PHYSIOLOGICAL PROCESSES
An Introduction to Mammalian Physiology

PHYSIOLOGICAL PROCESSES
An Introduction to Mammalian Physiology

M. W. Stanier

Formerly College Lecturer in Physiology and
Director of Studies in Medicine and Veterinary Science,
Newnham College, Cambridge

Mary L. Forsling

Reader in Reproductive Physiology, United Medical and Dental
Schools, University of London

McGRAW-HILL BOOK COMPANY

London · New York · St Louis · San Francisco · Auckland
Bogotá · Guatemala · Hamburg · Lisbon · Madrid · Mexico
Montreal · New Delhi · Panama · Paris · San Juan · São Paulo
Singapore · Sydney · Tokyo · Toronto

Published by
McGRAW-HILL Book Company (UK) Limited
MAIDENHEAD · BERKSHIRE · ENGLAND

British Library Cataloguing in Publication Data
Stanier, M. W.
  Physiological processes: an introduction to
  mammalian physiology.
  1. Mammals.   Physiology
  I. Title   II. Forsling, Mary L.
  599.01
  ISBN 0-07-084196-9

Library of Congress Cataloging-in-Publication Data
Stanier, M. W. (Margaret Wilson), 1919–
  Physiological processes: an introduction to mammalian physiology
  M. W. Stanier, Mary L. Forsling.
    p.   cm.
  Bibliography: p.
  Includes index.
  ISBN 0-07-084196-9
  1. Physiology.   I. Forsling, Mary L.   II. Title.
QP31.2.S73   1989
599′.01—dc 19   88-39018

1234 BP 9210

Typeset by Eta Services (Typesetters) Ltd, Beccles, Suffolk
Printed and bound in Great Britain by The Bath Press, Avon

Contents

Preface

This book is primarily for the use of first-year university and college undergraduates studying animal physiology as part of a course in biological sciences. Many such students will already have studied biology for A-level GCE or a senior high-school course. Some, however, including some preclinical medical students, may not have taken any advanced biology course at school. This book aims to bridge the gap between school and university or college studies of biology for students with varying extents of background knowledge.

The book may also be a useful lead-in to the more advanced studies of human and animal physiology for preclinical medical and veterinary students. It is in no sense a replacement for the more detailed and comprehensive textbooks of human physiology. But those who wish to gain an overall picture of, say, respiratory physiology before tackling all the intricate details and clinical applications of the subject may find their needs met by the appropriate chapter of this book. Brief discussions of some of the topics of human physiology—the electrocardiogram and blood groups for instance—will be found in some of the appendices at the end of the book.

Students will not find here much quantitative information or many formulae or equations. Boundaries between the fields of biological sciences are hazy and we have inevitably drawn on facts and explanations from the neighbouring areas of biochemistry, molecular biology and pharmacology. Limitations of space have forced us to omit, for the most part, accounts of the experimental evidence on which current knowledge of physiology is based, and we are therefore deprived of the pleasure of telling many fascinating stories of ingenuity and hard-won victories. However, we have tried to temper the inevitable dogmatism of an elementary textbook by pointing, at the end of some chapters, to the gaps in present-day understanding and the ways currently in use to try to fill them.

Physiology is not a complete, ordered and well rounded body of knowledge. It is itself, in a sense, a developing organism, with growing-points pushing out in many directions. If this book convinces its readers of how much more there is still to be known, it will fulfil one of its important functions.

Margaret Stanier
Mary Forsling

Acknowledgements

We acknowledge gratefully the help given by many people in the preparation of this book. Dr D. L. Ingram read most of the book in typescript and made useful comments, criticisms and suggestions. Dr F. P. B. Wooding gave much help with electron microphotographs. Dr E. Mawson, Dr B. Cross, Dr B. Broker and Mr F. Harrison read and criticized certain chapters. Members of the staff of the library and the photographic departments at the Institute of Animal Physiology and Genetics Research, Babraham, Cambridge gave much cooperation. Mrs J. Hood typed the manuscript and Miss J. Mander drew some of the figures.

Permission for the use of material in copyright has been granted by the following publishers, editors of journals, and authors. We thank them for this permission.

Academic Press; Appleton-Century-Crofts; Appleton & Lange; Edward Arnold; Cambridge University Press; Churchill-Livingstone; J. B. Lippincott Company; McGraw-Hill Book Company (New York); C. V. Mosby Co.; Oxford University Press; Rockefeller University Press; W. D. Saunders; Stanford University Press; Weidenfeld & Nicholson; Williams & Wilkins.

Editors of: *Acta Physiologica Scandinavica; Annals of New York Academy of Sciences; Annual Reviews Inc.; British Medical Bulletin; Journal of Applied Physiology; Journal of Neurophysiology; Journal of Physiology; Journal of Ultrastructural Research; Philosophical Transactions of the Royal Society; Proceedings of the National Academy of Sciences of the USA; Quarterly Journal of Experimental Physiology.*

H. Davson, R. L. Gregory, D. F. Horrobin, J. I. Hubbard, A. F. Huxley, H. Huxley, F. S. Kay, A. Leaf, T. Machen, V. B. Mountcastle, K. Schmidt-Nielson, A. P. Smolyo, J. B. West, D. R. Wilkie, S. H. Wollman.

For a figure taken or adapted from previously published material, by permission of the copyright holder, an acknowledgement is included in the figure caption.

1 Introduction

Physiology is the study of functions and processes within living organisms. Certain processes distinguish living organisms, both animals and plants, from non-living matter. Growth and reproduction are obvious examples. So too is movement, a property of nearly all animals, and shown in very limited capacity by plants also. The ability to respond to the environment, to its forms of energy such as heat, light, gravitational fields and their changes, is another distinctive feature of living things. A fundamental property is the capability of organisms to transform matter and energy, starting with sunlight and photosynthesis in green plants, and including assimilation, metabolic reactions of synthesis and breakdown of body tissue, and the respiratory processes generating the body's own energy supply.

Man as a prototype

This book is concerned with the physiology of animals. Although all species of animals have numerous functions in common, one species—man—seems to have dominated the study of animal physiology. There are two obvious practical reasons for this. One is that the human is to us the most familiar of living species, and therefore many of the functions under consideration can be readily observed on oneself. The other is the necessity for students of medicine to understand the normal functioning of the human body before they can usefully study its disorders and their correction. There is no great disadvantage in taking one single species as a prototype, example or 'model' for physiological study. But caution and provisos are necessary.

Since, obviously, many experimental studies in physiology have to be carried out on species other than man, one must guard against the assumption that the results are universally applicable. Many functions of the liver, for instance, have been revealed by taking samples of liver from freshly killed rats or pigeons and studying their enzymes; and also by perfusing blood or other fluids into the liver of anaesthetized animals and analysing the outflowing fluid. But does the human liver have the same enzymes? If, say, 20 different species of mammals and birds were all found to have precisely the same mechanism for breaking down liver glycogen to glucose, it would be fairly safe to assume something similar for man. Few physiological experiments, however, are performed on more than two or three species; and even if the results are indeed similar for these species, unquestioning acceptance of their validity for other species such as man should be avoided. On reading evidence derived from experiments or observations on other species, it is always fair to put the question: 'Do we know that this also happens in man?'

Conversely, man is recognized to be, in some respects, rather distinctive physiologically. There are of course the psychological properties of self-awareness, insight and imagination, and the accompanying abilities of the use of articulate symbolic speech and the making of tools, which are peculiar to the human. But apart from these psychophysiological phenomena there are the upright posture and movement on two legs, which though not unique to men are rare among mammals, and the very small amount of hair, which must have limited the geographical range of the human species for many millenia. The upright posture has necessitated adjustments of the circulatory system in the distribution of blood, as well as the development of intricate reflex activites of the muscles of the legs and back and of the nerves supplying them. The drawback of hairlessness with the consequent difficulty of maintaining body temperature was only gradually overcome, by the invention of shelters and clothing. These special features should remind the reader of any textbook of physiology to put the question: 'Does this apply *only* to man?'

Most of the material in this book describes physiological processes and systems common to all mammals, including man; and indeed much of it applies to all vertebrates. For any facts or observations peculiar to man or to an individual species, the particular species will be named.

Constancy of the internal environment

The distinguished nineteenth-century physiologist Claude Bernard asserted that 'The constancy of the internal environment is the condition for free life', a statement which over the years has given biological science a useful foundation for interpretation of diverse phenomena. By 'internal environment' is meant the extracellular fluid surrounding the cells, which for all vertebrate species comprises interstitial fluid and blood plasma. Many physiological mechanisms have as their outcome the maintenance of this constancy and stability. Indeed the cell itself (as explained in Chapter 3) is enabled by the activities of the cell membrane to maintain its volume and ionic composition within fairly narrow limits. Chapter 5 points out the rapid interchange of material at capillary level between blood plasma and interstitial fluid, an interchange which, together with the mixing and stirring effect produced by the circulation of blood, gives uniformity of composition to the whole internal environment: if plasma composition can be kept constant, stability of interstitial fluid will also be maintained. Chapter 7 considers the ability of the kidney to maintain constancy of volume and total osmolality of the entire extracellular fluid. Chapter 8 briefly discusses the cooperation of several organs and processes in maintaining constancy of extracellular pH, one of the most rigidly controlled variables. Chapter 14 describes the interlocking hormonal controls involved in maintenance of plasma glucose level, and also in calcium level.

The constancy is not absolute: there are small fluctuations in the chemical and physical properties of this aqueous medium. But considering the irregularity in the feeding and activity of most higher organisms, and in the demands made by the external environment as the animal moves around, the near-constancy of the internal environment is remarkable. This constancy depends on the proper functioning of many interlocking physiological and biochemical systems.

Systems of the body

For convenience of study, the physiology of animals can be subdivided into a number of processes, some of which can be closely attached to particular organs or systems in the body. These systems and their main functions are described in outline below. A more detailed description of the structure of the organs will be given in Chapter 2.

Alimentary canal and its related glands and organs

The alimentary canal, a much-coiled tube of soft tissue running the length of the animal body from mouth at one end to anus at the other, is the organ by which feeding, digestion and absorption take place. Digestive juices enter the lumen of this tube down slender ducts from the salivary glands and pancreas. The products of digestion are taken through the wall of the alimentary canal into the bloodstream or lymph system, and may be stored temporarily in the liver. From the liver, also, certain excretory products pass down a duct into the lumen of the alimentary canal; and these products together with unabsorbed food residues, outworn cells and symbiotic bacteria are passed outside the body through the anus.

Heart and circulatory system

Through the circulation of blood in the system of blood vessels (arteries, arterioles, capillaries, venules and veins), food and oxygen are supplied to all cells, and products of their metabolism are removed. The rhythmic pumping of the heart keeps the blood moving.

Respiratory system

Atmospheric air enters the blood of land vertebrates via the mouth and nose, into a rigid tube, the trachea, running through the neck into the thorax (chest). The trachea bifurcates into two narrower tubes, the bronchi, leading to the left and right lungs. By rhythmic inflation and deflation of the thoracic cavity, atmospheric gases enter and leave the lungs via the trachea and bronchi. Within the lung, well supplied with blood vessels, oxygen enters and carbon dioxide leaves the blood.

Excretory organs

There are two kidneys, left and right, in the abdominal region close to the vertebral column. The kidneys form urine, which includes among its constituents uric acid and other organic acids, traces of ammonium salts, urea, bile-pigment derivatives and creatinine. The fluid passes down a tube (ureter), one from each kidney, and is stored temporarily in the single centrally placed urinary bladder, whence it is passed to the outside from time to time through another short tube, the urethra.

Nervous system

The nerve supply, to all organs of the body except the interior of bones of the skeleton, acts as a messenger service through which coordination of function of all separate organs can be brought about; and by which the whole organism is enabled to respond to changes in the external world, as well as changes in its own internal condition. The network of nerves seen as thin white threads running into and among all organs of the body are the peripheral nerves. The coordination is carried out by the central nervous system (CNS)—the brain and spinal cord. Information in the form of nerve impulses enters the CNS via peripheral sensory nerves; these are afferent impulses. Impulses from the CNS to muscles or glands are conveyed by peripheral motor nerves; these are efferent impulses. The efferent peripheral nerves are of two kinds, which function rather differently: somatic, which carry impulses to striated muscle, and autonomic, which serve smooth and cardiac muscle and glands.

The CNS is more than just a sorting and coordination centre depending for its function on the input of afferent impulses. It can also initiate activity, both as conscious voluntary action and by way of inherent rhythms.

Sense organs

These include the eye and the ear. Vision and hearing are of such importance in man that they are called the special senses. Sense organs also include mechanoreceptors in muscles, tendons and walls of blood vessels, which respond to stretch, deformation, touch and pressure, including gravity; and chemoreceptors in the nose, mouth and near blood-vessel walls, which respond to chemicals in solution (smell, taste) and to dissolved gases.

Muscle

Muscles carry out the body's movements. Some muscles (the skeletal or striated muscles) are attached to bones and move the body over the earth or through air or water, as well as moving the limbs, head and trunk in relation to each other. Other muscles (smooth muscle) line the walls of hollow organs and move the contents of these organs; and others (cardiac muscles) perform the highly specialized function of pumping the blood through the circulation. (The terms 'voluntary' and 'involuntary' in defining types of muscle are now obsolete.)

Endocrine system

This system includes, first, a number of glands scattered in various parts of the body which produce specific chemical substances (hormones, endocrines) and secrete them into the blood, which then takes them to some other region of the body in which they act. The thyroid gland in the neck region, the pituitary gland at the base of the brain and the adrenal glands above each kidney are examples. Secondly the endocrine system includes secretions from other organs (for example the alimentary canal), of which the primary function may be conceived as something quite other than hormone production; again, the route between point of production and point of effect is via the bloodstream, but (for alimentary canal hormones for instance) this route may be quite short.

Reproductive system

The reproductive system includes not only those particular organs which form the germ cells (ovary and testes), but also the other organs involved in producing and rearing the young, such as the uterus and mammary glands; and also such 'temporary' organs as the placenta, which functions both as the route of exchange of materials between maternal organism and fetus, and as an important source of hormones maintaining pregnancy.

These are the main organs and systems which will be discussed in this book. In each of the physiological processes to be described, several organs or systems must participate. In movement, for instance, the nervous system and the muscles are involved and perhaps some sense organs also; excretion is the concern not only of the kidneys but also of the circulatory system supplying plasma to glomeruli for processing; reproduction is a function of the specific genital organs and also of several parts of the endocrine system; and so on. There is an interlocking and coordination of function of all processes and systems of the body—indeed sometimes even a rivalry or competition between them for available resources. It is this coordination and competition which permits the living organism to grow, thrive, reproduce, meet its biological needs and respond appropriately to the external world.

For the student of physiology, this close interlocking of function of physiological systems means that it is difficult to understand one system without first knowing something about all the others. Though the systems and processes have to be described and explained one by one, this is simply for convenience; we must not forget that the boundaries between them are somewhat arbitrary. So although we may abstract, say, the kidney, and study its function in some detail, it is only when we put it back into the context of the whole body that we understand its biological significance.

Another consequence of this interlocking of function within the body is that there can be no inherent logical order or sequence in which the several systems should be studied. Some authors start by describing feeding and excretion, dealing with the alimentary canal and kidneys. Others, remembering that blood vessels and nerve fibres penetrate all other body organs, start by describing one or other of the body's systems of distribution and coordination: the blood circulation or nervous system. The order chosen in this book is as arbitrary as any other. Frequent cross-references are a reminder of the flexibility of the boundaries between physiological systems.

In the next chapter, picturing and describing the structure of mammalian body organs, the reader's attention is drawn to the contrast between stylized textbook figures and the actual appearance of organs in the animal. In the chapter on cell structure and function, some of the material may already be familiar to many readers, but certain sections, especially those relating to the origin of the cell's membrane potential and the Gibbs–Donnan equilibrium, may serve as useful reminders. In the following 15 chapters (4–18) the main systems and functions of the body are described. The concluding chapter summarizes a few of the properties common to all physiological processes and indicates an approach to the study of physiology in greater depth.

2 Structure of the mammalian body

Introduction

This chapter is intended as an introduction to the structure and names of parts of the main organs of mammals, and their relative position in the body. It therefore consists largely of a series of labelled drawings of these organs. The order of sections in this chapter follows as far as possible the order in which functions are described in the later chapters. Emphasis is placed on the rather complex nervous system as it is likely to be less familiar to most readers. Since drawings are necessarily highly stylized for clarity

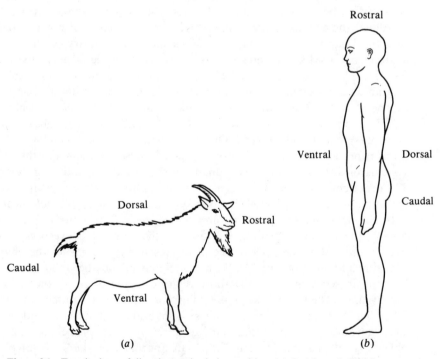

Figure 2.1 Terminology of direction and relative position. (*a*) Quadruped. (*b*) Man.

and labelling, they can rarely give any idea of the actual appearance of the organs. A few photographs have been included to help readers to visualize the organs of the thoracic and abdominal cavities of a mammal.

The following adjectives (Fig. 2.1), describing the direction and relative position of organs of the body, are useful: rostral, caudal, dorsal, ventral. The use of the words 'anterior' and 'posterior' needs care. Textbook diagrams are often labelled 'anterior surface of ...' when the meaning is 'ventral surface of ...'.

Alimentary canal

The alimentary canal or digestive tract, concerned primarily with feeding and the digestion and absorption of food, runs from the mouth at the rostral end of the body to the rectum and anus at the caudal end.* Figure 2.2a outlines the alimentary canal and related structures. Figure 2.2b shows the part of the alimentary canal caudal to the diaphragm.

Notice in particular the names of the various regions of the small intestine (duodenum, jejunum, ileum) and of the sphincters. A sphincter is a ring of robust, circular smooth-muscle fibres, usually with an innervation separate from that of surrounding smooth muscle; on contraction, this ring of muscle can close the lumen. There is no true sphincter at the point where the oesophagus enters the stomach, though the caudal end of the oesophagus performs a similar function and is sometimes called the 'cardiac sphincter'.

On the floor of the mouth is the tongue, which includes much striated muscle, and is covered by an epithelial layer containing mucus-secreting cells and taste buds. The back of the mouth (and of the nasal passage also) is formed by the pharynx, a funnel of curved sheets of smooth muscle and thick connective tissue, which extends downwards to lead into the top of the oesophagus.

The wall of the alimentary canal, surrounded by a thin sheet of connective tissue, is of similar basic structure throughout its length from oesophagus to anus. It is made up of two sturdy layers of smooth-muscle cells: an outer layer running longitudinally and an inner circular layer lying parallel to the circumference of the lumen. Secreting and absorbing epithelial cells, together with numerous blood capillaries, lymph vessels and nerves, lie inside the circular muscle layer, and form the submucosa and mucosa layers.

In Fig. 2.3 notice in particular the villi and crypts of the mucosal layer, characteristic of all regions of the small intestine.

Lying outside the wall of the alimentary canal but closely related to it, there are:

1. three pairs of salivary glands, which pour their secretions down salivary ducts into the mouth;

---

*The term 'gastrointestinal tract' is sometimes used as synonymous with 'alimentary canal'. Strictly speaking, the term 'gastrointestinal tract' does not include the mouth and oesophagus.

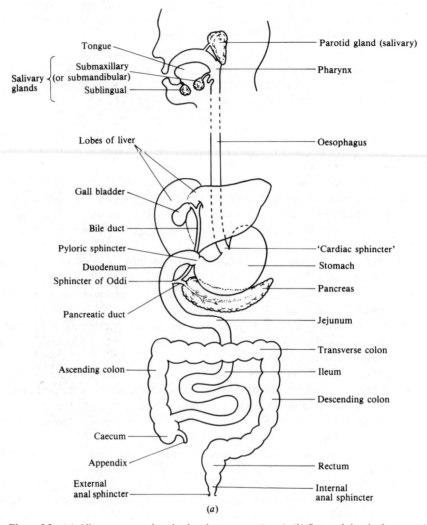

Figure 2.2 (*a*) Alimentary canal and related structures (man). (*b*) Some abdominal organs (rat).

2. the pancreas, the duct of which brings secretions into the upper part of the duodenum;
3. the liver and gall bladder.

The liver forms bile, which is stored and concentrated in the gall bladder and secreted eventually down the common bile duct through the sphincter of Oddi into the duodenum. In some species there is no gall bladder and the bile is taken directly from liver to duodenum.

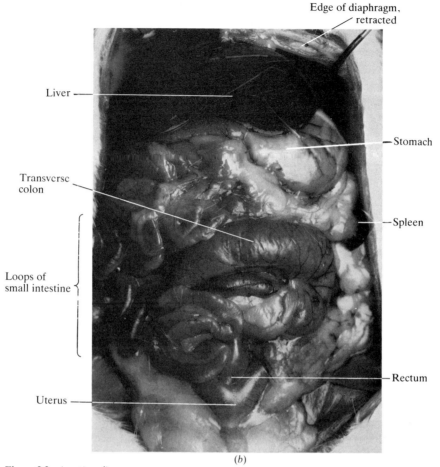

Edge of diaphragm, retracted

Liver

Stomach

Transverse colon

Spleen

Loops of small intestine

Rectum

Uterus

(b)

Figure 2.2 (*continued*)

The Brunner's glands are embedded in the wall of the duodenum. In addition, glandular epithelial cells are to be found throughout the lining of the alimentary canal. (Some secrete enzymes, many others secrete mucus.) In the intestinal wall there are numerous nodules of lymphatic tissue, particularly prominent in the ileum, where they are known as Peyer's patches (Fig. 2.3).

Circulatory system

Figure 2.4*a* shows in diagrammatic form some of the parts of the mammalian circulatory system. Figure 2.4*b–d* show the heart and main thoracic vessels. Arteries carry blood away from the heart, veins carry blood towards it.

The systemic circulation starts at the left side of the heart. From the left ventricle, blood is ejected through the aortic semilunar valve into the ascending aorta, and over

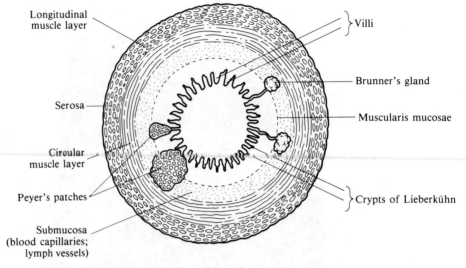

Figure 2.3 Transverse section through small intestine.

the aortic arch, where arteries taking blood to the head and upper limbs branch off. The blood moves down the descending aorta and enters a number of parallel pathways through the various organs. The coeliac trunk supplies the stomach, and also the spleen, an important abdominal organ where red blood cells are stored and destroyed. The mesenteric trunks supply the intestines. Other branches of the aorta supply the kidneys, lower limbs and so on. In every organ a capillary network brings the blood into close contact with all cells. Blood emerging from the stomach and small intestine is collected into the hepatic portal vein, and passes to the liver, where it goes through another capillary network before entering the hepatic vein and thence the inferior vena cava. The liver also receives blood via the hepatic artery, a branch of the coeliac trunk.

Blood from the head and upper limbs passes into the two superior venae cavae. The inferior vena cava takes blood from the abdominal organs and lower limbs. In mammals the venae cavae open into the right atrium (Fig. 2.4*d*).

This completes the systemic circulation, and the blood now enters the pulmonary circulation. Blood from the right atrium enters the right ventricle through the tricuspid valve. It is ejected through the pulmonary semilunar valve into the pulmonary trunk, which branches to form left and right pulmonary arteries supplying the lungs. Blood returning from the lungs passes by pulmonary veins into the left atrium; the blood then passes through the mitral valve into the left ventricle, and thence to the systemic circulation. The heart is thus a pair of pumps connected in series, and the systemic and pulmonary circulations are also arranged in series.

The term 'arterial blood' means fully oxygenated blood, emerging from the lungs and present in the left side of the heart and the main arteries. 'Venous blood' means

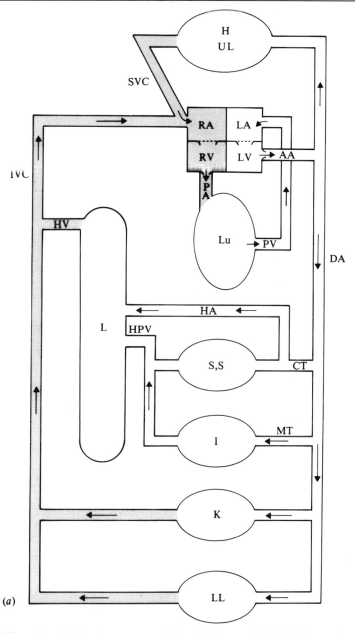

Figure 2.4 (a) Circulatory system. H: head; UL: upper limbs; SVC: superior venae cavae; RA, LA: right and left atrium; RV, LV: right and left ventricle; AA: aortic arch; PA: pulmonary trunk and arteries; PV: pulmonary veins; DA: descending aorta; CT, MT: coeliac and mesenteric trunks; Lu: lungs; S, S: spleen and stomach; I: intestines; HA: hepatic artery; HPV: hepatic portal vein; K: kidneys; LL: lower limbs; L: liver; HV: hepatic vein; IVC: inferior vena cava. Shaded vessels and chambers contain venous blood.

(*continued*)

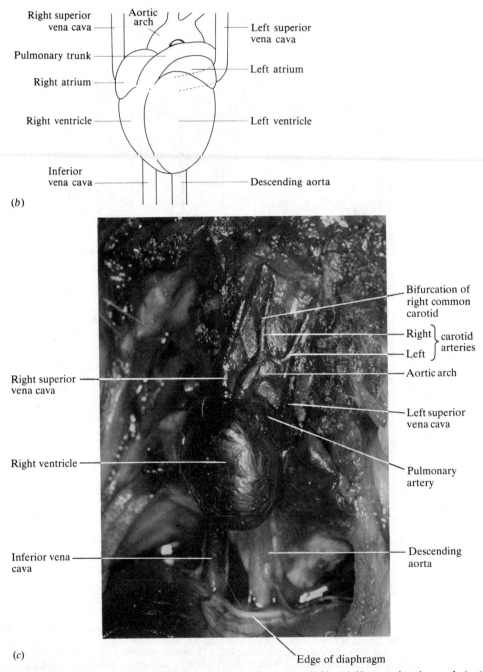

(b)

(c)

Figure 2.4 (b) Heart and main blood vessels viewed from ventral side. (c) Heart and main vessels (rat) viewed from ventral side. (d) Similar to (c), but heart has been displaced towards animal's right side, to show left superior vena cava passing below (dorsal to) heart, to join with other venae cavae at junction with right atrium.

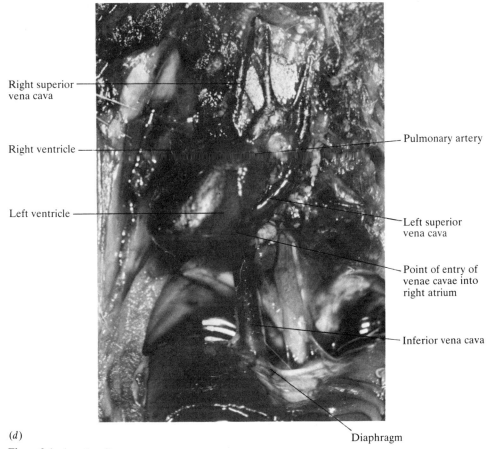

Right superior
vena cava

Right ventricle

Left ventricle

Pulmonary artery

Left superior
vena cava

Point of entry of
venae cavae into
right atrium

Inferior vena cava

(d)

Diaphragm

Figure 2.4   *(continued)*

blood which is at least partially deoxygenated. Note that the pulmonary trunk taking blood away from the right ventricle to the lungs contains venous blood, and the pulmonary veins bringing blood towards the left atrium contain arterial blood.

The walls of the main blood vessels contain circular smooth-muscle fibres (and a few elastic fibres) in concentric layers (tunica media). Outside the vessel is a thin skin of connective tissue including elastic fibres, the serosal layer or tunica adventitia; and within the layer of muscle is a layer of thin, flattened endothelial cells, the endothelial lining of the lumen (tunica intima) (Fig. 2.5).

In many areas and organs a main artery and main vein lie side by side. Veins have a thinner wall and a larger lumen than arteries, and much less elastic tissue. Another feature of main veins is the presence of flaps of connective tissue on their inner walls; these flaps form valves which prevent backflow of blood. The position of valves can often be seen as a small lump on a length of well-dilated superficial vein.

The walls of capillaries are one cell thick, and are continuous with the endothelial lining layer of the larger vessels. Arteriovenous anastomoses occur in the capillary

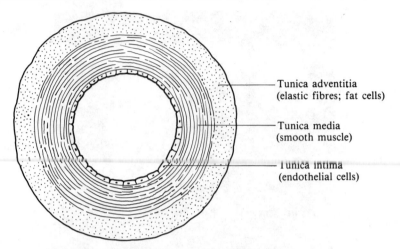

Figure 2.5 Cross-section through an artery.

beds and provide a short cut for the blood when a capillary bed temporarily closes down.

Respiratory system

The trachea, bronchi and lungs are shown diagrammatically in Fig. 2.6. The lungs and heart together occupy most of the space within the thoracic cavity.

In the walls of the trachea, bronchi and larger bronchioles there are nearly complete rings of cartilage, which prevent these tubes from collapsing completely but which also allow a small amount of dilatation. In the upper part of the trachea is the larynx. This consists of two complete rings of cartilage (the thyroid cartilage above, the cricoid below), to which are attached a number of small cartilaginous structures. One of these forms a flap, the epiglottis, which during swallowing is pulled down and covers the lumen of the trachea. Other small cartilages form the attachments of the vocal cords and the small muscles which move them. Figure 2.6a shows the trachea, bronchus and one lung.

The two bronchi divide repeatedly, giving rise to a series of bronchioles, with respiratory bronchioles at their final division leading to the alveolar ducts, respiratory atrium and alveoli, as shown in Fig. 2.6b. It is the alveolus which provides the actual gaseous exchange surface in the lungs.

Figure 2.7a and b show the trachea and lungs of a rat.

Renal system

The renal system consists of the left and right kidneys; their ureters, and the centrally placed urinary bladder into which the ureters open; and the urethra, through which urine is evacuated from the bladder (Fig. 2.8a–c).

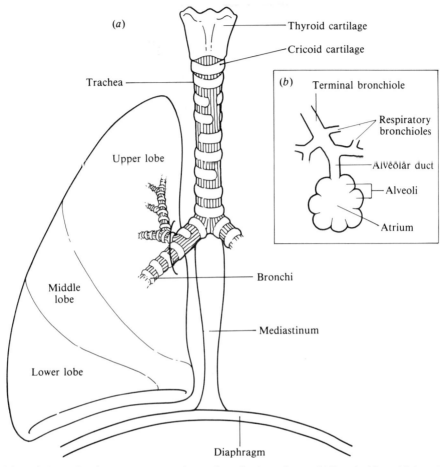

Figure 2.6 (*a*) Respiratory system: trachea and one lung are shown. (*b*) Terminal bronchiole and alveoli.

The kidneys lie close to the vertebral column. In most mammalian species the right kidney lies slightly more caudally than the left. They lie outside the peritoneum, the thin membrane of connective tissue which encloses most of the abdominal organs; and in many species the kidneys are firmly bound by connective tissue to the muscles of the back. The kidneys themselves are enclosed in a thin sheath, the renal capsule, which in many species including man has large quantities of fat embedded in it. The blood supply is via the renal arteries direct from the aorta; blood from the kidneys enters the renal veins and thence the inferior vena cava. The point at which the blood vessels enter the renal tissue is called the hilum.

The shape of the kidney differs in different species, as shown in Fig. 2.9.

The distinction between the outer layer (cortex) and the inner layer (medulla) is easily perceived in most mammals, because the cortex is more vascular (contains more

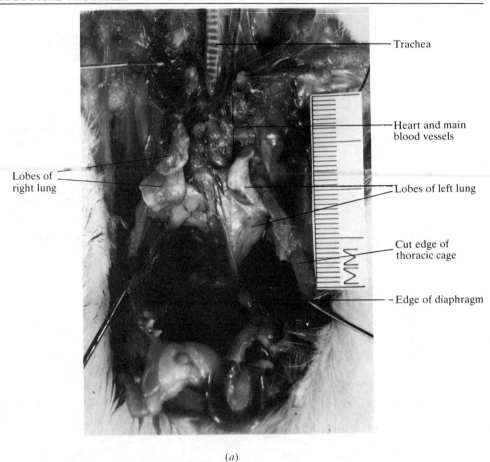

Trachea

Heart and main
blood vessels

Lobes of
right lung

Lobes of left lung

Cut edge of
thoracic cage

Edge of diaphragm

(a)

Figure 2.7 (a) Respiratory organs (rat), to show position relative to heart. (b) Trachea and bronchi after removal of heart and main blood vessels. Bifurcation of the bronchi lies immediately dorsal to the aortic arch; cut end of the aorta is visible; lungs have been removed to show the bronchi.

blood vessels) and is dark red in colour, whereas the medulla is pale pink. The term 'papilla' denotes the innermost tip of the medulla in each pyramid of renal tissue (Fig. 2.8c).

The upper end of each ureter opens out into a space within the kidney, the renal pelvis. The ducts of Bellini, formed by the joining of a number of collecting ducts of the nephrons (the small tubular units of renal tissue), open on the surface of the papillae, and discharge their contents into the renal pelvis, whence the urine is taken by peristaltic movement along the ureter into the urinary bladder.

Reproductive organs

In both sexes the gonads lie in the pelvic cavity, the most caudal part of the trunk, close to the urinary bladder and rectum.

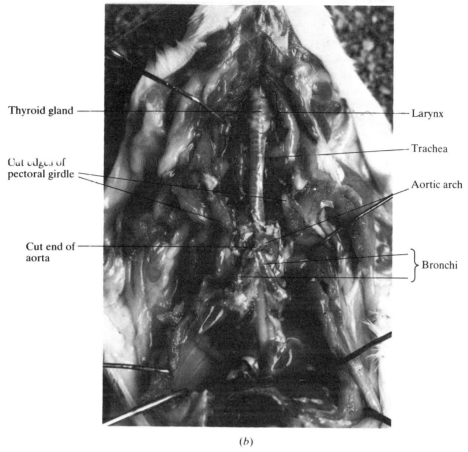

Thyroid gland

Cut edges of
pectoral girdle

Cut end of
aorta

Larynx

Trachea

Aortic arch

Bronchi

(b)

Figure 2.7   (*continued*)

The testes, the paired male gonads, are contained in most mammalian species within a pouch of the abdominal cavity, the scrotal sac, suspended outside the main part of the abdomen. The communicating passage (inguinal canal or spermatic cord) contains the spermatic artery and vein and the vas deferens.

Figure 2.10 is a side view of one testis and its associated structures. The spermatozoa, which develop in the main body of the testis, pass via the rete testis and vasa efferentia into a long coiled tube, the epididymis. This leads to the vas deferens at the end of which is the seminal vesicle, where the sperm are stored until ejaculated at coitus via the ejaculatory duct.

In the female the ovaries (paired left and right) shed ova into the abdominal cavity; cilia at the open end of the nearby uterine tube move the ovum into and along the tube where fertilization may occur. The embryo develops in the uterus. In many mammals this structure, too, is paired, being formed of a left and right horn (Fig. 2.11*a*). This arrangement is common to all species which are multiparous (producing many young

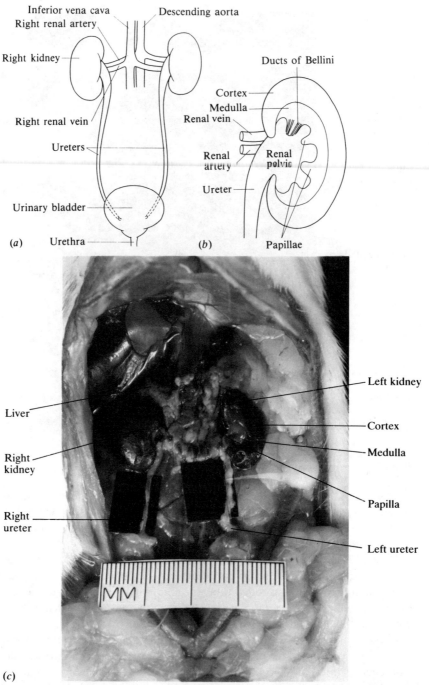

Figure 2.8 (*a*) Renal system. (*b*) Longitudinal section through multilobular kidney. (*c*) Kidneys and ureters (rat). Black paper has been placed below ureters, to show them against background of fat. Left kidney has been cut longitudinally to show (pale) medulla and papilla.

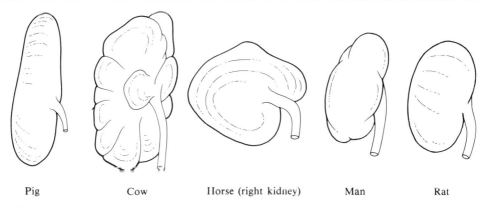

Pig   Cow   Horse (right kidney)   Man   Rat

Figure 2.9 Shapes of kidneys in various mammalian species.

at a birth), such as pig, rat and rabbit. In other species including the human the uterus is a single, centrally placed organ (Fig. 2.11*b*), the short left and right horns of which run up to the uterine tubes. The caudal end of the uterus in both types leads to the narrow cervix, and thence to the vagina or birth canal, which lies immediately dorsal to the urinary bladder. Figure 2.11*c* shows the relative position in the rat of several abdominal organs including the uterine horns. Most of the small and large intestines have been removed to reveal the more dorsal structures.

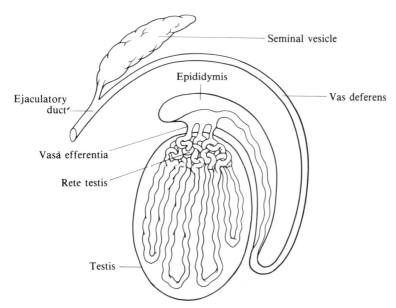

Seminal vesicle

Epididymis

Vas deferens

Ejaculatory duct

Vasa efferentia

Rete testis

Testis

Figure 2.10 Male reproductive organs.

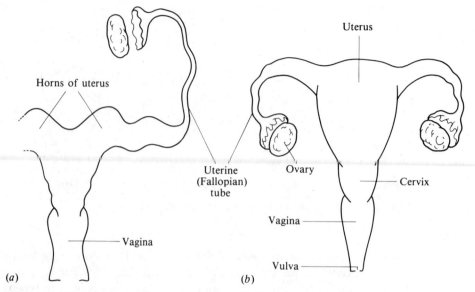

Figure 2.11   Female reproductive organs. (*a*) Rat. (*b*) Human. (*c*) Abdominal organs including uterine horns (rat).

The organs so far described—the alimentary canal, heart and main arterial and venous trunks, respiratory system, renal system and reproductive organs—fill the greater part of the cavities of the trunk (the thorax and abdomen). Figure 2.12*a* and *b* show how these organs are arranged within the trunk of a typical non-ruminant mammal.

Muscles

Muscles are of three types:

1. striated, also called skeletal;
2. cardiac;
3. smooth.

Striated muscles constitute about 40 per cent of the weight of the body of most mammals, and form the bulk of the soft tissue of the limbs and body wall. The function of most of them is to move the body in space or to move parts of the body in relation to each other. Cardiac muscle forms the wall of the heart, and its inherent rhythmic contractions move blood through the chambers of the heart and into the arteries. Smooth muscle forms the wall of hollow organs and tubes including the blood vessels, alimentary canal and urinary bladder; its function is generally to move the contents along or out of the tube or organ. Small smooth muscles occur elsewhere also:

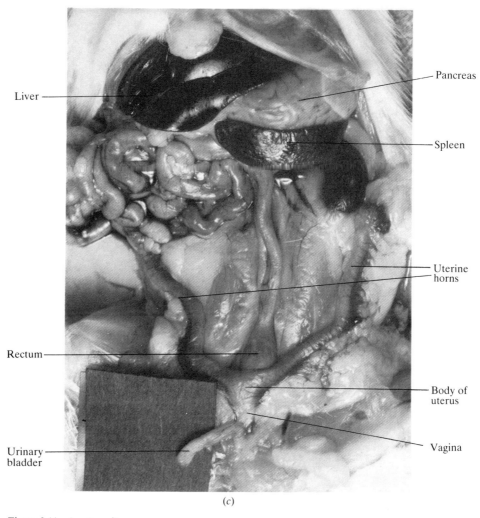

Liver

Pancreas

Spleen

Uterine horns

Rectum

Body of uterus

Vagina

Urinary bladder

(c)

Figure 2.11 (*continued*)

examples are the muscle closing the iris of the eye, and the muscles moving the hair. (Figure 2.13 shows the fibres of the main types of muscle.)

Striated muscle

Striated muscle consists of fibres lying more or less parallel, able to contract in such a way that the two ends come closer together. In striated muscle each fibre is a syncytium and the cell nuclei lie outside a cylindrical column of cytoplasm. Each fibre is contained within a sheath of connective tissue, the sarcolemma. The muscle as a whole is enclosed in a connective-tissue sheath, the epimysium (Fig. 2.14a). In many muscles the epimysium is prolonged at each end into a tough connective-tissue

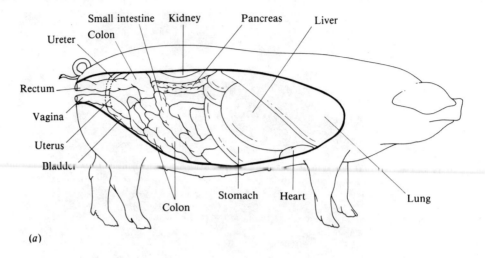

(a)

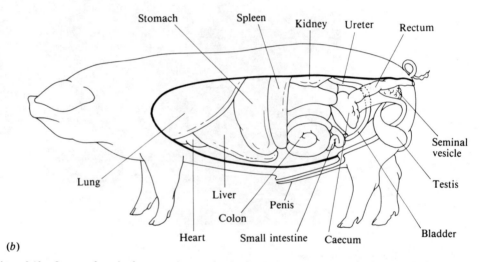

(b)

Figure 2.12 Organs of trunk of non-ruminant animal (pig) to show arrangement in thorax and abdomen. (a) Female from right side. (b) Male from left side. (Adapted from Sisson, S. and J. D. Grossman, *The Anatomy of Domestic Animals*, 5th edn, Saunders, Philadelphia, 1975.)

tendon, which attaches the muscle to a part of the skeleton. Limb muscles may be fixed to bones spanning a joint in such a way that the shortening of the muscle moves the joint (Fig. 2.14b and c).

The fibres of a skeletal muscle are arranged in bundles called fascioli. Within each fibre are numerous parallel myofibrils; microscopically visible transverse striations, reflecting the underlying molecular structure, are arranged in register for all myofibrils of one muscle fibre, and give the striated appearance to the fibre.

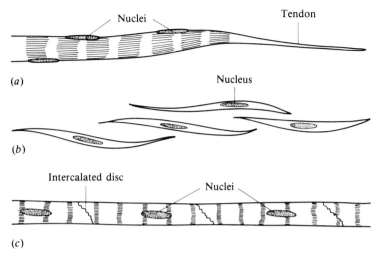

Figure 2.13 Muscle fibres. (*a*) Striated (skeletal) muscle. (*b*) Smooth muscle. (*c*) Cardiac muscle.

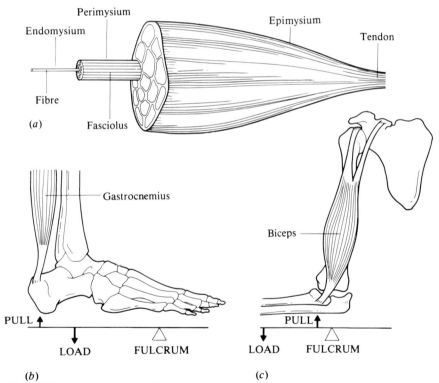

Figure 2.14 (*a*) Arrangement of striated muscle in fascioli. (*b*) and (*c*) Muscles spanning joints. In (*b*), shortening of the gastrocnemius lifts the heel, the fulcrum being near the toe. In (*c*), shortening of the biceps raises the forearm, the fulcrum being at the elbow.

Cardiac muscle

Cardiac muscle fibres have in microscopic appearance a somewhat similar cross-striated structure to that of somatic muscle, indicating a set of well-developed myofibrils. In contrast with somatic muscle, the cells are separated, each with its own nucleus; but there is very close contact between them, at points known as intercalated discs where fingers or ridges on one cell surface fit into holes or grooves in the other.

Smooth muscle

Smooth muscle, forming the wall of hollow organs and tubes, is arranged in curved or cylindrical sheets within which the individual muscle cells are long narrow spindle-shaped structures pointed at each end and with the nucleus lying centrally.

Nervous system

The nervous system consists of the central nervous system (CNS), comprising the brain and spinal cord, and peripheral nerves, emerging from the CNS, and consisting of bundles of nerve axons (fibres) running from the CNS to most regions and organs of the body. The word 'nerve' is used both for one of these bundles and for a single fibre within the bundle.

Nerve cells

The unit of structure of nerve tissue is the nerve cell, containing the nucleus, mitochondria and the usual cytoplasmic inclusions (Fig. 2.15). Scattered among these nerve cells are other cells called glial cells or neuroglia, which provide nutrients and also mechanical support. Nerve cells bear on their surface numerous branched processes, the dendrites; within the CNS these intertwine with dendrites of nearby cells forming a closely packed network. The main part of the cell, containing the nucleus, is termed the 'cell body'. In close proximity to the surface of each cell body there lie the tips of the dendrites of many other nerve cells; the point of proximity is called a synapse. The word 'synapse' is also used for the point of proximity between the end of a peripheral nerve and an effector organ (muscle or gland). Many nerve cells also bear one single process much longer than the dendrites, called the nerve axon; it is these axons which constitute many of the fibres of peripheral nerves. At its end the axon breaks up into separate threads, the terminal arborizations, each branch ending in a small swelling, the terminal button or end-foot. Axons are wrapped around with a protective layer of cells, called the Schwann cells. Along many axons the Schwann cells contain an abundance of a lipid substance (mainly phospholipid) called myelin. It is the myelin sheaths formed by the Schwann cells which give the white, glistening appearance to peripheral nerves as seen by the naked eye. Within the cytoplasm along the length of axons there are microtubules. Cell bodies within the CNS are called collectively 'grey matter', and nerve tracts in the CNS, consisting mainly of bundles of axons, are called collectively 'white matter'. A localized and well-

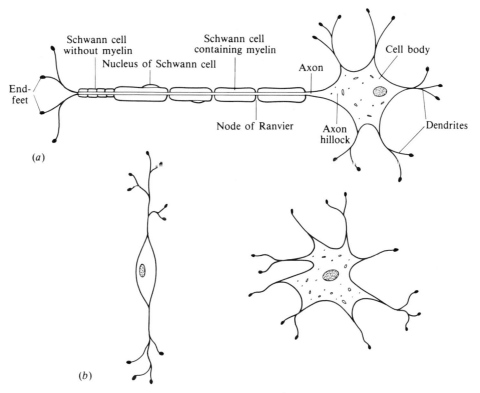

Figure 2.15 Some nerve cells. (*a*) Typical motor nerve cell with myelinated axon; Schwann-cell sheath contains myelin. (*b*) Cells from CNS.

defined group of cell bodies in the CNS is called a *nucleus*; a group of cell bodies outside the CNS, and surrounded by a capsule of connective tissue, is called a *ganglion*.

Central nervous system

The whole CNS—brain and spinal cord—is encased in three protective membranes called collectively the meninges. The outermost, the most firm and robust of the three, is the dura mater; it includes much collagen and elastic fibrous tissue. Firmly adherent to its inner surface is the second (much thinner) membrane, the arachnoid, in which run numerous blood vessels. Then comes a fluid-filled space (containing cerebrospinal fluid) and finally, closely wrapping the nerve tissue itself and following its shape, is a very thin membrane, the pia mater.

The presence of the cerebrospinal fluid (CSF) in the space between the arachnoid and the pia mater means that the CNS is surrounded by a supporting layer of fluid, which gives the nerve tissue buoyancy and prevents it from collapsing on itself.

Furthermore, the brain is hollow, and its cavities also contain CSF, which is in contact with the subarachnoid space via small channels in the roof of the fourth ventricle (cavity) of the brain. The CSF is being constantly but slowly renewed and replaced, by secretion from tufts of capillaries and gland-like cells (choroid plexuses) projecting into the ventricles of the brain; and by reabsorption into venous sinuses and lymph vessels.

Of the four cavities (ventricles) within the brain, two, the left and right lateral ventricles, are in the rostral part of the brain, and are larger than the other two. The third ventricle lies centrally between the lateral ventricles, and is connected with them by narrow tubes, the foramina of Monro. The fourth ventricle lies behind the third, connected with it by the aqueduct of Silvius (Fig. 2.16). It is via the roof of the fourth ventricle that CSF can seep through the tissue of the brain and bathe the outer surface of the whole CNS from end to end. The floor and walls of the third ventricle form an important structure, the hypothalamus, the nerve cells of which are concerned in integration of various non-conscious activities of the body such as temperature control.

The remainder of the CNS is a more solid structure, penetrated only by a very narrow central tube, the spinal (Haversian) canal, also containing CSF (Fig. 2.17). In

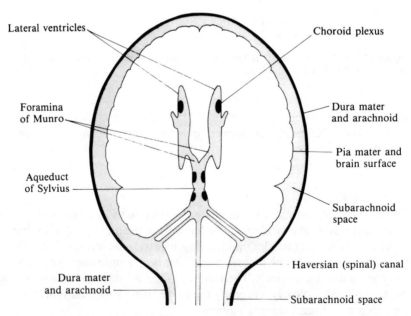

Figure 2.16 Cavities of brain, to show ducts and meninges. Central nervous tissue (nerve cells and neuroglia) white; fluid-containing spaces shaded. Subarachnoid space containing CSF runs the whole length of the trunk *outside* the spinal cord. Narrow spinal canal (also containing CSF) runs *inside* the spinal cord.

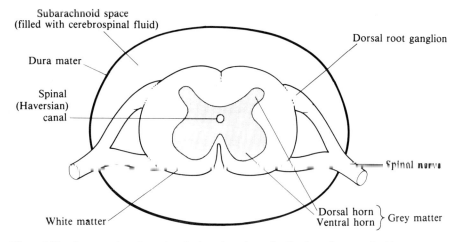

Figure 2.17 Cross-section through spinal cord to show distribution of grey and white matter.

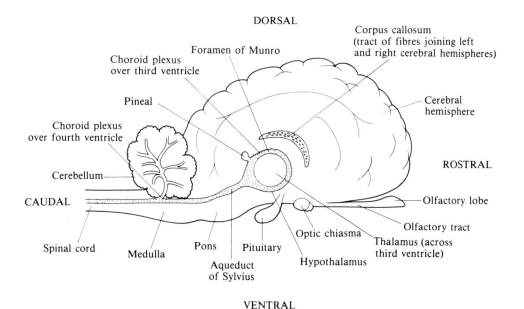

Figure 2.18 Brain of sheep; longitudinal section viewed from animal's right side.

the rostral region of the brain, the cerebral cortex, most of the cell bodies (grey matter) occur in the much-folded outer layers of tissue, the inner layers consisting of bundles (tracts) of fibres. In the spinal cord, on the other hand, the grey matter is near the centre, and the tracts are on the outside. In the hypothalamus and brain stem the distribution of grey and white matter follows a complicated pattern; cell bodies occur in nuclei of grey matter.

The brain stem connects the brain with the spinal cord. It consists of the pons (short and wide) and the medulla oblongata, long and narrower, continuing caudally into the spinal cord. On the dorsal side of the pons lies a large structure, the cerebellum, more or less spherical, with many parallel grooves and ridges on its outer surface. It is concerned in coordination of movement and balance.

Figure 2.18 is a vertical section through the brain of a sheep, viewed from the right side, to illustrate the relationship of the structures described.

Peripheral nerves

The peripheral nerves emerge in pairs, left and right, from the CNS. There are in man 12 pairs of *cranial* nerves, and these are numbered with roman numerals, I–XII. The other peripheral nerves are numbered with arabic numerals with a letter-prefix to show the region from which they emerge: C_{1-8} (cervical (neck) region), T_{1-12} (thoracic), L_{1-5} (lumbar) and S_{1-5} (sacral). Numbers of pairs differ slightly in different mammals.

A few peripheral nerves contain only sensory fibres (carrying impulses towards the CNS), a few only motor fibres (taking impulses away from the CNS), but the majority contain both sensory and motor. Cranial nerves I and II (olfactory and optic), for instance, contain only sensory fibres from the olfactory surface and the eye, respectively, and cranial nerve III (oculomotor) is entirely motor, carrying impulses to eye muscles. Cranial nerve X (vagus) is mixed, containing both sensory and motor fibres; it is a large nerve, passing from the brain down the neck and innervating many organs in the thorax and upper abdomen. Sense organs (innervated by sensory fibres) are present not only on or near the surface of the body (eye; ear; skin sensory organs) but also deep within it, as for example stretch receptors of muscle and tendon, and chemoreceptors responsive to the composition of plasma.

Each spinal nerve from T_1 down to S_5 has two roots, easily identified in cross-sections of the spinal cord (Fig. 2.19). The dorsal root contains only sensory fibres, which carry impulses towards the CNS, from the sense organs. The ventral root contains only motor fibres, taking impulses from the CNS to muscles and glands, the effector organs. Nerve cells whose the axons lie entirely within the CNS are called interneurones (Fig. 2.19).

The cell bodies of the spinal sensory nerves lie not within the spinal cord but in a small spherical mass of tissue, the dorsal root ganglion, close to the dorsal root of the nerve. (Since an *axon* is defined as a fibre conducting impulses *away* from the cell body, the long fibre bringing impulses from the sensory organ towards the CNS is not strictly speaking an axon, and is called a 'sensory nerve fibre'.)

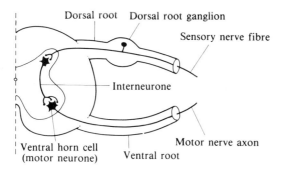

Figure 2.19 Transverse section of spinal cord (half) to show arrangement of neurones in roots.

The grey matter along much of the spinal cord is arranged in two dorsal and two ventral horns. The cell bodies of many of the motor fibres taking impulses to the striated muscles of the limbs and trunk lie in the ventral horns of the grey matter, and are called *ventral horn cells.*

In addition to the peripheral afferent and efferent nerves already described, there exists a set of efferent nerves emerging from the CNS via the ventral roots, and supplying smooth muscles and glands. These peripheral nerves comprise the *autonomic nervous system* (Fig. 2.20), and their arrangement is described in Chapter 10. A characteristic feature of the autonomic system is that there are always two nerve fibres between the CNS and an innervated organ: the axon emerging from the CNS forms a synapse on the cell body of another nerve cell outside the CNS and it is the axon from this cell that innervates the organ.

This chapter gives the reader an opportunity of becoming familiar with the main organs fo the mammalian body, their structure and position, and the names of their

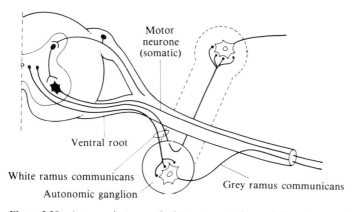

Figure 2.20 Autonomic (sympathetic) system, to show relation to sympathetic nerves in spinal roots.

parts. Certain groups of mammals possess organs or structures specialized or adapted to a particular way of life. Examples are the alimentary canal of ruminants and the position within the abdomen of the testes of seals.

Some of these adaptations will be described in the appropriate chapters. This chapter is designed to give a general picture of features common to most mammals.

3 Cell structure and function

Introduction

The many organs within the body of the higher animals are specialized for the various tasks and processes which contribute to the growth, maintenance activity and reproduction of the organisms. In consequence the cells of many of these organs are highly differentiated for their roles. Nevertheless it is possible to describe a generalized cell, and to define the structures and organelles present in nearly all cells of the body. This chapter will first attempt to describe cells using an epithelial cell as a prototype. The function of organelles seen within cells by light microscopy (LM) and electron microscopy (EM) will be explained (Fig. 3.1). Some of the modifications and varieties of cell types in different organs in the body will be indicated. A description will be given of how cells are held together in tissues, and how they may influence other cells. The processes occurring in cell membranes by which the cell is able to exchange chemical substances with its environment will be described. Finally, an account will be given of some of the physicochemical and biological processes enabling cells to maintain their composition and volume.

Morphology and intracellular structures

The following is a description of the nature and function of the main features visible by EM in a 'typical' cell. Figure 3.1a shows an epithelial cell in diagrammatic form. Figure 3.1b–d and Fig. 3.2a–f are EM photographs of some cellular organelles.

Plasma membrane

This membrane, approximately 7.5 nm thick, consists mainly of two layers of phospholipid. The hydrophobic ends of these long-chain molecules are arranged towards each other in the centre of the layer. The hydrophilic ends lie towards extracellular fluid (outer layer) and towards cytoplasm (inner layer). Proteins are spread over or attached to these hydrophilic ends, both inside and outside. Protein molecules also span the membrane, passing through the phospholipid layers. It is likely that ions or small molecules pass through the membrane in either direction by way of these membrane-spanning proteins. These protein molecules are not fixed structures but shift around in the plasma membrane. So, too, do the phospholipids. The term 'liquid mosaic' has been used for the cell membrane; the pattern of the mosaic is continually changing. Very high resolution EM has revealed the presence on

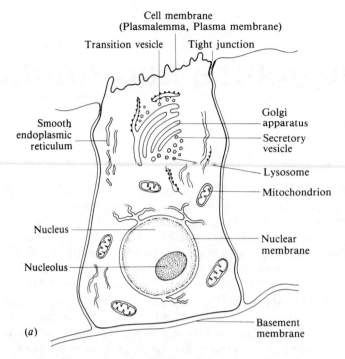

Cell membrane
(Plasmalemma, Plasma membrane)

Transition vesicle   Tight junction

Golgi apparatus

Secretory vesicle

Smooth endoplasmic reticulum

Lysosome

Mitochondrion

Nucleus

Nuclear membrane

Nucleolus

Basement membrane

(a)

Figure 3.1   Cell and organelles. (a) Typical cell: an epithelial cell forming part of a surface layer, standing on basement membrane. Several of the organelles visible by EM are shown. (b) Intestinal epithelial cell (pig). n: nucleus; o: nucleolus; r: rough ER; m: mitochondria; white arrows: lateral plasmalemma; white arrowheads: apical tight junctions (see Fig. 3.4); open arrow: basement membrane; asterisk: Golgi apparatus. × 3400. (c) Section through mitochondrion showing double mitochondrial membrane and cristae (c). × 4700. (d) Placental cell (sheep). n: nucleus; o: nucleolus; y: lysosomes. × 3000. (b–d: Courtesy of F. P. B. Wooding.)

the outer surface of the cell of a thin layer of material called the glycocalyx or 'fluffy layer' (Fig. 3.2g); it is probably made of a carbohydrate-linked protein (mucopolysaccharide).

Nucleus

The nucleus contains the chromosomes, invisible through most of the life of the cell as structureless 'nucleoplasm', but becoming apparent at cell division. The chromosomes contain the genes, the hereditary elements which are passed on by each cell to its daughter cells, and which control the activities of the cell. The genes determine, for instance, which particular enzymes and other proteins the cell can synthesize. All cells in an organism have the same genes; yet they manufacture different proteins and enzymes in different tissues. So we surmise that in different organs or tissues the activities of many of the genes are suppressed, and only those few appropriate to that tissue are active. The nucleus is itself bounded by a double-layered membrane, the

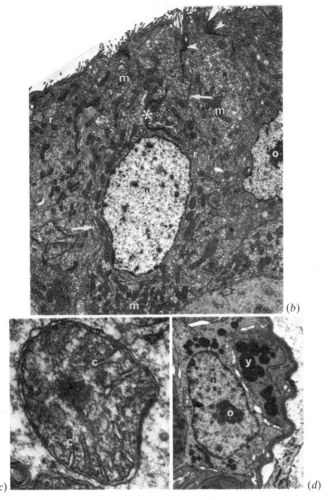

Figure 3.1 *(continued)*

inner layer of which has many pores. A more densely staining structure, the nucleolus, is sometimes visible within the nucleus.

Mitochondrion

It is in the mitochondria, both on their much-folded internal membranes (cristae) and within the matrix between the membranes, that the enzymes concerned with the cell's oxidative metabolism (and energy production) are situated. It is likely that the cristae form a solid base or structure, giving a stable position to a series of enzyme molecules and thus allowing them to work in a particular sequence, the product of one enzymic reaction being the substrate of the next.

Mitochondria of the cells of epithelia which are occupied in active absorption (small intestine, for instance, and renal tubules) are all lined up along the end of the cell towards which the material is being moved. We may speculate that it is in this region of the cell that the greatest energy production is required.

In striated muscle fibres, where much of the cytoplasm is filled with orientated structural proteins, the mitochondria are tucked away in a row along the edges of the myofibrils. Red cells of the blood (erythrocytes) have no mitochondria and no oxidative metabolism; their energy source is the glycolytic breakdown of glucose.

Endoplasmic reticulum

This series of tubes and cavities running through the cytoplasm is made of a single layer of lipoprotein similar to that of the plasma membrane. It is continuous with the outer of the two membranes around the nucleus: the nucleus bounded by its inner membrane thus lies in one of the cavities of the endoplasmic reticulum (ER). Attached to the wall of the *rough* ER are ribosomes, spherical particles 10 nm in diameter consisting of nucleoprotein, on which the cell's proteins are synthesized. *Smooth* ER has no ribosomes on its wall. In myofibrils of striated muscles the (smooth) ER is called sarcoplasmic reticulum. It lies among the contractile actin and myosin filaments and is concerned with the repeated release and reuptake of calcium ions during muscle contraction. There is very little rough ER in striated muscle. A few types of cell lack ER altogether. Figure 3.2 shows some cell organelles not present in the epithelial cell of Fig. 3.1.

Golgi apparatus

This is a series of membrane-enclosed flattened cavities or tubes, often forming a dome-shaped stack, which conjugate and package proteins made on the ribosomes. Portions of rough ER bud off to form transition vesicles which then enter the convex surface of the Golgi stack. The Golgi apparatus is prominent in cells such as those of digestive glands which are synthesizing digestive enzymes and of endocrine glands synthesizing hormones. The enzyme molecules are packaged into vesicles during storage within the Golgi apparatus, and then carried to the cell surface where they are released by exocytosis into a channel (the acinus) in the middle of a group of glandular cells. Thus the active enzymes never come into contact with the cell's own cytoplasm.

Lysosomes

Small vesicles called lysosomes (smaller than mitochondria) are sometimes formed in the ER and Golgi apparatus. Lysosomes contain hydrolytic enzymes. The function of these enzymes is to destroy organic material, either foreign material such as bacteria invading the cell, or else material derived from the cell itself as its structure is remodelled during growth and development; in both cases the particle of organic material is sealed off in a membrane-enclosed vesicle, and the lysosome discharges its enzymes into this vesicle, where digestion proceeds. The cytoplasm itself is thus protected from digestion. Lysosomes are particularly prominent in white blood cells (leucocytes).

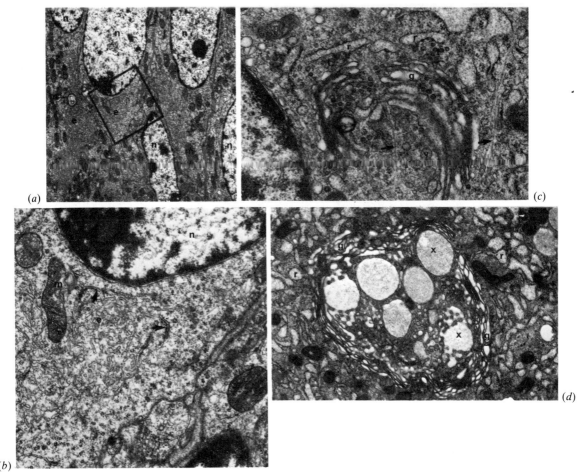

Figure 3.2   Some cell organelles. (a) Uterine epithelium (cow). Portions of five cells (five nuclei) are visible at this magnification. Note relative sizes of nucleus (n), mitochondria (m) and ER (e). ×3400. (b) Enlargement of area in the square in (a), to show abundant smooth ER (e) and short lengths of rough ER (arrows). m: mitochondrion; n: nucleus. ×16 800. (c) Golgi apparatus (g) associated with rough ER (r). Transitional vesicles (t) budded off from rough ER take protein formed on the ribosomes into the Golgi, where they are processed, packaged and extruded as secretory vesicles (v). Note the microtubules (arrows) along which the secretory vesicles are moved around the cell. ×21 400. (d) Mature Golgi apparatus showing production of large secretory vesicles (x). Rough ER (r) has dilated cisternae in these cells. ×9400.

(*continued*)

Microtubules

These organelles are made of a protein called 'tubulin'. In certain situations they may be transient structures, formed, for example, at cell division, when they constitute the thread-like structure of the spindle along which the chromosomes migrate to opposite

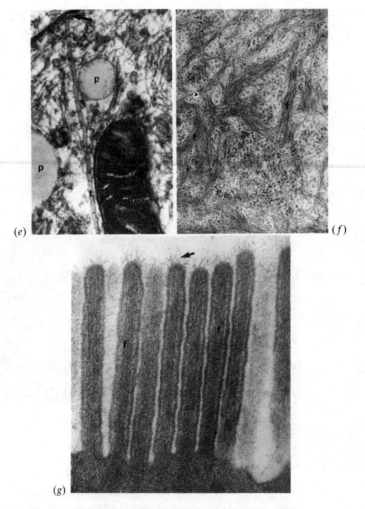

Figure 3.2   (*e*) Mammary gland epithelium (sheep). Microtubule (t) is visible, attached to cell membrane (arrow). p: lipid droplet. × 60 300. (*f*) Mammary duct epithelium (sheep). Bundles of microfilaments (f) are present, and give robustness to the tissue. × 33 500. (*g*) Intestinal cell (pig). Microvilli at surface show plasma membrane and glycocalyx (fluffy coat) (arrow). Note filament bundles (f), which give rigidity to the microvilli. × 54 900. (*d, g*: Courtesy of F. P. B. Wooding.)

poles of the cell prior to cleavage. Microtubules are also formed in any cell which is undergoing growth, regrowth or remodelling. They are seen as permanent features in nerve cells, running parallel with the long axis of an axon or dendrite, and may help to give firmness to its structure. They are also present in structures concerned in cell movement, such as the flagellum of the spermatozoon and the cilia of the bronchiolar mucous membrane.

Microfilaments

Filaments much finer than the microtubules are sometimes seen in cells by EM. They appear at cell division when the cytoplasm of a single cell is cleaving to form two daughter cells; and they may even cause this cytoplasmic rearrangement. Microfilaments, however, are also seen in cells which are not dividing. Perhaps they help to form a cytoskeleton within the cytoplasm, giving the cell a certain architectural structure.

Summarizing, it is clear that all cells have a plasma membrane, and all have a nucleus at some stage in their life history. Other organelles are more prominent in some types of tissue than in others; they are not universally present, and indeed when present may have only a transient existence. The function of some cellular structures seen by EM is still under investigation.

Cells as components of tissue

Some types of tissue

From the description already given it would not be difficult for a beginner in the use of LM to recognize many tissues as consisting of cells, and to identify individual cells and their contents. Epithelial tissue, including glandular epithelium, liver or kidney tissue or nerve tissue, could be identified as recognizably cellular. Each cell is bounded by a membrane, and one nucleus is present in each cell. Problems might occur for the novice, however, who looked for the first time at cross-sections of cartilage, or bone or at fat, or striated muscle.

Some of these less obviously cellular tissues are shown in Fig. 3.3. For cartilage and bone the cells are few, and are embedded in a large extracellular solid or semisolid matrix. In cartilage, which contains no blood vessels, the cells must receive their nutrition by diffusion of substances through this gel-like matrix; in bone the cells are present in spaces (lacunae) among the layers of solid bone crystals, and are in touch with each other through minute canaliculi formed between the lacunae and penetrated by processes from each cell. The cells can thus communicate with each other and ultimately with those in the vicinity of blood vessels. In fat (adipose tissue) the very large cells (up to 120 μm in diameter) may be spherical but are often squashed into polyhedral shapes by mutual deformation. Almost the whole volume of the cell is occupied by a fat droplet so it is quite hard to find the nucleus. There is a thin layer of cytoplasm around the fat droplet, in which can be found a small Golgi apparatus, a few mitochondria and some ER.

In striated muscle, groups of cells have coalesced to form muscle fibres. Each fibre is completely bounded by a membrane, and (in the adult) the nuclei of all the cells which have joined to form it lie side by side along the length of the fibre immediately below the membrane. This arrangement is called a syncytium. The nuclei within the fibre do not divide further, and enlargement of a muscle during growth takes place by development of existing fibres. (The total number of fibres in each muscle is fixed well before birth in mammalian development.)

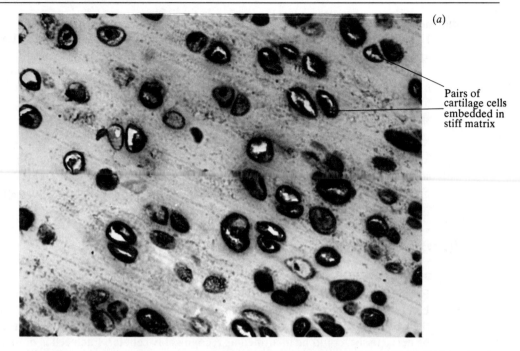

Pairs of
cartilage cells
embedded in
stiff matrix

Figure 3.3 Three types of tissue. (*a*) Cartilage. × 180. Cells secrete collagenous material which hardens to a semisolid matrix; when cells embedded in the matrix subsequently undergo mitosis, the daughter cells are unable to move apart, so cells in cartilage are often found in pairs. (*b*) White fat. × 180. Cells are almost entirely occupied by a large droplet of fat, the cytoplasm and flattened nucleus forming a thin film around the droplet. (*c*) Striated muscle. × 130. Each cylindrical fibre is formed by merging of several cells, producing a syncytium; flattened nuclei of the component cells are visible packed around the cylinder just below the fibre membrane. (Courtesy of P. Harris and P. Taylor.)

Contacts between cells

There is some speculation on the question of what material or process keeps cells joined together to form a tissue. One possibility is that each cell's outer 'fluffy layer' (glycocalyx), consisting of mucopolysaccharide molecules with projecting negatively charged carboxyl groups, is bound to that of adjacent cells by Ca^{++} ions, which function as intercellular bridges; so the combination of calcium and mucopolysaccharide acts as a kind of glue sticking cells together. The fact that removal of calcium from the medium surrounding tissues tends to make the tissue cells fall apart is in line with this idea.

In tissues lacking any sign of a glycocalyx, adjacent cell surfaces have been carefully studied by EM, and several types of junction have been observed. An artefact of preparation for EM studies shows the plasma membrane of cells as a pair of electron-dense lines, each line being the uranyl-salt 'staining' attached to a protein layer at the hydrophilic ends of the phospholipids. There is often a gap of about 20 nm between the plasma membranes of adjacent cells, as revealed by EM. But there are at least

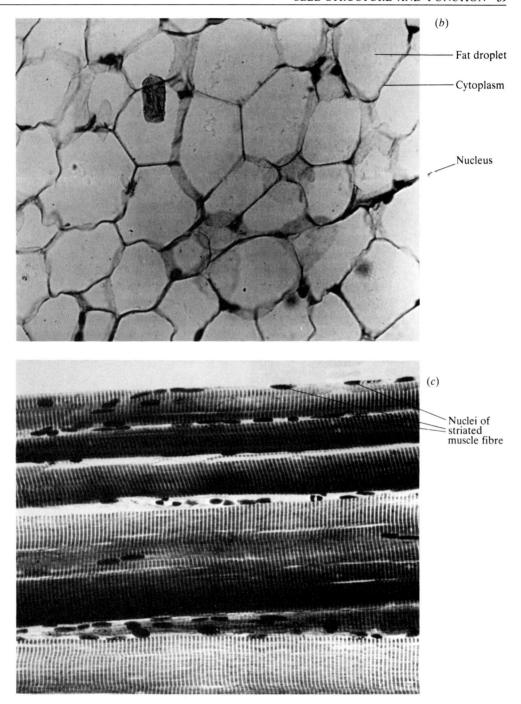

(b)

— Fat droplet

— Cytoplasm

Nucleus

(c)

Nuclei of
striated
muscle fibre

Figure 3.3 (*continued*)

three types of junction observable by EM in which adjacent cells come closer than this. These are shown in Fig. 3.4.

At *tight junctions* the outer electron-dense lines of the two cells actually fuse to form a single line. Tight junctions can be observed in many tissues, for instance between epithelial cells in the lining of the intestine. The tight junction does not extend along the whole length of the surface-to-surface contact line. In the intestinal epithelium it is present only at the part closest to the intestinal lumen. It would prevent most organic molecules and many ions from slipping out of the intestine between the cells, but it might still allow intercellular passage of water.

At *gap junctions* (or nexuses) the two plasma membranes come closer than 20 nm; they may be only about 2–4 nm apart. Water, ions and small molecules can pass between cells at a gap junction. Also, at this point the cell walls themselves are rather permeable, so there may be effective electrical continuity and even passage of ions from cell to cell here. The electric charge spreading over heart muscle fibres during cardiac contraction probably does so by way of gap junctions.

Desmosomes are points where the walls of adjacent cells are particularly close and the lines of the plasma membrane appear thickened, in EM staining. The desmosomes

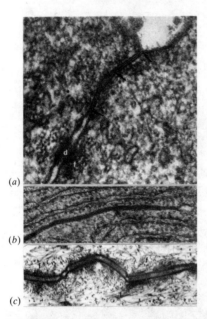

(a)

(b)

(c)

Figure 3.4 Contacts between cells. (*a*) Tight junctions (between arrows) and desmosomes (d). At points along the tight junctions (arrows) the outer electron-dense 'lines' of the two cells merge to give a single line. Cytoplasm adjacent to the desmosome contains dense electron-opaque microfilaments (f). Mammary epithelium (goat). × 72 000. (*b*) Gap junction. The lines of the plasma membrane run parallel, with uniform density; there are no dense bodies or organelles in the adjacent cytoplasm; molecules up to a molecular weight of 1000 can pass from one cell to the next through such junctions. Stomach epithelium (rabbit). × 32 000. (*c*) Series of desmosomes joining cells of amnion (sheep); such a group of desmosomes together with their associated microfilaments (f) provides considerable resistance to tearing. × 28 000. (*a–c*: Courtesy of F. P. B. Wooding.)

may be thought of as a pair of circular discs, one on each cell, which keep the cells tightly pressed together at this point, like the two halves of metal press-studs. Microfilaments are seen in the dense cytoplasm close to the desmosomes; and there is often an abundance of mitochondria near the desmosomes, suggesting that there is energy-requiring work being done here, in holding the cell together. Desmosomes are especially common in tissues such as skin where some mechanical rigidity is required. They hold cells together but do not form a barrier to intercellular passage of material.

Cell division (mitosis)

During growth, cells divide frequently, each division forming two daughter cells. This process of division, called *mitosis*, occurs in all tissues during prenatal life. After birth, cells of many tissues, notably nerve and muscle, cease to divide, and subsequent growth consists of development and enlargement of existing cells. Muscle fibres in particular can undergo much enlargement with use, a process called 'physiological hypertrophy'; and it is possible, too, that nerve cells in the CNS can form new dendritic connections after birth. Cells of other tissues continue to divide throughout life: the precursors of red cells (erythroblasts) and white cells (leucoblasts) are notable examples. Another example is the surface layer (endothelium) of the alimentary canal; and again, the cells of bone (osteoblasts) divide during the postnatal growth of the skeleton. In other organs (kidney and liver for example), although the cells do not divide in normal postnatal life, they are able to restart the process of cell division if the total amount of tissue is decreased. If one complete kidney, or about two-thirds of the liver, is removed, cells of the remaining organ, or portion of the organ, suddenly start dividing, and continue to do so until the original weight of tissue of the appropriate type has been restored. This remarkable phenomenon has led to much speculation. What signal initiates it? And what terminates the process, at restoration of the original weight of tissue? Chemical signals are probable but the details are still under investigation. Cell division in the formation of new tissue is called *hyperplasia*, in contrast with *hypertrophy*, the enlargement of existing cells.

Several aspects of the series of cell divisions involved in reproduction are considered in Chapter 15. The process of cell division, studied particularly in embryonic tissue, has been known in broad outline for many years. Typically, a cell division takes 1–2 h. The process is shown diagrammatically in Fig. 3.5, and EM photographs of several stages are given in Fig. 3.6.

A cell not undergoing division is said to be at interphase. At this stage two small bodies, the centrioles, are just visible (by LM). Electron microscopy has revealed that the centrioles are rigid cylinders about 400 μm in length, closed at one end; and at this stage they are arranged with their long axes at right angles to each other. The first event in cell division is that the centrioles divide.

The members of the centriole pairs thus formed migrate to opposite poles of the nucleus, and simultaneously there appears between them a set of microtubules forming a spindle-shaped structure (prophase). Meanwhile within the nucleus the amorphous mass of granular chromatin forms itself into a series of threads, the

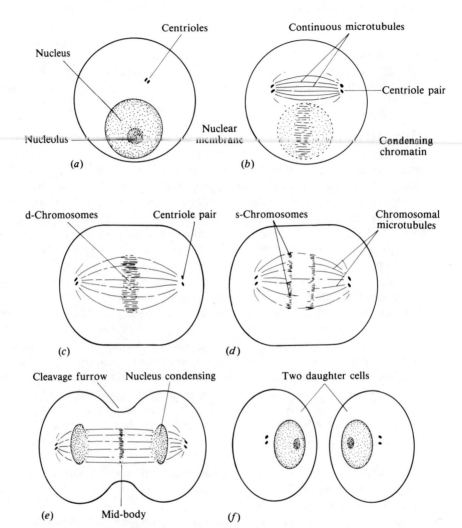

Figure 3.5 Stages of mitosis. (*a*) Interphase. Nucleolus clearly visible in nucleus, centrioles just visible in cytoplasm. (*b*) Prophase. Centrioles have divided and separated, continuous microtubules forming spindle between them, nuclear membrane distintegrating and chromatin condensing. (*c*) Metaphase. Condensed chromatin forming d-chromosomes aligns in equatorial plane of spindle; chromosomal microtubules develop and pass to poles of spindle. (*d*) Anaphase. s-Chromosomes, formed by splitting of d-chromosomes, move to opposite ends of spindle. (*e*) Telophase. Cleavage furrow forming between two ends of spindle; chromatin condensing into nuclei; microtubules degenerating; mid-body appears. (*f*) Two daughter cells entering interphase. Nuclear membrane complete and nucleolus present; centrioles visible.

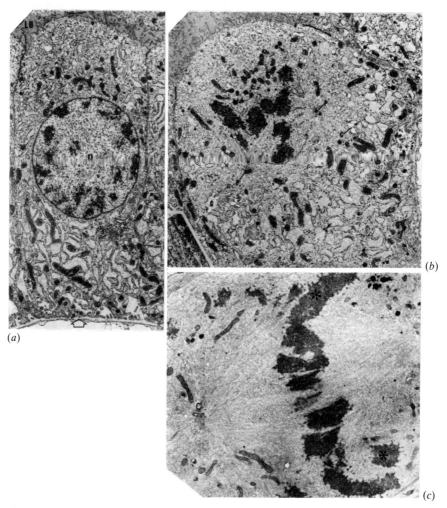

Figure 3.6 Stages of mitosis in thyroid gland (*a, b, d–f*) and fibroblast (*c*) (rat). (*a*) Cell at early prophase. Nucleus (n) has moved to central position between basement membrane (open arrow) and lumen of follicle of gland (LU). × 3800. (*b*) Late prophase. Nuclear membrane has disappeared, chromatin is condensing (*); centrioles have divided and the pairs so formed have moved to opposite poles of the nucleus (P, P); residual nuclear membrane material is visible between arrow-heads; arrows show groups of lysosomes; G: Golgi bodies. × 4700. (*c*) Metaphase. Continuous microtubules have formed between the poles; chromosomes (*) are arranged in equatorial plane of spindle; pair of centrioles (c) is clearly visible at one end of the spindle. × 5800.

(continued)

chromosomes (sometimes called d-chromosomes, because the DNA within them is double-stranded). At this stage the chromosomes can be identified as pairs, each member of a homologous pair having the same size and shape and general appearance. The nuclear membrane breaks down and the nucleolus disappears. The spindle, with paired centrioles at either end, moves to a central position in the cell,

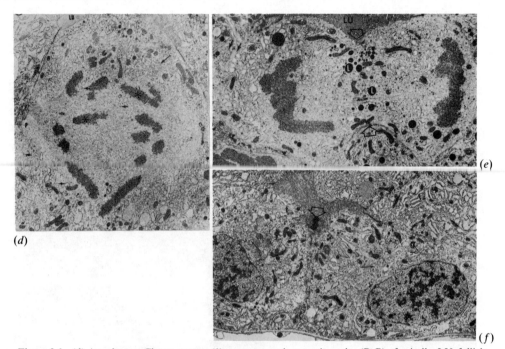

(d)

(e)

(f)

Figure 3.6 (d) Anaphase. s-Chromosomes (*) move towards opposite poles (P, P) of spindle; LU: follicle lumen; long arrow: 70-nm vesicles; short arrows: apical vesicles. × 4900. (e) Telophase. Chromosomal material aggregates and a cleavage furrow (open arrows) appears at centre of spindle. LU: follicle lumen; L: lysosomes in central furrow. × 3400. (f) Very late telophase. Nuclear membranes have formed round each daughter nucleus; a few residual microtubules of the spindle (i) and a mid-body (open arrow) can be seen. g: Golgi body; arrow: cluster of apical vesicles. × 4900. (a, b, d–f: Reproduced by permission from Zeligs, J. D. and S. H. Wollman, *Journal of Ultrastructural Research*, **66**, 53–77 and 97–108, 1979. c: Reproduced by copyright permission of Rockefeller University Press from Brinkley, B. R. and J. Cartwright, *Journal of Cell Biology*, **50**, 416–431, 1971.)

entangling the chromosomes in the microtubules, and the chromosomes arrange themselves in such a way that a particular point on each one, called its centromere, lies in the equatorial plane of the spindle (metaphase). From the centromeres another set of microtubules grows outward, towards each centriole, between the existing microtubules of the spindle.

Each chromosome now splits longitudinally into two chromatids (also called s-chromosomes). This splitting means that each of the daughter cells will have exactly the same set of genes. When the chromosomes are completely split, the two sets of s-chromosomes move apart, the spindle elongates, and the cell itself becomes longer in shape (anaphase). The result is that the two sets of s-chromosomes come close to the ends of the spindle. At this stage a constriction appears at the centre of the cell, forming a waist (telophase). This waist becomes narrower, pulled in by encircling actin microfilaments. Finally, the waist pinches off the cytoplasm into two separate cells, though residual microtubules of the spindle sometimes remain attached for a short time to one or other daughter cell. The two daughter cells then enter the stage of interphase. It is during interphase that the DNA of the s-chromosomes reduplicates to form double-stranded DNA, as is present in d-chromosomes which will undergo the next mitosis. The process of DNA synthesis takes about 8 h—much longer than mitosis itself.

In eukaryotic organisms genetic information is contained in the DNA of the chromosomes. The genetic information is carried in the form of a code of triplet sequences of nucleotides (bases) within the DNA strands. When the triplet code is transcribed to messenger RNA (mRNA), the DNA double helix is parted in the region of the gene and transcription occurs under the influence of an enzyme: DNA-dependent RNA polymerase. Messenger RNA moves from the nucleus to the cell cytoplasm for the translation of the message with the formation of proteins.

Protein synthesis

Molecular biologists have exploited this final stage of cell division to help to identify amino-acid sequences of proteins, and also to prepare specific proteins in bulk. Use is made of a rapidly dividing bacterium, *Escherichia coli*, or else of isolated mammalian cell lines, which can be grown in a culture medium. The appropriate DNA is introduced into the cultured cells by the help of a phage, and the newly synthesized protein is harvested from the culture medium. Protein hormones such as human growth hormone prepared in this way are in fact safer to use in treatment than hormones prepared from cadavers.

Meiosis

A different type of cell division, known as meiosis, occurs during the formation of the male and female gametes (sperm and eggs) in all organisms which reproduce sexually. During meiosis, each chromosome splits longitudinally. In each homologous pair of chromosomes, one chromatid from each member of the pair migrates to one end of the spindle and the other two chromatids to the other end; and the two chromatids unite to form a single chromosome. In consequence the daughter cells from this division have only half the original number of chromosomes; such cells are called haploid cells; cells with the normal full number of chromosomes are called diploid. Each daughter cell formed from the meiotic division divides once more (by mitosis), forming a group of four cells. In males, all four of these become spermatozoa; in females, only one of these four develops into an ovum and the remaining three degenerate. (These three are known as polar bodies.) At fertilization the nuclei of sperm and ovum fuse and the diploid number of chromosomes is restored.

Chemical signalling and receptors

Cells make up tissues and tissues form organs, all of which contribute to the survival of the living organism. So there must be the possibility of communication between cells and organs, and routes through which one cell or organ can influence another. Much of the communicating and influencing is carried out by chemicals released from one cell and received by another. If the chemical substance affects only a few cells in the immediate neighbourhood of its point of release, the process is called *paracrine*. If the releasing cell is a nerve cell and the receiving cell is a muscle or gland or another nerve cell, it is called *neurocrine*. If the chemical is released into the blood circulation and carried to a target cell or organ elsewhere, it is called *endocrine*. These processes are shown diagrammatically in Fig. 3.7. They will be considered in more detail in Chapter 14.

An example of a paracrine system is provided by bradykinin, a short-chain polypeptide made from one of the plasma proteins. It has the property of dilating small blood vessels in the immediate vicinity of its point of production, and is then rapidly broken down. It is formed from plasma protein by a proteolytic enzyme released during the activity of sweat glands and salivary glands. Another example is provided by prostaglandins, made in and released from many types of cell, and affecting cells nearby; again, one of the effects is transient dilatation of arterioles. For neurocrine processes a typical example is the release of the transmitter acetylcholine into the synaptic cleft at the neuromuscular junction, the first stage of the process by which a nerve excites a muscle. Neurocrine secretions, too, are quickly destroyed by enzymes in the immediate neighbourhood of their point of action. As for endocrine activity, most readers will already be familiar with such processes. An example is provided by the release of the hormone insulin from the islet tissue of the pancreas, from which it circulates in the blood and promotes uptake of plasma glucose into many cells of the body.

In general these chemical messengers do not themselves enter the cells which they influence, but attach themselves to a specific molecule (or part of a molecule, or

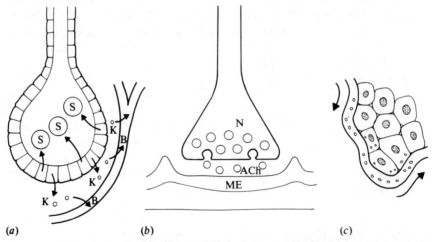

(a)   (b)   (c)

Figure 3.7   Chemical signals between cells. (a) Paracrine. Sweat gland and small capillary. Gland cells release sweat (S) into lumen, and also a proteolytic enzyme, kallikrein (K), into interstitial fluid; this diffuses into capillaries and hydrolyses a plasma protein to produce the polypeptide bradykinin (B), a vasodilator. (b) Neurocrine. Vesicles containing acetylcholine (ACh) fuse with membrane and release their contents by exocytosis from the nerve terminal (N); ACh diffuses across the synaptic cleft to affect the motor endplate (ME) on a muscle fibre. (c) Endocrine. Islet cells in the pancreas form the protein hormone insulin and pass it directly into the blood in capillaries permeating the gland.

chemical group) called a 'receptor', which lies on the surface of the cell. For neurocrine and endocrine activities the receptor groups are easily demonstrated and in many cases their actual structure is known. For paracrine actions the receptors are harder to identify but can be assumed to exist. In some cases the receptors are present only on certain particular cells of certain organs; the endocrine vasopressin (antidiuretic hormone) of the posterior pituitary gland for example, on reaching the kidney, becomes linked onto receptors found only on cells in a specific region of the nephron. In other cases the appropriate receptors are present in numerous organs and tissues. Adrenaline secreted from the adrenal medulla circulates in the blood for several minutes and reaches receptors in the heart, blood vessels, bronchioles of the lung, liver cells and several other places. For many of these quick-acting endocrines the immediate effect of their attachment to the surface receptor is to increase within the cell the level of a certain enzyme, adenyl cyclase, which splits ATP in the cytoplasm to give cyclic AMP (cAMP); and this increase in cAMP is itself the signal causing the particular cell to alter its level of a certain intracellular enzyme, or to change its plasma-membrane permeability, or perhaps to secrete yet another endocrine. These points will be further considered in Chapter 14. New receptors can be formed on cell surfaces under certain conditions. If a nerve to a muscle is cut and allowed to degenerate, the muscle develops on its surface a number of additional acetylcholine receptors, the effect of which is to make the muscle abnormally sensitive to acetylcholine. If the nerve regrows, these additional receptors disappear. Again, in opium addiction, receptors on the smooth muscle of organs innervated by parasympathetic nerves increase in number. A decrease in receptor numbers can also occur, sometimes in response to a chronically high level of a circulating hormone. This decrease in receptors is called 'down-regulation'. In some forms of diabetes there are too few receptors of the hormone insulin.

Movement of material across the cell membrane

The cells of all tissues lie in interstitial fluid which is in close contact with the capillaries of the blood circulation and is in fact similar in composition to an ultrafiltrate of blood plasma. Exchanges between cell and interstitial fluid of nutrients (e.g. glucose, amino acids and fatty acids), oxygen and excretory products (e.g. carbon dioxide and creatinine) are continually occurring; so the energy supply of the cells, and thus their structure, activity and integrity, is maintained. The movement of molecules and ions across the membrane takes place by several processes, a few of which themselves require a supply of energy for their performance. But consideration will first be given to processes explicable in terms of simple structure, physics and chemistry, occurring without any additional energy supply.

Diffusion, lipid solubility, size and osmosis

The rate of diffusion of a substance (s) across a membrane is proportional to the area (A) of the membrane, and to the difference in concentration ($C_1 - C_2$) between the two sides of the membrane; that is:

$$\frac{ds}{dt} = kA(C_1 - C_2)$$

where t is time (in seconds) and k is the permeability coefficient (measured in cm/s). This applies to the cell's plasma membrane, and many substances cross the membrane by simple diffusion. Oxygen is one such substance. Within the cell it is immediately taken up in a series of enzymically catalysed reactions, so the level of dissolved oxygen within the cytoplasm is low; in consequence, the diffusion gradient $(C_1 - C_2)$ is kept steep and the rate of entry is kept rapid. This is the case for many rapidly metabolized molecules. They become so rapidly involved in intracellular reactions that their concentration within the cytoplasm is effectively zero, and rate of entry by diffusion is high and constant.

Since the plasma membrane is composed largely of lipid, it is not surprising to find that lipid-soluble molecules diffuse into cells rapidly; and in fact for many small molecules their rate of entry is predictable from their oil–water partition coefficient: ethanol has a high partition coefficient and enters rapidly, glycerol a low coefficient and enters very slowly. The lipid-soluble molecules would enter into the lipid of the membrane quickly and in large quantity from the exterior and would thus maintain a steep concentration gradient through the thickness of the membrane. Size of molecules is also a factor in membrane diffusion, the smaller molecules being favoured. Small molecules have more energy of random kinetic movements than larger ones and thus a more rapid rate of diffusion. Also, the membrane behaves as if it contained narrow water-filled pores about 4 nm in diameter which, for small molecules, would provide an additional route of diffusion not available to a molecule of similar oil–water partition coefficient but too large to squeeze through the pore.

Osmosis is the movement of water across a membrane, and is a special case of diffusion: the water moves from the region where it is at higher 'concentration' (in relation to solute) to the region of lower 'concentration'. Water moves quickly in both directions across the membrane, and the cell cytoplasm is close to osmotic equilibrium with the interstitial fluid (though as we shall see later it may be slightly hypertonic to interstitial fluid, i.e. of greater solute concentration). If cells are placed in a solution more dilute than normal interstitial fluid, they swell by entry of water; in a more concentrated medium, they shrink.*

No biological membrane is a perfect hypothetical 'semipermeable membrane', permeable to water and impermeant to all solutes. Solutes readily move in and out of cells and there is rarely a situation in which cells either swell or shrink, to any great extent, in normal life. But as we shall see, osmosis is of great importance in the movement of water from one compartment of the body to another, through membranes composed of sheets of cells, not just a single plasma membrane.

---

* After brain injury small quantities of hypertonic solutions may be infused into the cerebral blood vessels, causing the brain cells to shrink, and thus making the brain tissue less liable to further damage by pressure within the cranium.

Carrier-mediated diffusion

All transport processes so far considered would take place just as well across an artificial membrane of phospholipid containing a few small water-filled pores. There is nothing peculiar to biological systems in these processes, all of which are predictable from well-established physical and chemical principles. In contrast, carrier-mediated diffusion is a uniquely biological process. In this process, diffusion proceeds down the concentration gradient but far more quickly than could be predicted from the known properties of the molecule concerned. Several types of hexose sugar enter cells faster than pentoses, which have smaller molecules and similar solubility properties. Glycerol penetrates most cells very slowly. Its permeability coefficient is only 2×10^{-7} cm/s. But it penetrates human red cells 100 times faster, with a permeability coefficient of 2×10^{-5} cm/s. These rapid movements are explained by postulating in the cell surface a carrier molecule to which the penetrating molecule becomes attached, and which somehow passes the molecule into the cell's cytoplasm very rapidly. There is much evidence to support the suggestion of this attachment, but few clear accounts of how the attachment then leads to the transfer of the carried molecule. One idea is that the attachment somehow causes a reorientation of the carrier within the membrane, so that the part of the carrier to which the transferred molecule is linked flips over towards the cytoplasm, drops off its load there, and flips back again, and picks up another molecule (Fig. 3.8a). In any case, the result is that molecules reach the cytoplasm faster than they otherwise would do, but they cannot be transferred 'uphill', that is, against a chemical or electrical gradient.

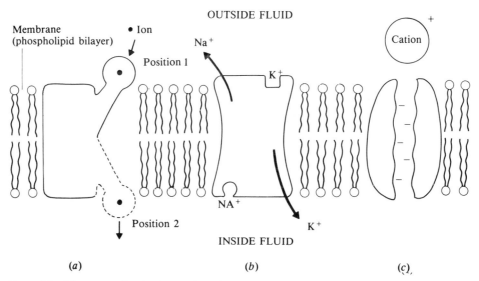

Figure 3.8 Movement of molecules and ions through membranes. (a) Specific carrier taking up ion from extracellular fluid and 'flipping' into a changed orientation in the membrane, releasing ion within cell. (b) Sodium–potassium exchange pump, requiring energy in movement of ions against chemical gradients. (c) Ion channels, membrane-spanning proteins specific for certain ions; when the channel opens, the passive movement of the ion is allowed.

It is assumed that the carrier molecules are permanent structural proteins of the plasma membrane, enabling the cell to carry out this activity. The usual substances for which carriers exist are sugars, amino acids and other small metabolizable organic molecules. But, in addition, cells can make new carrier molecules. Bacterial cells are particularly successful in this respect: if grown on a medium containing a type of sugar which does not normally penetrate the cell wall, they are soon induced to form carrier molecules which facilitate its penetration.

Active transport

Active transport means the movement of materials by a specific energy-requiring process, i.e. not simply the continuous non-specific cellular metabolic processes required in keeping the cell alive and its membranes normal, but a defined energy-releasing reaction linked to this particular transport process. Many though not all of such active transport processes involve 'uphill transport', leading to the accumulation of material against its electrochemical gradient. The essential property of active transport, however, is that it is dependent on metabolism and stops almost immediately if the energy-releasing reaction is inhibited.

The transport mechanisms considered so far have been illustrated by examples of movement of whole molecules, and the term 'concentration gradient' across the membrane has been appropriate. However, the best-known example of active transport involves movement of ions: the cations Na^+ and K^+ (Fig. 3.8b). These are charged particles and the plasma membrane itself is charged (the interior of the cell is electronegative relative to the exterior). So passive movement *towards* a thermodynamic equilibrium and active transport *away* from such an equilibrium must take into account not only the concentration gradient, but also the electrical gradients, since charged particles move towards areas of opposite polarity to their own. In this case, therefore, we must consider *electrochemical potential gradients* rather than mere chemical gradients (see Appendix 2). An 'uphill' movement of an ion across a membrane would comprise a movement against its concentration gradient, or towards the side of the same polarity as its own, or both. Like carrier-mediated diffusion, active transport requires a carrier molecule in or close to the membrane.

At all surfaces of animal cells there is active transport of Na^+ ions *out of* the cell, and K^+ ions *into* it. These two processes are linked and their source of energy is the strongly exothermic reaction of splitting ATP. Indeed the enzyme catalysing the ATP breakdown is identical with or closely related to the carrier molecule of the Na^+ and K^+ ions. If ATP breakdown is inhibited (by cooling mammalian cells, or depriving them of glucose), the active transport abruptly ceases. (Two substances moving in opposite directions across a membrane by closely linked processes are known as *antiports*. The Na^+ and K^+ ions are antiports in this active transport.)

A primary function of active sodium transport is the maintenance of the ionic composition of cells. There is a steep electrochemical potential gradient for Na^+ ions inwards (steeper than the gradient for K^+ ions outwards). In consequence, if active transport were to cease, Na^+ ions would quickly enter the cell by passive processes and accumulate in the cytoplasm. Active transport of Na^+ and K^+ ions helps to maintain the appropriate composition of intracellular fluid. Fortunately for the cell's energy balance, the plasma membrane's passive permeability to these ions is fairly low anyway (k for the K^+ ion is about 10^{-8} cm/s and for the Na^+ ion, 10^{-10} cm/s). Thus, the metabolic work involved in the active transport is not too large.

In addition to maintaining cytoplasmic composition, Na^+ transport (the 'sodium pump') has other functions in certain tissues. For instance in intestinal cells the carrier molecules for glucose and for amino acids require (or function more rapidly with) an Na^+ ion; so during absorption, Na^+ and (say) glucose, bound to the same carrier, enter the cell together from the intestinal lumen. The Na^+ is immediately pumped out by active transport, thus keeping the chemical gradient from lumen to cell as high as possible and facilitating the entry of another glucose–sodium complex. So glucose movement is linked to sodium movement and, in the complete absence of sodium, glucose enters the cells only at the rate predicted from passive diffusion. (In the carrier-mediated entry of Na^+ and glucose into the cell, the Na^+ ion and the glucose are described as *symports*: two substances passing through a membrane in the same direction by linked processes.) Another function of active sodium transport is in assisting the movement of water across epithelia, from one fluid compartment to another, perhaps of the same osmolarity so that water could not move between the compartments by simple osmosis. The sodium pump builds up a hypertonic solution in a limited extracellular space forming a third compartment between the two isotonic compartments; and water is transferred by osmosis plus hydrostatic pressure. This process will be described in more detail in the next chapter, in connection with intestinal absorption of water.

Ion channels

Some of the transmembrane proteins may form specific ion channels, allowing rapid passage of certain ions. One may visualize a large membrane-spanning molecule as containing a channel lined with, say, negatively charged groups on side-chains of amino acids, which would pass on a cation from group to group down the channel (Fig. 3.8c). These channels may be highly specific, allowing the passage of one ionic species but excluding another of similar size and charge. Their specificity is demonstrable by means of specific blockers: for instance tetrodotoxin, a poisonous derivative of a certain fish, blocks Na^+ ion channels, and another poison, tetraethyl ammonium, blocks K^+ ion channels; Mg^{++} ions bind at the outer end of Ca^{++} ion channels at nerve endings, not moving through the channels themselves but preventing Ca^{++} ions from passing. Many ion channels appear to have 'gates' at one or other end, which have to be 'opened' (perhaps by a rearrangement of chemical groups or charges at the surface) before the ions can rush through down their diffusion gradient. An example of this process of opening and shutting is observed during impulse conduction in excitable cells (Chapter 9).

Ionic movement through such channels is quite different from transport via carrier molecules in the membrane. It is thought that carrier molecules (for example the carrier involved in the sodium–potassium exchange pump) actually have to move through (or turn around in) the thickness of the membrane, picking up a K^+ ion at one side and an Na^+ ion at the other. The ion-channel molecules cannot move around in the membrane. Ionic movement through open channels is considerably faster than movement via carriers; and once the channel has opened, the passage of the ions requires no energy.

It is interesting that some of the antibiotics, large molecules of high molecular weight, work by inserting themselves into bacterial membranes and forming ion channels, thereby disturbing bacterial metabolism by allowing entry of ions which are normally completely or partially excluded.

Endocytosis and exocytosis

These processes are the means by which large particles—say, fat globules or proteins or even whole bacteria—enter cells. The particle touches the plasma membrane which at that point invaginates to form a cup or cavity; the cytoplasm curves in at the lip of the cup, closing around the particle, which thus becomes contained in a vacuole within the cytoplasm. This is endocytosis. In the converse process, a fat droplet or other material in a vacuole within the cytoplasm sticks to the inside of the cell wall which at that point opens, releasing the contents of the vacuole to the exterior (Fig. 3.9).

The processes described above refer to the exchange of substances between the cell and its environment, the extracellular fluid. However, all these transport mechanisms—both the active and the passive processes—can also be observed across intracellular membranes. For example the membrane of the mitochondrion can accumulate many ions by active transport from the cytoplasm into its interior. Furthermore these same processes are involved in the movements of water, ions, organic and inorganic molecules and particles through multicellular barriers within the body, such as the walls of the intestine, capillary and kidney tubule. However, in these multicellular membranes additional processes are at work as well, notably hydrostatic pressure and bulk flow between cells.

Maintenance of cellular volume and composition

The previous sections have dealt with exchanges of material between cells and their environment, and with the influence of one cell on others through such exchanges. The environment (interstitial fluid) is itself of rather uniform composition, and (in mammals and birds) of rather steady temperature also. This comparative constancy of interstitial fluid or 'internal environment' is remarkable considering that all actively metabolizing cells are rapidly taking up molecules from it and pouring other molecules into it. Such constancy is, however, essential for the functioning of all tissues; and a number of the body's organs and systems—notably the kidneys, lungs and endocrine glands—have specific roles in contributing to the constancy of the internal environment.

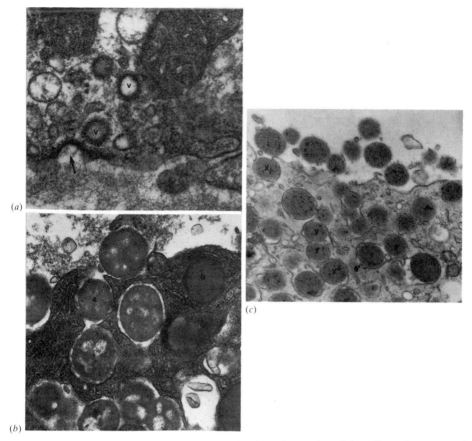

Figure 3.9   Endocytosis and exocytosis. (*a*) Invagination of a portion of the cell membrane (arrow) of mammary gland epithelial cell (sheep) is the first step of entry into the cell of material for milk production; this process forms coated vesicles (v) within the cell. × 63 800. (*b*) Pituitary gland cells (sheep) secreting a hormone; granule a has been extruded from the cell and the edges of the cytoplasm will retract and realign below it; granule b is bounded by a membrane and is still within the cytoplasm. × 30 200. (*c*) In this pituitary cell (sheep) secreting prolactin, secretory granules may be secreted individually (x) or in groups (yy) by prior fusion of membranes of individual granules within the cytoplasm. Prolactin within the granules is unequivocally identified by an immuno-gold label (black dots). × 15 100. (*a–c*: Courtesy of F. P. B. Wooding.)

In this section we consider the maintenance of constancy not of the cell's environment but of the cell itself—the composition of the cytoplasm, especially in relation to water and ions.

Non-diffusible anions

A characteristic of living cells is their function in the formation of large organic molecules from smaller ones: proteins from amino acids; glycogen or starch from sugar; or neutral fat from glycerol and fatty acids, for example. These large molecules, often aggregated into particles, once formed commonly remain in the cell until broken down. The only way in which such large molecules can pass out as such from the cell is by exocytosis; and this indeed is the process by which albumin formed in liver cells reaches the plasma, and enzymes found in digestive glands are secreted into the ducts. The large molecules in the cytoplasm are often in colloidal solution. Some of them are electrically neutral. If they bear any charge, it is negative (at the pH of the cell); that is, there is a preponderance of electronegative groups on their surfaces, and they behave as non-diffusible anions; they cannot diffuse through the cell membrane.

The relative ionic composition of cytoplasm (intracellular fluid of a muscle cell) is indicated in Fig. 3.10a, and that of interstitial fluid is shown for comparison in Fig. 3.10b. The striking features are that:

1. Within the cell the main cation is K^+, and the main anions are organic phosphates and proteins.
2. Na^+ and Cl' are the main ions of interstitial fluid, but are present in the cell in only minute amounts.
3. Protein forms about a quarter of the anionic component of intracellular fluid but only about one-twentieth of that of interstitial fluid.

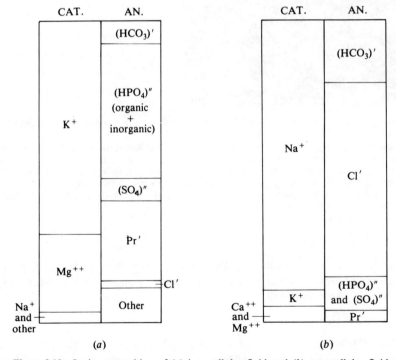

Figure 3.10 Ionic composition of (a) intracellular fluid and (b) extracellular fluid. CAT.: cations; AN: anions; Pr': protein anions.

There are some important physicochemical consequences resulting from the presence of non-diffusible anions inside a membrane. One can imitate the processes involved in the biological situation by the use of a completely inert inelastic non-biological membrane, such as cellophane or Visking tubing. In a bag made of such a membrane may be placed a solution of a soluble protein in anionic form; such a solution may be made, say, by dissolving albumin in 6 mM NaOH; the bag may then be immersed in a solution of 6 mM NaCl. The initial state of the bag and of the solutions inside and outside is shown in Fig. 3.11a. The 6 mM sodium 'albuminate', and 6 mM NaCl are ionized; the total number of particles on each side of the membrane is the same, so there is no osmotic gradient. For the Na^+ ions there is no chemical diffusion gradient either way, as their concentration is 6 mM on each side. For the albumin anions there is an outward chemical gradient, but these ions are not free to cross the membrane.

However, for Cl' ions there is a steep chemical gradient inwards into the bag. So Cl' ions at once start to move into the bag down the chemical gradient, even though this renders the bag slightly electronegative on its inner surface. By electrostatic attraction the Cl' ions drag in with them an equal number of the outside Na^+ ions (if this did not occur, the bulk of the outside solution would be left positively charged). This, of course, gives an increased Na^+ concentration inside the bag, which in turn leads to an outward diffusion of a few Na^+ ions down their chemical gradient. In this way the surfaces of the bag become charged: negatively inside, positively outside. (One may visualize this charged surface as being a local small accumulation of Na^+ ions close against the outer wall of the bag, held there by electrostatic attraction of a local accumulation of a few Cl' ions against the inner wall, although in the *bulk* of the outer solution $[Na^+] = [Cl']$.)

The 'later' condition of the cellophane/Visking bag is in fact attained within a few seconds, and is shown in Fig. 3.11b. Note that in this state:

1. The total number of particles, and thus the osmolarity, is greater inside the bag than outside.

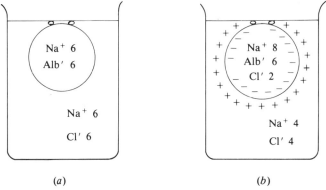

| (a) | (b) |

Figure 3.11 Separation of charge at the surface of a membrane. During movement of diffusible ions from the initial state (a) to a later state (b) in the presence of a non-diffusible anion, albumin (Alb.'), a membrane potential is developed. Na^+ and Cl' are the diffusible ions. For explanation see text.

2. In the bulk of each solution, there is electrical neutrality: inside, 8 positive charges balance $6 + 2$ negative charges; outside, 4 positive charges balance 4 negative charges.
3. The wall of the bag becomes electrically charged, inside negative to outside.
4. Na^+ inside $>$ Na^+ outside.
5. Cl' inside $<$ Cl' outside.

It is important to recognize (see (3) above) that the build-up of electrical charge at the surface of the bag is the direct consequence of the rearrangement of *diffusible* ions resulting from the presence in the bag (and not outside) of the *non-diffusible* albumin anion. There is no active transport or biological process or external work being done on the system. There is simply a separation of charge, as those ions which are free to do so move along their electrochemical potential gradients.

Note also that because of (1) above, the situation would be osmotically unstable. Water would tend to enter by osmosis if the walls were elastic; ionic concentrations would therefore alter; more ionic movements would occur, and so on.

Now we may consider how these processes as described for an inert, non-biological membrane apply to living cells. There certainly is a great excess of non-diffusible anions inside the cell, the place of manufacture of proteins; but the cations involved, and the diffusible anions, would be of many different kinds, not merely Na^+ and Cl' as in the example.

Taking the properties in order:

1. It is likely that the total osmolarity within the cell is indeed slightly greater than that of interstitial fluid, but it is difficult to measure intracellular osmolar 'concentration' accurately. The tendency for water to move osmotically into the cell is counteracted in the living animal cell by the removal of some of the internal solute by active extrusion of Na^+ ions. Living plant cells normally show turgor, indicating tendency towards osmotic entry of water, but their strong cellulose walls prevent bursting.
2. As far as is known, the bulk charges within the cell give electrical neutrality.
3. There is a charge across the cell membrane of all cells, such that the interior is electronegative.
4. The concentration of diffusible cations inside the cell is greater than that outside.
5. The concentration of diffusible anions inside is less than that outside.

Gibbs–Donnan equilibrium

If the distribution of the *diffusible* ions across a membrane in the presence of a non-diffusible anion on one side is studied, it can be observed that when equilibrium is reached, the product of the concentrations of any *pair* of diffusible ions on one side of the membrane is equal to the product of the concentrations of those same ions on the other side. (By 'pair' is meant a cation species and an anion species.) This distribution of diffusible ions is known as the Gibbs–Donnan equilibrium. In the example illustrated in Fig. 3.11b, Na^+ and Cl' are the pair of diffusible ions. Inside the bag the product of their concentration is $(8 \times 2) = 16$; outside, it is $(4 \times 4) = 16$. So the ions have attained their Gibbs–Donnan equilibrium. In cells and interstitial fluid, there are, of course, numerous ionic species involved, all of which are moving down their electrochemical potential gradients towards their Gibbs–Donnan equilibrium concentrations. If they ever succeeded in reaching this equilibrium, they would produce these concentration ratios (subscript 'o' or 'i' indicates that a concentration is outside or inside the cell, respectively):

$$\frac{[Na^+]_o}{[Na^+]_i} = \frac{[Cl']_i}{[Cl]_o} = \frac{[K^+]_o}{[K^+]_i} = \frac{[HCO_3']_i}{[HCO_3']_o} = \frac{[H^+]_o}{[H^+]_i} \text{ and so on.}$$

Of course this perfect equilibrium is not attained in living cells. For one thing, although all these ions are diffusible through the membrane to some extent, the membrane is not equally permeable to all of them. For another thing, some of these ionic species undergo active transport which takes them right away from an equilibrium attained by passive movement.

Charge on the membrane, and the Nernst equation

Referring again to Fig. 3.11b, a few Na^+ ions have left the bag under their chemical gradient $(8 > 4)$, but are being pulled back towards it by an electrostatic attraction, the interior of the membrane being electronegative. They attain their equilibrium when these two forces balance. Referring to the description of 'useful energy' in Appendix 2, we can predict how large the membrane charge must be to counteract the effect of the chemical gradient. At equilibrium, the chemical component of the driving force (outwards)

$$= RT \ln \frac{[Na^+]_i}{[Na^+]_o}$$

must be equal to the electrical component (inwards)

$$= ZF \, \Delta\Psi$$

(R = gas constant, T = absolute temperature, Z = valency of ion, F = Faraday's constant).

$\Delta\Psi$, the electrical potential difference across the membrane, is usually written as PD. Thus

$$PD = \frac{RT}{ZF} \ln \frac{[Na^+]_i}{[Na^+]_o}$$

We may convert natural logarithms to common logarithms (base 10) by the conversion factor 2.303. We may then insert numerical values for the constants R and F, and for Z, and include an appropriate value (mammalian body temperature) for T. Thus:

$$PD = \frac{RT}{ZF} \times 2.303 \times \log \frac{[Na^+]_i}{[Na^+]_o}$$

$$= \frac{RT}{ZF} \times 2.303 \times \log \left(\frac{8}{4}\right)$$

$$= \frac{RT}{ZF} \times 2.303 \times \log 2$$

$R = 8.2$ joules/mol/degree, $F = 96\,500$ coulombs/mol, and Z for a monovalent ion $= 1$. If $T = 310$ K $(=37\,°C)$,*

$$\frac{RT}{ZF} \times 2.303 \text{ becomes } \frac{8.2 \times 310 \times 2.303}{96\,500} = 0.06 \text{ V} = 60 \text{ mV}$$

and $PD = 60 \times \log 2$ mV
$\qquad = 18.1$ mV

This is called the equilibrium potential for the Na^+ ion and is usually written ε_{Na}. An analogous procedure can be carried out for the Cl' ion, but in this case, as the ion is electronegative the concentration ratio of which the logarithm is taken becomes $[Cl']_o/[Cl']_i$. The equilibrium potential for the Cl' ion, ε_{Cl}, is of course the same, in the example above, as

$$\frac{[Cl']_o}{[Cl']_i} = \frac{4}{2} = 2$$

The equation above, in its general form

$$PD = \frac{RT}{ZF} \ln \frac{[ion]_i}{[ion]_o}$$

is called the Nernst equation. (For a derivation of the Nernst equation, see Appendix 1.) It is very useful in interpreting the distribution of ions across biological membranes, whether the cell membrane, mitochondrial membrane, or multicellular membranes such as frog skin or the wall of the nephron. Suppose that the actual membrane potential difference across the membrane is measured, and suppose that the concentrations of a certain ion on each side of the membrane are measured. The equilibrium potential for that ion can be readily calculated from the Nernst equation, and if the millivoltage is identical with, or close to, the observed membrane potential, it can be assumed that the ionic distribution is passive: there is no need to invoke 'active transport', 'secretion', 'absorption' or any biological or energy-requiring process to explain the concentrations. In general, biological membranes are by no means equally permeable to all ions, or to any given ion all the time; and the observed membrane potential is likely to be close to the equilibrium potential of the ions to which the membrane (at that moment) is *most* permeable.

---

* For tissues of invertebrates and non-mammalian vertebrates a value of $T = 288\,°A$ $(=15\,°C)$ is appropriate. This gives 56 instead of 60 for the value of $[(RT/F) \times 2.303]$.

If, for any ion, the calculated equilibrium potential is very different from the observed membrane potential, this is a much more interesting situation biologically. It could mean, for instance, that the ion is not after all freely diffusible across the membrane, or that it has not reached its equilibrium, perhaps because of some additional biological process ('active transport' or 'ionic pumping') going on in the cell.

Here is an example of this use of the Nernst equation, using concentrations of the ions K^+, Cl' and Na^+, within frog muscle fibres and in the extracellular fluid surrounding them. The concentrations in mM are:

	Inside	Outside
K^+	126.0	2.5
Cl'	1.6	74.0
Na^+	15.0	145.0

$$\text{So } \varepsilon_K = -56 \log\left(\frac{126}{2.5}\right) = -56 \times \log 50.4 = 56 \times 1.7 = -95.2 \text{ mV*}$$

$$\varepsilon_{Cl} = -56 \log\left(\frac{74}{1.6}\right) = -56 \times \log 46.2 = -56 \times 1.66 = -93.0 \text{ mV}$$

$$\varepsilon_{Na} = -56 \log\left(\frac{15}{145}\right)$$

or, reversing the sign and using the reciprocal of the concentration ratio,

$$+56 \times \log\left(\frac{145}{15}\right) = +56 \times \log 9.67 = +56 \times 0.985 = +53.0 \text{ mV}$$

Now, the observed membrane potential for a muscle cell at rest is about -93 mV. So the Cl' distribution, and a major part of the K^+ ion distribution, are accounted for by purely passive processes occurring in the attainment of an electrochemical equilibrium.

For the Na^+ ion, however, the observed membrane potential is very far away from the Na^+ equilibrium potential as calculated from the Nernst equation: the Na^+ ion could not possibly be at an equilibrium here.

Before commenting further on the distribution of the Na^+ ion, it may be useful to mention another use for the Nernst equation in biological study. It can be used occasionally to measure the concentration of an ion inside the cell, or in some inaccessible medium in which ordinary chemical analysis may be difficult. If one knows on independent grounds that, say, the H^+ ion is distributed passively across a cell membrane, one can measure the $[H^+]$ outside the cell, and also the membrane potential (E_m), which would be approximately equal to ε_H. Then, the only unknown

---

* For the use of the constant 56, see previous footnote.

value in the equation

$$E_m = -56 \log \frac{[H^+]_i}{[H^+]_o}$$

is $[H^+]_i$, which can then be calculated by simple algebra.

Significance of the sodium pump

It has been found that, as for the muscle fibre for which a calculation was made previously, for many cells the observed membrane potential is far from the equilibrium potential of the Na^+ ion, and this ion cannot therefore be in an equilibrium state across the membrane. Most animal cells (but not cells of terrestrial plants) lie in a medium containing a much higher Na^+ ion concentration than that of their own cytoplasm. The membrane is slightly (but not very) permeable to Na^+, so Na^+ ions are continually leaking in at a low rate, down their diffusion gradient, and are being actively extruded, by a biological pumping mechanism which is present in the wall itself. This sodium pump is a prime example of an 'active transport' process. In fact it has been found that about a quarter of the energy produced in a cell is used in the pumping out of Na^+ ions.

It was seen in the example of the muscle cell on that the observed membrane potential, E_m, was close to, but not identical with, the equilibrium potential for the K^+ ion, ε_K. This implies that some small part of the K^+ distribution across the membrane may also be due to an active biological process. It turns out that the sodium pump, in extruding the inwardly leaking Na^+ ions, pulls in a few K^+ ions from the medium; but since the membrane is comparatively permeable to K^+, these ions quickly diffuse out again. The pump is often called a sodium–potassium exchange pump. For many cells (but by no means all), three Na^+ ions are extruded for every two K^+ ions pulled in. The sodium–potassium exchange pump is closely related to, if not identical with, the enzyme which hydrolyses ATP (ATPase).

If, for any reason, the sodium pump of a cell is inhibited or slowed, Na^+ ions will continue to leak in but will not be extruded. This will have the effect of reducing the potential difference across the membrane. The charge, instead of being, say, -93 mV, will slowly drift closer towards zero, say, to -50 mV. If the medium also contains a high [Cl'], Cl' ions will also leak in, the membrane potential opposing such movement having become lower; and the additional Na^+ and Cl' within the cell will exert an osmotic effect, drawing water into the cell also, so the cell will swell up. This can readily be seen if a piece of mammalian tissue (liver for instance) is placed in plasma (or Ringer solution with the ionic composition of plasma) in a refrigerator for a few hours. The low temperature slows down energy release to the sodium pump, the cells swell, and the tissue weight increases. If the tissue is then returned to a warm environment, 37 °C, and given oxygen and glucose, the sodium pumping restarts, and the cells extrude all the excess Na^+ ions and go back to their former size, shape and condition. At the restarting, the excess internal Na^+ causes the pump to work very rapidly (by the Law of Mass Action), and the rate gradually decreases as normality is restored.

In summary, it can be seen that the ionic distribution across the cell membrane of animal tissues is maintained partly by an electrochemical equilibrium and partly by active transport, mainly of the Na^+ ion, a process requiring metabolic energy. These processes result in the attainment of the charge on the membrane, making the interior electronegative to the extracellular fluid.

The question of the maintenance of cell volume must be closely related to the problem of distribution of solutes, because the greater part of the volume of all cells consists of water, and movements of water in biological systems occur only by physical processes, mainly osmotic and hydrostatic pressures. The movement or distribution of solutes will thus determine much of the movement and distribution of water, by osmotic gradients. Since there are proteins and other osmotically active colloidal particles inside but not outside the cell (or anyway at much lower concentrations outside), there is a much greater colloid-osmotic pressure inside, which might be expected to draw water into the cell, and this is one factor contributing to the slightly greater total osmolar 'concentration' of intracellular fluid as compared with extracellular fluid. The animal cell lying in the aqueous medium of constant composition will keep its shape and volume (in spite of the positive colloid-osmotic pressure within it) *only* so long as the sodium pump works efficiently. Anything which inhibits this pumping—cold, or lack of energy supply in the form of glucose and oxygen, or certain drugs—will allow passive entry of Na^+ ions down their electrochemical gradient, entry of Cl' ion with the Na^+ by electrostatic attraction, and entry of water by osmosis. The sodium pump therefore maintains not only the ionic distribution and consequent membrane potential of the cells of animal tissue but also their water content and consequently their volume.

Animal cell membranes, as compared with membranes of most plant cells, are very fragile, and extremely permeable. Their low surface tension makes possible a very rapid exchange of materials with their environment, but also makes them vulnerable. The significance of the sodium pump mechanism may be explained in this way, as described by the physiologist Alexander Leaf:

> The alternative adjustment possible to the cell to prevent the swelling that would result from its content of intracellular colloid would be to surround itself with a rigid casing to withstand this force. However, a high membrane tension would be very disadvantageous to small cells, which are dependent for many processes on a high surface–volume relationship. Furthermore, in those instances in which membrane tensions have been measured, very low values have been obtained. ... These low membrane tensions are possible, I believe, because animal cells have learnt to avoid disastrous swelling by developing the ion pumping mechanism just discussed. Certain cells seem to have evolved secondary uses for the energy stored in the ion gradients or in the resulting cell membrane potentials. Nervous conductivity and muscular contractility, perhaps, represent examples of such secondary evolutionary adaptations. Thus we owe the contractility of the myocardium and, in fact, our very mobility, as compared with the sessile members of the vegetable kingdom, to this method of preserving cell volume which avoids the cumbersome cellulose casing the plants chose as their answer to the threat of cell swelling.
>
> (Leaf, 1958)

A tree limits the exchange of matter and energy with its environment to its leaves and root hairs; most of the cells of the trunk and branches once formed are more or less static conduits and supports, and energy of maintenance is saved. The cost paid by the higher animals for their independent mobility over the earth's surface is that a quarter of their energy is spent simply on excluding sodium and water from their cells.

Summary

The structure and components of a typical animal cell are described; and a brief account is given of the process of cell division—a process particularly active during early growth and development, continuing throughout life in some tissues. The routes of interaction between cells, either in the same tissue or in other tissues or organs of the body, are mentioned. Several processes are described by which the cell is enabled to exchange chemical substances through its membrane with materials in its environment. An account is given of a physicochemical factor (Gibbs–Donnan equilibrium) and a biological process (sodium–potassium exchange pump) in the establishment of the voltage charge on the cell membrane. The use of the Nernst equation in interpreting ionic equilibria is explained. The value of the sodium pump in maintaining the volume of all animal cells is indicated.

4 Feeding, digestion and absorption

Introduction

All living organisms require a continuous input of energy for their maintenance. For nearly all animals this energy is the chemical energy liberated by the oxidation of organic molecules derived from other living organisms, plant or animal. These molecules are mainly sugars, amino acids and fatty acids. The feeding of animals on other organisms supplies not only energy but also the material for the structural components of the body. This material is necessary for the young growing animal and also for the adult, in which the tissue material is slowly and constantly being replaced. Food also includes inorganic molecules and water, which are just as necessary as organic molecules are. Finally, food must contain vitamins—organic molecules without which certain metabolic reactions cannot occur, but which the body is unable to synthesize from other food components. This chapter is concerned with the entry of food into the body.

The route of entry is the alimentary canal. The structure of this organ and its related tissues will be briefly described, and an account of its movements will be given. Then comes a section dealing with the enzymic digestion of the foodstuffs by the digestive juices secreted into the alimentary canal, and with the control of this secretion. The lumen of the alimentary canal can be considered in a sense to be 'outside' the body, and the digested derivatives of the food make their entry into the body as they pass through the wall of the small intestine; the numerous intricate processes of absorption are described. Finally, a brief mention is made of possible mechanisms underlying the sensation of hunger and satiety, by which food intake is controlled.

Structure of the alimentary canal

Figure 4.1 shows the main parts of the alimentary canal of a human, together with the associated organs (salivary glands, liver, gall bladder and pancreas) which produce secretions that reach it.

Food entering the mouth may be chewed and moistened by saliva before being swallowed. The oesophagus takes the partly macerated food from the mouth to the stomach where it is temporarily stored and where the process of digestion may start.

Rings of smooth muscle are present at the points of entry and exit of the stomach; the ring at the exit point, the pyloric sphincter, is anatomically a true sphincter muscle. The most active region for both digestion and absorption is the small intestine. The semiliquid material, called chyme, consisting of partly digested food and digestive juices, next enters the large intestine (colon and rectum). There is no further secretion of digestive juices but much bacterial activity and absorption. The chyme enters the rectum just before defaecation via the anus.

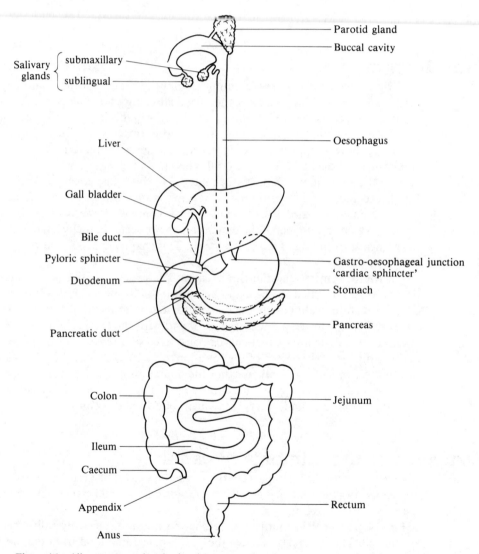

Figure 4.1 Alimentary canal and related structures (man).

The same general histological pattern is present throughout the alimentary canal from oesophagus to anus. This pattern is shown in diagrammatic form in Fig. 2.3 and indicated in the photograph, Fig. 4.2. Within a thin layer of connective tissue forming the outermost part of the wall, there lie two layers of smooth muscle, the outer running longitudinally and the inner circular. Between the two muscle layers lies a network of thin nerve fibres, called the myenteric or Auerbach's plexus. Within the circular muscle lies the submucosal layer containing glands, numerous small lymphatic vessels, blood capillaries (mainly branches of the hepatic portal vein) and also another nerve network, Meissner's plexus. Within this is another very thin smooth-muscle layer, the muscularis mucosae; and finally comes the innermost layer, the mucosa, adjacent to the lumen.

Superimposed on this general pattern are regional differences. For instance in the mucosal layer of the oesophagus and large intestine there are especially numerous goblet cells secreting mucus. In all regions of the small intestine (duodenum, jejunum and ileum) the mucosal surface is thrown into many finger-like processes, the villi (each one is a villus). The individual mucosal cells of the villi carry on their luminal surface minute projections visible by EM, forming the so-called 'brush-border', or microvilli. The villi are in constant motion, waving, contracting and elongating. Simple tubular glands (crypts of Lieberkühn) open at the surface between the villi. It is in the upper part of the duodenum that the main extrinsic secretions (pancreatic juice and bile) enter the intestine; in the duodenal wall, too, there is, inside the muscularis

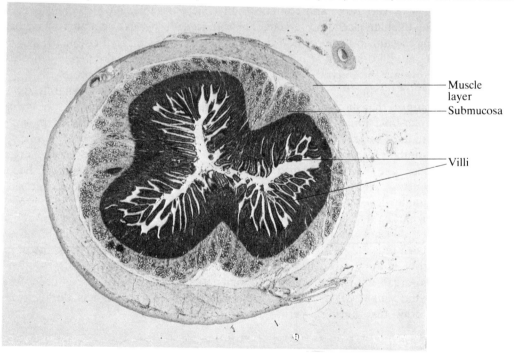

Figure 4.2 Transverse section of duodenum (cat). × 3.6. (Courtesy of P. Harris and P. Taylor.)

mucosae layer, an additional set of glands (Brunner's glands) secreting mucus and a weak proteolytic enzyme. In the jejunum the villi and crypts are particularly long and prominent. In the ileum, follicles of lymphoid tissue (Peyer's patches) are found in the submucosal layer. In the colon the outer longitudinal layer of muscle fibres is gathered up into three bands, the taeniae coli, which give this region a triangular appearance in cross-section.

The sphincter muscle between the small and large intestines is the ileocaecal valve. The large intestine is shorter and wider than the small intestine. Its widest part is the first part, the caecum (which carries on one edge a small diverticulum, the vermiform appendix). The caecum forms the first part of the ascending colon, running up the right side of the abdominal cavity; the transverse colon and descending colon run across and down the left side, and the descending colon merges with the sigmoid colon which leads to the rectum. This ends at the anus, where there are two bands (inner and outer) of sphincter muscle, through which undigested material, bacteria and shed mucosal cells are evacuated as faeces.

This general pattern of the structure of the mammalian alimentary canal is modified in various groups and species. Carnivores do not chew or macerate the food into small particles; they use the teeth mainly for cutting and tearing, then swallow the food as large lumps. In ruminants the stomach consists of a series of chambers in which bacterial breakdown of food occurs, and from which food is regurgitated to the mouth where it may be further masticated and mixed with saliva. In many herbivores the caecum is very large and contains many micro-organisms which convert carbohydrates (including cellulose) to fatty acids. Indeed all species of mammals have bacteria in the caecum and colon, and some have micro-organisms in the stomach also. Many other modifications of structure and function occur, and make the alimentary canal appropriate to the type of food eaten by different groups and species.

Before leaving the subject of the structure of the alimentary canal, it should be mentioned that there occurs a remarkably rapid turnover and renewal of the cells of the intestinal mucous membrane. This has been thoroughly studied in the small intestine of mice, in which rapid cell division (as shown by many mitotic figures consisting of spindles and chromosomes) occurs at the base of the crypts of Lieberkühn. The newly formed cells migrate up the crypts and the villi, pushed up by even newer cells. During the process the cells mature and alter their properties. They eventually degenerate and are extruded at the tips of the villi. The whole process (in mice) can be traced by radioactively labelled thymidine incorporated into cell nuclei at cell division. From cell division to eventual extrusion takes only 2 days. The extruded cells are passed out in the faeces. Indeed it is likely that most faecal matter consists, not of unabsorbed food residues, but of these extruded cells, together with micro-organisms and excreted bile pigments and cholesterol. It has been observed that the weight of faecal matter passed daily is not much less during complete starvation than during a period of normal food intake.

Movements of the alimentary canal

The only movements of the alimentary canal which are under voluntary control are mastication and the initiation of swallowing in the mouth, and defaecation by control of the external anal sphincter, composed of striated muscle.

Swallowing is initiated by the pushing of a bolus of food onto the back of the tongue. Thereafter, the process is entirely by reflex action, resulting from the stimulus to the touch receptors on this part of the tongue: even an anaesthetized animal on the tongue of which a drop of oil is placed will make all the complicated series of swallowing movements. During the swallowing reflex, respiration is also reflexly inhibited.

The tongue throws the bolus back against the pharynx, and the soft palate is raised, shutting off the base of the nasal passage. Then the epiglottis turns downward, ahead of the bolus, and shuts off the top of the larynx at the upper part of the trachea (see Fig. 4.3). The pharynx, which is continuous with the upper part of the oesophagus, contracts, forcing the bolus downwards, while the larynx ('Adam's apple') jerks upward, accommodating the oesophagus, which is made to bulge by the bolus as it passes behind the larynx. A wave of peristalsis, initiated by touch-receptor nerves on the surface of the pharynx, flows along the oesophagus, carrying the bolus into the stomach. By this time the cardiac sphincter has relaxed and the bolus simply falls into the stomach.

Peristalsis occurs throughout the alimentary canal and is the only process pushing food onward. It consists of contraction of circular smooth muscle behind the bolus or chyme, this wave of contraction then moving along down the tube. There is

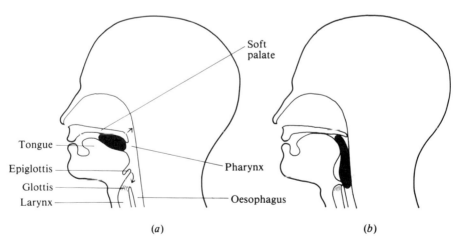

Figure 4.3 Movements of swallowing (men). When the bolus of food is placed on the back of the tongue (*a*), the soft palate moves up, closing off the back of the nasal cavity, and the epiglottis moves down, closing the glottis at the top of trachea. As the bolus of food passes down the top of the oesophagus, the larynx is pushed forward (*b*).

disagreement about whether or not an active relaxation of smooth muscle simultaneously occurs ahead of the bolus. Oesophageal peristalsis is slightly different from that elsewhere, in that it is initiated by sensory nerves, and is coordinated by, and dependent on, a swallowing centre in the medulla oblongata of the brain stem. Elsewhere, peristalsis is propagated myogenically or by the intrinsic nerve plexuses. The so-called 'cardiac sphincter' is not a true sphincter (i.e. a thickened, sturdy band of circular smooth-muscle fibres); it is simply a slight thickening of the circular smooth-muscle layer of the base of the oesophagus, close to its junction with the stomach where the oesophagus enters the stomach wall at an oblique angle. The arrangement must be efficient enough to prevent regurgitation, during stomach contractions, of the gastric contents into the base of the oesophagus—a mishap which never normally occurs.

The stomach is mainly an organ for the storing of food. The smooth muscle of its three-layered wall accommodates itself to meals of varying size in such a way that there is little or no increase in intraluminal pressure. In the main part (fundus) of the stomach, there may not be much mixing of food within the bolus. The first food to be swallowed at a meal is pushed to an outside layer lying against the greater curvature, and succeeding portions form concentric layers; these layers may remain unmixed for some time, and it is only the outermost which comes into contact with the gastric juice. Movement of the stomach wall is influenced by the stomach contents. In man, movement may stop almost completely for half an hour after a meal—even longer if the meal contains much fat. Then, after such a pause, peristalsis starts, and part of the effect of the movement is to churn the food around and mix it with gastric juice. The pyloric sphincter muscle is continuous with the circular muscle of the pyloric antrum and gradually participates in these peristaltic movements. Little by little, food from the stomach is moved on into the duodenum. The duodenum then remains relaxed for a short time after the entry of food, while the pyloric sphincter is contracted. The presence of hypertonic solutions, fatty acids, or liquid of low pH in the duodenum inhibits gastric peristalsis. (This feedback mechanism might be by an enterogastric nerve reflex, and also by a hormone, enterogastrone.) The consequence is that no more food passes through to the duodenum until the first lot has been moved on, by the peristalsis of the duodenum itself.

Throughout the length of the small and large intestines, peristalsis keeps the chyme moving slowly onwards. In addition, there occurs in the small intestine another type of activity, called 'segmentation', which produces a mixing of the chyme but no onward movement. The small intestine appears as a series of segments like a string of sausages with a constriction between each; suddenly each segment constricts in the middle; then a moment later, the halves of adjacent segments join up, to form new whole segments. Then, these in turn are split by a constriction and rejoin. This activity goes on at the rate of about 18 per minute in the duodenum, and rather less in the ileum.

During the passage of chyme the villi lining the small intestine are in continuous movement. The mechanism of this movement may involve fibres in the muscularis mucosae, or a hypothetical hormone 'villikinin', or both.

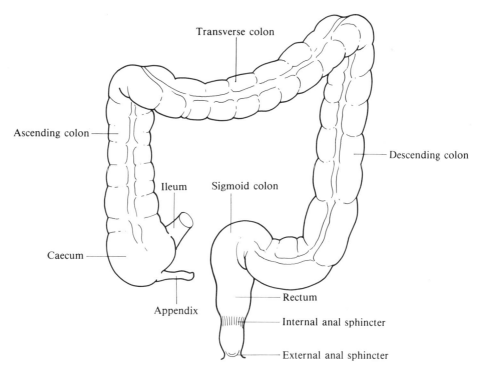

Figure 4.4 Large intestine and related structures. (Adapted from Davson, H. and M. B. Segal, *Introduction to Physiology*, vol. 1, Academic Press, London, 1975.)

In the large intestine, where there is much reabsorption of water, the chyme becomes the semisolid faeces, and the onward movement is slow.

The rectum, that portion of the large intestine close to the anal region, is normally empty. The entry of faeces into it, from the sigmoid of the colon, is the stimulus for defaecation. This consists of the relaxing of internal and external anal sphincters, the external one being under voluntary control (Fig. 4.4). The muscles of the abdominal wall contract and the diaphragm descends; the increase in intra-abdominal pressure expels the faeces.

Digestion

The chyme, the mixture of food and secretions moving through the alimentary canal, always contains much water, and NaCl, and abundant mucus, secreted not only by the various extrinsic glands but also by numerous goblet cells interspersed throughout the mucous membrane. So a viscous protective coat of mucus is always present, and helps to protect the lining of the alimentary canal from attack by its own digestive enzymes.

The pH of the chyme varies. In the stomach it is markedly acid, and can have a pH as low as 2, because of the HCl of gastric juice. In the upper duodenum the pH is about 6 because the sodium bicarbonate ($NaHCO_3$) of the pancreatic juice partially neutralizes material entering the duodenum from the stomach. The chyme becomes almost neutral in the large intestine, unless organic acids formed by bacterial action are present in abnormally large amounts. The digestive enzymes each have a pH optimum and normally work close to this point.

The cells producing the secretions which bring about the changes of pH of the chyme—the oxyntic (parietal) cells of the stomach and the centro-acinar cells of the pancreas—have been studied in some detail (Fig. 4.5). Pure gastric juice unmixed with food or saliva can have a pH as low as 1, and pure pancreatic juice can be as high as pH 8. The oxyntic cells secrete the H^+ and the Cl' ions at different points on their apical membrane, both mechanisms involving active transport. The Cl' secretion

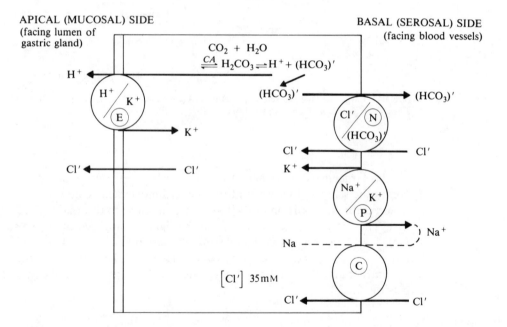

Figure 4.5 Processes involved in H^+ and Cl' secretion in parietal cell. At the apical surface the electrically neutral exchange pump (E) secretes H^+ in exchange for K^+. Cl' is passed out, even in the 'resting' cell, down the diffusion gradient from the high internal Cl' generated by activity at the basal surface. At the basal surface the electrically neutral anion exchanger (N) exchanges Cl' inwards for $(HCO_3)'$ outwards. The usual sodium–potassium exchange pump (P) operates, but much of the Na^+, in re-entering the cell (dotted line) takes Cl' with it by electrical attraction (C). H^+ of pump E and $(HCO_3)'$ of pump N are derived ultimately from the reaction of H_2O and CO_2 catalysed by carbonic anhydrase (CA). (Reproduced, with permission, from the *Annual Review of Physiology*, **42**, © 1980 by Annual Reviews Inc.)

continues even when the stomach is empty and resting; and because of this, when the stomach is in this state the electrical gradient across its wall is as high as -40 mV (lumen negative). After gastric stimulation by a meal, the transmembrane potential difference falls to about -4 mV, as H^+ ions then accompany the Cl'. The H^+ ions move down an electrical gradient but against a very steep chemical concentration gradient. The separation of the H^+ ions (derived ultimately from water) is dependent on the activity of the intracellular enzyme carbonic anhydrase. This catalyses the first of the two reactions shown:

$$H_2O + CO_2 \rightleftharpoons H_2CO_3 \rightleftharpoons H^+ + (HCO_3)'$$

bringing the equilibrium to the right. The bicarbonate, $(HCO_3)'$, ions then move across the basal membrane of the cells, into the blood, exchanging with Cl' ions. The secretion of Cl' into the lumen of the stomach is in some way dependent on the presence of K^+ ions. Sodium is actively extruded at the basal membrane. The overall result is an increase in plasma sodium bicarbonate occurring at the same time as active HCl production in the stomach: gastric venous blood has been found to be 0.09 pH unit more alkaline just after a meal than during fasting. This so-called 'alkaline tide' of the blood is sometimes large enough, in humans, to cause temporary alkalinity of the urine just after a heavy meal.

The enzyme carbonic anhydrase occurs in the body wherever there is a marked pH gradient across a membrane. The enzyme is present in the pancreas also, and at least part of the sodium bicarbonate production by the pancreatic centro-acinar cells may take place by an analogous process to that occurring in the gastric oxyntic cells, but in the reverse direction; however, since at least some bicarbonate production can still occur even after inhibition of carbonic anhydrase, it is surmised that some other mechanism must also be present.

The secretions entering the alimentary canal are listed in Table 4.1, together with their sources and their main components.

Digestion occurs by hydrolysis of large organic molecules into smaller ones. Hydrolysis of starch (catalysed by amylases) forms dextrins and disaccharides. Hydrolysis of proteins catalysed by pepsin, trypsin and chymotrypsin forms polypeptides, peptones and amino acids; and hydrolysis of neutral fats by lipase forms fatty acids and monoglycerides. Some hydrolysis would probably occur even in the absence of digestive enzymes, for instance during the mixing of the macerated food with warm HCl in the stomach. But obviously the presence of the digestive enzymes speeds the process enormously. There has been speculation about why the digestive enzymes do not attack the wall of the alimentary canal itself. The proteolytic enzymes exist in the gland cells, and are secreted, in the form of inactive precursors (zymogens), which become activated on entry into the lumen. In the stomach, for instance, inactive pepsinogen becomes active pepsin on contact with the HCl simultaneously secreted, and this pepsin can itself activate pepsinogen secreted later. The trypsinogen of the pancreatic juice is converted to active trypsin by enterokinase secreted in the intestinal juice, and trypsin is in turn the activator of chymotrypsinogen and carboxypeptidases. This necessary activation of the powerful proteolytic enzymes means that the wall of

Table 4.1 Secretions of the alimentary canal

Secretion	Position	Sources	Components
Saliva	Mouth	Three pairs salivary glands: parotid, sublingual, submandibular; also buccal glands lining mouth	Mucus (glycoprotein) Also amylase (ptyalin) in some species
Gastric juice	Stomach	Tubular glands in mucous membrane of stomach	Mucus Pepsinogen (precursor of pepsin) HCl Intrinsic factor Gastrin
Bile	Duodenum	Liver (via gall bladder in most species)	Bile salts Cholesterol Bile pigments
Pancreatic juice	Duodenum	Pancreas	Trypsinogen Chymotrypsinogen Carboxypeptidases Lipase Amylase Ribonucleases $NaHCO_3$
Brunner's glands secretion	Duodenum	Brunner's glands	Mucus
Intestinal juice	Small intestine	Paneth cells Goblet cells	Peptidases Mucus Enterokinase Secretin Cholecystokinin

the intestine and the pancreatic duct cannot itself be digested by them, because they do not occur in the active state unless a mass of chyme is initially present, stimulating the secretion of the activator enterokinase. Preventing the stomach lining from contact with HCl, which is secreted in small amounts even during starvation, there is a continuously secreted protective layer of mucus.

As mentioned earlier, the three main organic foodstuffs of animals are proteins, carbohydrates and fats. Protein digestion starts in the stomach, where pepsin in the presence of HCl catalyses the hydrolysis of peptide bonds, particularly those involving the aromatic amino acids—tyrosine, phenylalanine and tryptophan. The process continues in the duodenum, where the trypsin, chymotrypsin and carboxypeptidases of the pancreatic juice act on the peptones and polypeptides resulting from gastric digestion. The enzymic breakdown produces and presents for absorption mainly single amino acids, with a few di- or tripeptides.

Digestion of carbohydrate may be started by the enzyme amylase (ptyalin) in the saliva which is swallowed with the food and acts on starch (at α 1–4 links) while the food is stored and mixed in the stomach. The main part of carbohydrate digestion is carried out by the amylase of the pancreatic juice, which hydrolyses starch to maltose. This sugar, together with the other disaccharides lactose and sucrose, is converted to monosaccharides by enzymes in the brush-borders of the mucosal cells of the small intestine. It seems that the disaccharidase enzymes are not secreted into the intestinal lumen as part of the intestinal juice, but function at the moment when the sugars are undergoing absorption.

Fat digestion is carried out in the small intestine. The process starts by emulsification of triglycerides (esters of glycerol with long-chain fatty acids) by the bile salts entering the duodenum from the gall bladder. The fine droplets of triglyceride thus formed can be attacked by the enzyme lipase of the pancreatic juice; this hydrolyses the triglyceride at the first and third positions, giving free fatty acid and monoglycerides. If the chyme remains long enough in the small intestine, the monoglyceride may itself be hydrolysed further, to glycerol and fatty acid. Fatty acid and monoglyceride together with bile salts and phospholipid form very small particles called micelles, which (unlike finely emulsified fat droplets) are water-soluble. It is mainly from micelles that the products of fat digestion are eventually absorbed.

Control of secretion

Control of secretion occurs partly by autonomic nerves and partly by the action of hormones formed in the wall of the alimentary canal and carried by the blood to nearby glands. Control in the mouth is entirely by nerves, in the stomach by both systems, and in the intestine almost entirely by hormones.

Secretion of saliva is a reflex action, originating in the sense organs of smell and taste. Afferent impulses arising from these sense organs when the animal smells or tastes food are sent to the salivary nucleus in the brain stem, whence parasympathetic fibres in the facial and glossopharyngeal nerves (cranial VII and IX) reach the three pairs of salivary glands and stimulate secretion. This reflex can readily be conditioned by other sensory stimuli associated with food. Sympathetic nerves as well as parasympathetics innervate salivary glands, but their role in normal feeding is a matter of controversy. In man they may inhibit parotid secretion, a process which causes the sensation of 'dry mouth' associated with fear, when there is widespread sympathetic stimulation; sympathetic stimulation of human submandibular glands produces a small secretion rich in organic constituents.

The initial step of gastric secretion also occurs by a reflex, initiated by the taste of food in the mouth (and also, through conditioning, by the sight or smell of food). The efferent nerve is the vagus (cranial X), innervating both the oxyntic (parietal) cells producing HCl, and the peptic (chief) cells producing pepsinogen. The chyme may remain for some time (an hour or two, in man) in the stomach, and is released little by little through the pyloric sphincter. During this time a further stage of secretion occurs, mediated by a hormone, gastrin, a 17-amino-acid polypeptide. Its production from the pyloric (non-acid-secreting) part of the stomach wall is elicited by the presence of protein breakdown products, and also by vagal stimulation of the gastrin-producing cells. Gastrin enters the blood and is carried to the oxyntic cells, which are thereby stimulated to further production of HCl. As the chyme enters the duodenum a further phase of gastric secretion is stimulated. The mechanism is not well defined; the hormone involved may be cholecystokinin (CCK), and the stimuli for its release include mere mechanical distension of the duodenum and the presence of solutions of high osmolarity. Another influence of the duodenum, this time a negative one, is shown when strong acid (pH 5 or less) or fatty acids are present in the duodenum. These substances have the effect of *decreasing* secretion and motility of the stomach. The mechanism is thought to be hormonal, and a hormone called enterogastrone has been postulated but not yet isolated.

The flow of pancreatic juice starts when food enters the duodenum. Two hormones, secretin and CCK, are involved, the first acting on the centro-acinar cells of the pancreas, producing water and sodium bicarbonate; the second acting on acinar cells, producing enzymes. These hormones are released when acid or the products of protein or fat digestion are present in the duodenum. They have been well characterized as polypeptides of known structure, and they can be chemically extracted from the duodenal wall; they are also present, in small amounts, further down the small intestine. A nerve reflex also gives a small stimulation of pancreatic secretion; the afferent limb of the reflex is in vagal fibres from the wall of the stomach stimulated by distension of the stomach; the efferent limb is in vagal fibres to the pancreas.

Bile enters the duodenum under the influence of CCK (also known as pancreozymin) which causes the gall bladder to contract. Bile may be stored and concentrated for some time in the gall bladder; it contains no enzymes but it helps the digestion and absorption of fats because of the emulsifying effect of the bile salts. Bile is also the route of excretion of sterols (cholesterol and cholic acids) and of haemoglobin derivatives (bilirubin and biliverdin). Some bile salts recirculate: they enter the portal vein after absorption, reach the liver, and stimulate further production of bile—the so-called 'enterohepatic circulation'. This circulation has an important function; in man, for example, the total volume of bile stored in the gall bladder would be inadequate for emulsifying and aiding absorption of the fat of an average meal. Some animals have no gall bladder; bile enters the duodenum directly from the liver. Such animals include continuous feeders such as rats, and continuous digesters such as ruminants.

In the duodenum the secretion of the Brunner's glands is stimulated by feeding and by movement of the duodenal wall, the response involving probably both the vagus and secretin. Further down the small intestine there appears to be a continuous secretion of intestinal juice even during fasting, which is not increased by feeding. Whether this secretion is normally controlled in any way is not yet known, but secretion is increased after irritation by mechanical or chemical means.

Before ending this account of the control of secretion in the alimentary canal, it should be mentioned that several biologically active polypeptides, in addition to gastrin, secretin and CCK, have been found in various parts of the gut, and may have an endocrine or paracrine function, released from one tissue or cell and influencing another. (Details of these processes of chemical release are given in Chapter 14.) Some of these peptides have been given names denoting their biological activity; for instance vasoactive intestinal polypeptide dilates blood vessels; gastric inhibitory polypeptide (obtained during purification of CCK preparations) inhibits acid secretion from the stomach; motilin from the duodenum, released from the duodenal wall by alkali, causes vigorous movement of the stomach. Further research is needed to define the exact physiological role (if any) of these substances. It is interesting that many of these intestinal polypeptides are similar to, or identical with, peptides found in the brain; and this observation has led to speculation that the same chemical substance may act as a neurotransmitter in the brain and as a hormone in the gut. The question of whether this identity of structure between neurocrine and endocrine chemicals has some biological significance or is purely fortuitous must await further study

Absorption

In most higher animals feeding is discontinuous, and so also are digestion and absorption. The barrier through which materials must pass during absorption from the gut is formed by a single layer of epithelial cells on the surface of the villi, the finger-like projections, 0.5–1.5 mm long, lining the whole surface of the small intestine. Some villi and adjacent tissues are shown in Fig. 4.6. The cells on the surface of villi touch each other at tight junctions at the outer (lumen) edge, and at their inner surface

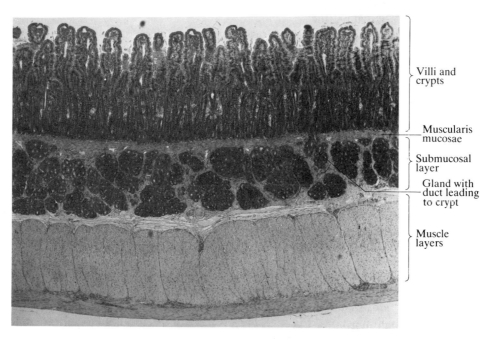

Villi and crypts

Muscularis mucosae

Submucosal layer

Gland with duct leading to crypt

Muscle layers

Figure 4.6   Longitudinal section, ileum (cat). Gland with duct leading to crypt is marked. × 5. (Courtesy of P. Harris and P. Taylor.)

there are narrow spaces (lateral intercellular spaces) between them. But the so-called tight junctions are not in fact very tight and certain substances can be absorbed between the cells as well as through them. Below the villi in the mucosal membrane is a thick network of blood capillaries and small lymphatics, and each system (blood and lymphatic) sends a small loop up into each villus. In addition, minute smooth-muscle fibres from the muscularis mucosae enter each villus.

The area of the apical luminal surface of each epithelial cell is greatly increased by the presence of the brush-border. The basal side of the cell rests on a very thin basement membrane, which is close to the basement membrane of the underlying capillary. The cells of the capillary wall include fenestrations (that is, areas where the layer of cytoplasm is extremely thin). So there is only a very slight diffusion barrier between the intestinal epithelial cell and the blood, the rapid flow of which removes material as soon as it is absorbed, thus keeping the diffusion gradient steep.

Besides the hydrolysed foodstuffs the digestive juices themselves must be absorbed from the intestinal lumen, and their volume may be considerable. In man, perhaps 8 litres of digestive juices are secreted into the intestine per day—a greater volume than that of the whole circulating blood. Between the periods of food intake small amounts of fluid are trickling into the intestine, and there are continuous slight peristaltic movements of the smooth muscle of the wall of the small intestine. During and after a meal the movements become vigorous, and the villi themselves shorten and lengthen rhythmically, as already described, providing a pumping motion which squeezes fluid into the underlying plexuses of vessels, and hence to portal blood and thoracic lymph ducts.

Before the start of the process of absorption there is an osmotic equilibration across the intestinal wall. This occurs high up in the duodenum, as chyme enters from the stomach and the pancreatic juice and bile are secreted. If the chyme is hypotonic, water is osmotically removed into the blood; if hypertonic, water is drawn out from the blood into the duodenal lumen. So all absorption of solute occurs from a chyme which is almost isosmotic with blood plasma.

Water and sodium

The mechanism of the regular daily passage of large quantities of fluid in one direction only—that is, intestinal fluid to plasma—between two fluids in osmotic equilibrium clearly requires something more than a mere physicochemical explanation. The intestinal transfer of water and Na^+ ions has been studied intensively, and the resulting hypothesis, called *standing-gradient osmotic flow*, has been used to explain the unidirectional movement of water and salt across many other epithelia besides that of the intestinal villus. It is suggested that in a partially enclosed space, the lateral intercellular space, a hypertonic solution can be formed by the active transport of Na^+ ions by sodium pumps on the lateral walls of the adjacent epithelial cells below the tight junctions (Fig. 4.7). The presence of this localized hypertonic solution would have the effect of moving water by osmosis from the cell into the lateral intercellular space. This space, however, is narrow and of limited capacity, so that as the volume of

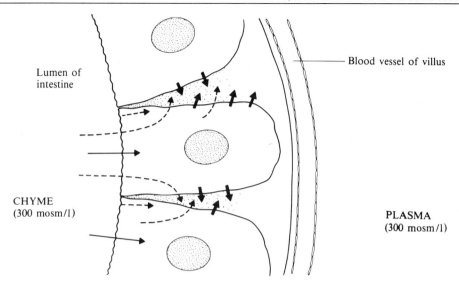

Figure 4.7 Standing-gradient osmotic flow. Thin arrows: passive diffusion of Na^+ ions down chemical gradient. Thick arrows: active transport of Na^+ ions into lateral intercellular spaces of limited capacity. Dotted lines and arrows: movement of water by osmotic gradient, through and between the cells. Formation of a highly concentrated solution in a compartment of limited volume is a step in the process of moving solute and water from chyme to blood plasma, to isotonic solutions.

fluid within it increases, this fluid would be squeezed by the build-up of hydrostatic pressure, down towards its open end to the basement membrane of the capillary epithelium and thence across the capillary wall into the blood. The presence of colloid (proteins) in plasma gives the blood a slightly greater total osmolarity than that of the surrounding interstitial fluid, and this too would favour movement of water from interstitial space to blood. The sodium pumps would keep the level of Na^+ ions within the epithelial cells very low, so there would be a steep gradient for diffusion of Na^+ ions from the intestinal lumen into the cell; and these Na^+ ions would be accompanied as usual by the isosmotic amount of water, and Cl' as negative ions. The tight junction at the apical end of the lateral intercellular space is not completely tight; a stream of water from the intestinal lumen could be drawn through by osmosis; and solutes, if small enough, would also come in this aqueous stream, by 'mass filtration' or 'bulk flow'. The lateral intercellular space is thus a compartment of great activity (active transport, hydrostatic pressure and mass filtration), interposed between two compartments (the intestinal lumen and the blood vessel), the contents of which are isosmotic with each other.

This hypothesis has been used to explain the transfer of water and Na^+ ions across other epithelia where the final transferred fluid is isosmotic with the starting fluid; examples are the absorption of fluid of glomerular filtrate in the proximal tubule of nephrons, and concentration of bile by the wall of the gall bladder. The same hypothesis has been used to explain processes in which the fluid produced is hypertonic to the starting fluid (such as the fluid produced by the salt gland at the base of the beak of many birds); or hypotonic to the starting fluid (such as sweat). The differences in the tonicity of the final transferred fluid or secretion could be explained mainly by differences in the relative activity of sodium pumping and passive water permeability at the lateral cell surface.

Though this standing-gradient hypothesis is useful, one must remember that it is still only a hypothetical model. It is hard to see how to obtain any direct evidence supporting (or disproving) the hypothesis. Efforts have been made to detect a swelling of the lateral intercellular spaces of epithelia during water absorption, by comparing electron microphotographs of bladder walls fixed during water absorption with those fixed while not absorbing water. But in observations of this type it is difficult to avoid artefacts, or alternative explanations of the results, and unequivocal evidence supporting the hypothesis is still lacking. Nevertheless it remains a convenient way of thinking about the movement of water through epithelial membranes.

This account of the mechanism proposed for the movement of water and Na^+ ions from the intestinal lumen into the blood illustrates many of the processes—physicochemical and physiological—by which substances move in the body. The Na^+ ions move from the lumen into the cell down a chemical diffusion gradient, accompanied by Cl' ions by electrostatic attraction; active transport extrudes the Na^+ against a gradient into the lateral intercellular spaces. Water flows into the spaces by osmosis from the cell, and also (probably) via the tight junctions; molecules or ions may be swept through the tight junctions in the stream of water, by bulk flow; hydrostatic pressure forces the contents of the lateral intercellular space down towards the basement membrane of the capillary and thus into the blood. These processes, together with the other mechanisms mentioned in Chapter 3 allowing movement across membranes of single cells (carrier-mediated transport, endocytosis and exocytosis), can help to explain the whole of the absorptive function of the small and large intestines.

The following paragraphs describe, in terms of these general processes, the absorption in the small intestine of sugars, protein and fat derivatives, certain divalent ions and a vitamin, vitamin B_{12}. A final section describes the specific activities within the colon.

Carbohydrate

Carbohydrate is absorbed as monosaccharides—mainly glucose, galactose and fructose—these being formed from the disaccharides maltose, lactose and sucrose by enzymes on the brush-border of the intestinal villi. (A lactose-splitting enzyme occurs in young animals and infants, but disappears from the intestine of adults who do not habitually drink milk or eat milk products.) Pentose sugars from nucleic-acid breakdown are also absorbed, by passive diffusion. There is a specific carrier molecule for glucose and galactose; the affinity of glucose for this molecule is high, so this sugar is absorbed especially rapidly.

As mentioned in Chapter 3, the presence of Na^+ ions in the intestinal lumen is

LUMEN   MEMBRANE   CELL

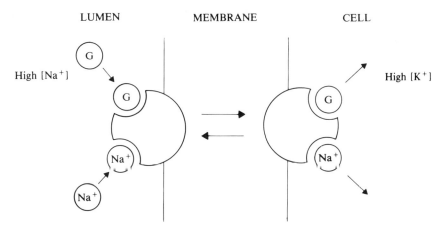

Figure 4.8   Entry of glucose (G) into cell: suggested carrier mechanism (see text).

necessary for the rapid entry of glucose into the cell. One suggestion is that Na^+ may modify the structure of the carrier to give it a greater affinity for glucose; then the complex (carrier, Na^+ and glucose) moves in such a way that the Na^+ and glucose are offloaded into the cytoplasm, and the carrier returns to the external cell surface and picks up another Na^+ ion and another glucose molecule (Fig. 4.8). The Na^+ brought into the cell is immediately extruded through the basal surface of the cell by active transport, which keeps the intracellular Na^+ very low; and this process, by making a steep lumen-to-cell gradient for Na^+, speeds the process of entry at the apical surface of the carrier-mediated Na^+ plus glucose. As the intracellular glucose level builds up, a diffusion gradient for glucose from cell to blood is formed and so glucose diffuses into the capillaries. The whole process is called the sodium-gradient hypothesis. It assumes that the only energy-requiring process in glucose absorption is that of the sodium pump creating the steep gradient for Na^+ ions across the apical membrane of the cell; and that glucose itself is not actively transported into the cell, but moves by virtue of the structure of the carrier, along with the Na^+ ion (a process called 'co-transport'; Na^+ and glucose are called 'symports'—see page 51). The hypothesis also assumes that the basal membrane of the cell is extremely permeable to glucose, or else that there is another carrier-mediated transport system for glucose at this surface; otherwise, passive diffusion of glucose at the basal surface would become the rate-limiting step for the whole process of glucose absorption. The study of the movement of substances from epithelial cell to blood has not yet proceeded very far; and we may hope in time for confirmation (or disproof) of the sodium-gradient hypothesis.

Protein

The derivatives of protein—single amino acids or dipeptides—are absorbed rapidly. There are dipeptidases in the cells of the villi, so most of the luminal dipeptides are hydrolysed at the moment of absorption; but a few di- and tripeptides and perhaps even larger protein-derived molecules may appear in the portal vein. Small traces of protein can be absorbed (by endocytosis) particularly in newborn animals. This is of some advantage since colostrum, the initial secretion of the mammary glands formed after the birth of the young, contains immunoglobulin antibodies (and in some species also a trypsin inhibitor). The globulins can be absorbed, and give the young animal or infant some degree of immunity from disease.

Absorption of amino acids is carrier-assisted. Experiments using competitive inhibition have revealed that there are four different carrier molecules: one for the neutral amino acids, one of the basic amino acids, one for the dicarboxylic amino acids (glutamic and aspartic), and the fourth for proline, hydroxyproline and glycine. Only the naturally occurring L-isomers are carried; in experiments using isolated loops of intestine it is found that D-isomers are absorbed by passive diffusion only. The presence of the Na^+ ion speeds the carrier-mediated movement of amino acids into the intestinal cell. The role of sodium here may be similar to (or slightly different from) its role in glucose absorption. The activity of the Na^+ ion as a symport is of some interest in the study of membrane transport. But it should be emphasized that in life the amount of sodium is never rate-limiting in the absorption of other molecules: there is always more than enough sodium present to assist the movement of sugars and amino acids into cells.

Fat

Fat may be absorbed in the form of extremely small particles. These may be droplets of an emulsion of monoglyceride, free fatty acids and bile salts, which, if less than 5000 nm in diameter, could pass down between the threads of the microvilli forming the brush-border, and enter by pinocytosis. Most fat absorption, however, involves the micelles, the formation of which was described earlier. A few molecules of fatty acid and monoglyceride may exist free in solution in the intestinal lumen, and being fat-soluble can pass rapidly through the walls of the mucosal cells (see Chapter 3 under Movement of material across the cell membrane). These freely floating molecules in the lumen are in equilibrium with the fatty acid and monoglyceride bound in the micelles. As soon as the free molecules are removed by passing into cells, more are released from the micelles, and then these too are removed into cells, and so on. So the function of the micelles is to store the products of fat digestion temporarily and to present them to the absorbing surface in an available form in which they can pass through the cell membrane.

Within the cell, free fatty acids and monoglycerides are resynthesized to neutral fat in the endoplasmic reticulum. Small droplets of this neutral fat, together with cholesterol and fat-soluble vitamins, are coated with a layer of protein and phospholipid which stabilize them. Soon they appear in the lacteals (lymphatics) of the villi, presumably having left the cells by reverse pinocytosis (or exocytosis). These droplets, called chylomicra (each one is a chylomicron) are between 0.33 μm and 1 μm in diameter. The chylomicra move along the thoracic lymph duct and enter the general circulation via the vein at the base of the neck. Any bile salts which enter cells of the villi leave via the capillaries of the portal vein and return to the liver where they are available for resecretion; bile salts are not normally present in the general systemic circulation.

Calcium, iron and vitamin B$_{12}$

Most salts as ions are absorbed readily by passive diffusion. Divalent ions enter much more slowly than monovalent ones, and in the case of Ca^{++} and Fe^{++}, special mechanisms are present. The absorption of calcium is related to the body's current requirement. Calciferol (1,25-dihydroxycholecalciferol), the active form of vitamin D, is necessary for calcium absorption (see Chapter 14). It seems that calciferol assists the synthesis of a protein carrier for calcium, within the intestinal cell wall. Entry of iron also requires a carrier, a protein called apoferratin, which with iron forms ferratin, the storage form of iron.

Iron enters the body in the ferrous form. It is carried in the blood not as ferratin but as a beta-globulin called transferrin. For iron, also, the amount entering the body is in some way regulated by the body's requirements. In fact only a small proportion of dietary iron actually enters the blood; there is a large re-use of the body's stores of iron, so the same Fe^{++} ions may be used several times over, as haemoglobin is broken down and resynthesized. The iron not absorbed (which would be probably more than 90 per cent of the iron ingested in a normal adult human) remains as ferratin in the mucosal cells, and is lost when these cells are shed into the intestinal lumen and leave the body in the faeces.

The water-soluble vitamins enter the body by diffusion, and the fat-soluble vitamins which are associated with dietary fat are absorbed in close association with fat. Vitamin B$_{12}$, necessary for the synthesis of haemoglobin, has a special mechanism of absorption. It combines in the stomach with a glycoprotein of molecular weight 60 000, called 'intrinsic factor', which is secreted from the oxyntic cells along the HCl. The complex of vitamin B$_{12}$ and intrinsic factor moves along the upper part of the small intestine, and is absorbed in the ileum, probably by pinocytosis. It is possible that the intrinsic factor helps the binding of the vitamin to a receptor site. Vitamin B$_{12}$ is stored in the liver and used in the bone marrow. People in whom the stomach has lost the power to produce intrinsic factor were at one time treated for the consequent pernicious anaemia by being given large supplies of animal's liver, so that some vitamin B$_{12}$ was forced into their blood by passive diffusion.

Absorption in the large intestine

Two processes of great physiological importance occur in the colon. One is the continued absorption of salt and water. It is largely this process which reduces the water content of the chyme, about 95 per cent at the ileocaecal valve, to about 80 per cent in the excreted faeces. The sodium pump of the wall of the colon is different from that in the small intestine. It is stimulated by the hormone aldosterone (from the adrenal cortex) and inhibited by the drug amiloride, but not by oubain which inhibits sodium–potassium exchange pumps elsewhere in the body. It is this colonic sodium pump which is damaged in the disease cholera, in which the consequence is a very rapid depletion of the body's sodium and water.

A second important process carried out in the colon is the synthesis by the bacterial flora of several vitamins of the B-complex, and their subsequent absorption. This process is sometimes called 'refection'. The intestinal flora thus perform a valuable nutritional function. This becomes apparent if a person is given a drug which kills the intestinal bacteria; such a person will soon suffer from symptoms of deficiency of B-complex vitamins, unless he is also given extra quantities of these vitamins in his diet.

Adaptations in ruminants and other herbivores

The processes of digestion and absorption are broadly similar among mammalian species. One particular group, the ruminants (e.g. cow, sheep, goat, deer, antelope), show an interesting structural and physiological adaptation to their strictly herbivorous diet. The grass when cropped and swallowed passes down the oesophagus to a large cavity, the rumen, which connects with a smaller more rostral cavity, the reticulum. Both cavities contain bacteria and protozoa in which the enzyme cellulase can break down cell walls; the micro-organisms use the vegetable matter in their metabolism, and the byproducts of this fermentation, mainly short-chain organic acids, are absorbed through the wall of the rumen. Later, some of the food initially cropped and swallowed is regurgitated into the mouth, where it is chewed and mixed with saliva; this process of 'chewing the cud' is called rumination. When reswallowed, this finely ground material passes through the reticulum to the omasum, where there is much absorption of organic and inorganic material including the sodium and water of the saliva. Finally, the food reaches the abomasum or true stomach, the only one of these cavities which is lined with glandular epithelium, and where gastric juice is secreted as in other mammals.

The rumen is a very large organ, occupying (in the cow) the whole of the left side of the abdomen (Fig. 4.9). The organic acids produced in fermentation form a considerable proportion of the energy requirements of ruminant species. The copious parotid-gland saliva, a dilute solution of sodium bicarbonate and alkaline sodium phosphate, partially neutralizes the organic acids produced in fermentation, and provides the appropriate medium for the activity of the micro-organisms. The recycling of the salts and water of the saliva is essential for the animal's fluid balance. The gaseous byproducts of fermentation, methane and carbon dioxide, are eliminated by eructation (belching).

It is not certain what stimulates regurgitation and initiates the process of rumination. It might be a chemical signal: a certain level of organic acid in the rumen for instance; or it might be a mechanical stimulus: grass particles of a certain size touching the sensitive partition between rumen and reticulum. Nor is it known exactly how the finely chewed material is directed towards the omasum instead of re-entering the rumen. A pair of longitudinal muscular folds at the base of the oesophagus, the

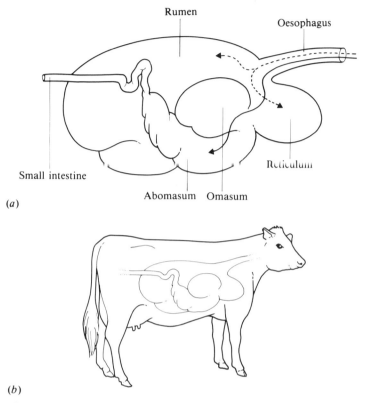

Figure 4.9 (*a*) Rumen and related structures. Grass when swallowed enters rumen and reticulum (dotted line) and undergoes fermentation. Fermented material is regurgitated into the mouth and chewed. When it is reswallowed it enters the omasum and abomasum (true stomach). (*b*) Position of rumen in abdominal cavity (cow). (*a, b*: Adapted from Schmidt-Nielsen, K., *Animal Physiology: Adaptation and Environment*, 3rd edn, Cambridge University Press, Cambridge, 1983.)

oesophageal groove, on contraction form a furrow along which the chyme would run straight towards the omasum. In the lamb this muscle is indeed contracted during suckling so the milk goes to the omasum and abomasum, and does not enter the rumen. But in adult sheep the muscle of the oesophageal groove appears to be relaxed for most of the time so the mechanism directing chewed material is uncertain.

Nitrogenous material as well as organic acids can be absorbed via the walls of the rumen. Indeed the nitrogen of urea can be recycled by this route. Urea as an endproduct of the mammal's metabolism is secreted in the saliva: in fact in ruminants on poor-quality pasture or forage, the urine is almost free of urea and most urea leaves the blood via saliva. The bacteria of the rumen metabolize the urea, and the ammonia thus produced can be absorbed and re-used in the animal's protein metabolism. Urea is sometimes added to the foodstuffs of farm animals as a cheap source of nitrogen.

The energy of a vegetarian diet is in a more dilute form than that of animal material and is contained in cells, the walls of which cannot be digested by any vertebrate species. All herbivores therefore have the problem of either mechanical or bacterial breakdown of the cell walls. In non-ruminant herbivores such as the horse the caecum and colon are extremely large, forming a huge 'fermentation vat' functionally similar to the rumen; they too are full of bacteria and can absorb organic acids. The great length of the herbivores' gastrointestinal tract means a slow passage for the chyme and a lengthy period available for absorption. But the food of such species obviously cannot be as finely ground as it is in the ruminants, and there is more faecal wastage. The particulate matter often visible in the faeces of the horse contrasts with the smooth homogeneous faeces of the sheep or cow.

An interesting behavioural adaptation called coprophagy (faeces-eating) is seen in rabbits and some small rodents. This enables maximum use to be made of the diet by its passing through the digestive tract twice. The rabbit forms a certain kind of faeces from the contents of the caecum, softer in texture and lighter in colour than the normal small spherical faecal pellets. These soft faeces which include a mass of bacteria are eaten by the rabbit, and further fermentation, digestion and absorption can occur during the second passage through the alimentary canal.

Hunger and satiety

Many mammals including man eat at fairly regularly spaced intervals. Herbivores, for which the food is rather low in energy content, spend much of their waking life grazing or browsing; in contrast, large carnivorous mammals may eat only at intervals of three or four days. There is a wide variation of eating habits among humans: some people eat a large meal once a day, others eat five or six small meals. Despite such variations most adult mammals maintain a fairly constant body weight over long periods. Clearly there is some degree of regulation in the intake of food, both at the short-term hourly or daily level ('It is time to eat') and at the longer-term level ('I am losing weight, and must eat').

Many attempts have been made to identify the signals which alert the central nervous system to the energy requirements of the body, initiating the search for food, and food intake; and also the signals causing cessation of eating when hunger is satisfied. Hunger and satiety centres exist in the hypothalamus (see Chapter 14 under Central autonomic control) and are probably influenced both by afferent nerve input and by blood-borne chemicals. Possible signals are glucose level or fatty-acid level in the blood. Certainly intravenous infusion of glucose in experimental animals diminishes their food intake, and injections of insulin, which lower the circulating glucose level, increase it. But in fact hormonal control mechanisms normally maintain blood glucose at a fairly steady level, and there is no evidence of a fall in blood glucose associated with the sensation of hunger just before a meal. Again, in man even a light meal takes about an hour to be fully absorbed, but one feels satiety after only 10 minutes. A plausible suggestion is that stretch receptors in the walls of the stomach give the sensation of fullness, and signals from stomach to satiety centre cause cessation of eating, allowing the central nervous system to make an assessment of the energy content of the meal. When the stomach is emptied, biochemical signals determine the time of onset of the next period of hunger. If the last meal contained much inert bulk but little energy, the sensation of hunger comes soon; if the meal supplied abundant energy, hunger will not return for some hours.

Conclusion and problems

In the alimentary canal the processes of digestion, refection and absorption supply all the necessary materials for growth, maintenance and energy input in the animal. Faecal output is normally very low in available energy and consists mainly of bacteria, shed epithelial cells and excretory products derived from the bile. Although the function of the digestive enzymes is now well known, certain problems remain. One is the relationship of hormones and intrinsic nerve plexuses in the control of secretion. The process of absorption provides examples of all the various mechanisms, physical chemical and biological, by which molecules and ions move through membranes; but the mechanisms of the passage of material from cell to blood are less well known than those of the passage from intestinal lumen to cell. Another topic of current biochemical interest is the mechanism, at the cellular level, by which the current physiological requirement of the body can control the rate of entry of certain ions or molecules. The last word on absorption has not yet been written.

5 Cardiovascular system

Introduction

The cardiovascular system through which blood is supplied to all organs in vertebrates (and in many invertebrates) is a means of distributing structural and energy-supplying materials—glucose, amino acids, fatty acids—to all cells; and of conveying the products of metabolism—carbon dioxide, lactic and pyruvic acids— from the cells to the points at which they are removed from the body, the lungs and kidneys. The blood also carries hormones, the chemical messengers released from glands and other organs, and conveys them to their site of action. This regular movement of blood, which is part of the extracellular fluid, ensures some degree of uniformity in the internal environment of all cells. The cardiovascular system consists of the heart, which pumps the blood, and the blood vessels—arteries, arterioles, capillaries, venules and veins. The first part of this chapter describes the work of the heart, the activity which keeps the blood circulating.

Heart

The mammalian heart is a double pump—two pumps arranged in series. The right side pumps blood through the lungs (pulmonary circulation) and the left side through all the rest of the body (systemic circulation). The muscle fibres in the wall of the heart have an inherent rhythm, totally independent of nerves. This can be strikingly illustrated by removing a single fibre from the embryonic heart of a developing chick at an early stage of incubation, and growing it in tissue culture. It has been beating rhythmically within the embryo before any nerve fibres have reached it, and continues to beat when removed from the embryo. The activity of the muscle fibres is related to drifting, reversal and restoration of their membrane potential; and this inherent instability and cycle of rhythmic changes of potential is present in the membrane of certain parts of the cardiac musculature (myocardium) throughout their existence. The rhythm can be modified by temperature, by the chemical composition of the blood, and by impulses from nerves reaching the pacemaker areas of the heart; but the initiation of the beat is myogenic: that is, a property of the pacemaker muscle fibres themselves.

Cardiac cycle

The heart beat of mammals is so quick that the sequence of events is difficult to observe directly. The events of the cardiac cycle—the processes from the start of one atrial contraction to the start of the next—can be more readily seen in the slower heart of the amphibian, which can be slowed still further if the isolated heart is perfused with blood or Ringer solution that has been cooled. Also, since contraction of each portion of the myocardium is accompanied by a characteristic electrical change acting as the stimulus for the sequential activity, contraction can be observed indirectly by recording these electrical signals from electrodes on the heart's surface.

Contraction is initiated at a region on the right atrium where the main veins bringing blood from the systemic circulation enter this atrial cavity: the sinoatrial (SA) node (Fig. 5.1). The inherent rhythm of the cardiac muscle fibres at this node is faster than that of any other part of the myocardium. Since the whole myocardium acts as a syncytium (as defined in Chapter 3), with effective electrical transmission between the fibres, the electrical signal and consequent contraction spreads quickly from this node across the right and left atria, the right contracting slightly before the left. The signal then reaches another node of myocardial tissue, the atrioventricular (AV) node, close to the septum between right and left parts of the heart, and the junction between right atrium and ventricle. From the AV node, a bundle of specialized rapidly conducting muscle fibres (Purkinje fibres) carry the electrical signal. After a short distance this group of fibres (the bundle of His) divides into right and left branches running down to the tip of the respective ventricles, then turning back and splaying out over the ordinary ventricular muscle cells. Since Purkinje fibres conduct 10 times faster than the ordinary myocardial fibres around them, the electrical signal quickly reaches the tip (apex) of both ventricles, so it is at this point

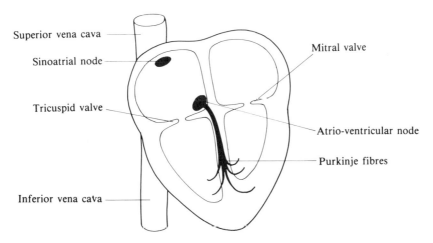

Figure 5.1 Chambers of the heart, RA, LA: right and left atrium. RV, LV: right and left ventricle.

that ventricular contraction starts, and then spreads throughout the ventricular myocardium. The contraction, or period of contraction, of the myocardium is called systole, and its relaxation, diastole. While the ventricles have been undergoing systole, the atria are in diastole; then the ventricles also relax, and the cardiac cycle is complete.

The electrical changes in cardiac muscle fibres are described in detail in Chapter 11. Appendix 3 describes the electrocardiogram.

The changes in pressure, blood flow and position of the valves in the chambers of the heart during one cardiac cycle will now be described. There are no valves between the veins and atria, so when the walls of the atria are relaxed, with low pressure within them, blood from veins on left and right sides of the heart rushes into these chambers. This increases the pressure in them, and thus when the ventricles start their diastole, the tricuspid and mitral valves (AV valves) open, and blood from the veins pours straight through the atria, through these valves, and down into the ventricles. In fact during a normal cardiac cycle, two-thirds of the blood in the ventricles enters them during the phase of diastole of all four chambers of the heart. Only the final third enters by the force of atrial systole. The atria act simply as a booster pump.

During the diastolic phase of the ventricles the semilunar valves between the ventricles and main arteries are shut as the pressure in the main arteries filled with blood from the previous heart beat is greater than that in the relaxed ventricles. However, the pressure within the ventricles builds up as they fill with blood from the veins, helped finally by a push from the contracting atria. At this point the ventricles start to contract, the pressure within them rises, and the tricuspid and mitral valves snap shut. The ventricular myocardium contracts further, but the ventricles are now effectively a closed box, as both sets of valves are shut; so the pressure inside the ventricular chambers rises enormously, from about 5 to 150 mmHg in 0.3 s (in man). Arterial pressure in the aorta and pulmonary artery has by now dropped slightly, since the blood forced into them by the previous heart beat has moved further on. So the high pressure in the ventricles can force both semilunar valves open, and blood is quickly ejected from the ventricles into the arteries. The elasticity of the arterial walls is sufficient to accommodate the added load of blood by bulging outwards. The flow of blood into the arteries continues, but with decreasing velocity, until in the now-relaxing ventricles the pressure drops so much that the semilunar valves shut again; and in this relaxed state of the ventricles, blood from the veins can once more start pouring through the atria and AV valves into the ventricular cavities.

In most humans at rest the heart beats between 70 and 80 times per minute, so each cardiac cycle lasts just under one second, say 0.8 s. For about half of this time, all four chambers of the heart are undergoing diastole, and it is in this phase that blood from the veins is filling the heart. When the heart rate quickens, as in exercise for instance, it is mainly this diastolic phase that is cut short. The rate of blood flow back to the heart (venous return) from actively working muscles is high, so even in this shortened diastolic phase an adequate amount of blood can enter the ventricles. If the heart rate is extremely rapid, however, the time of ventricular diastole becomes too short, the ventricles fail to fill sufficiently and the rate of the heart's output into the arteries decreases.

Starling's Law

The heart muscle, besides its inherent rhythmicity, has another important property, which is shown also by striated muscle. This is that when the muscle is passively stretched, the next contraction will be more forcible. This fact, for cardiac muscle, has been summarized as Starling's Law of the Heart: the force of a contraction is proportional to the initial length of the ventricular muscle fibres. (This point is discussed in Chapter 11, p. 222.)

The operation of Starling's Law of the Heart could serve to keep the two sides of the heart 'in step'. If, for instance, there were to be a slight blockage or congestion in some part of the pulmonary circulation, blood in the lungs would be dammed back towards the right ventricle, which would now be fuller than usual at the end of diastole. The fibres of this ventricle would therefore be stretched, and at the next systole would contract more powerfully, overcoming the obstruction and forcing an adequate amount of oxygenated blood over to the left atrium. Without the Starling effect, there would have been too little blood coming to the left side of the heart, so during the next few beats, the left ventricle would be insufficiently filled, and its beat would therefore have become weaker. In this way small moment-to-moment changes in pressure and flow of pulmonary and systemic circulations are corrected at the next heart beat by the Starling effect, and the output per minute from the two ventricles is kept equal.

There are few physiological conditions in which the ventricular muscle fibres are stretched (thus enlarging the heart) for longer than a beat or two. It is doubtful, for instance, whether such enlargement occurs during physical exercise. The heart does indeed beat more forcibly during exercise but this is by the action of nerves, not by the Starling effect. In trained athletes there is some evidence that the heart is enlarged, not only by a thickening of the ventricular walls ('physiological hypertrophy' of the myocardium) but also by actual enlargement of the cavity. Certainly the resting heart rate of trained athletes is slow, suggesting a larger stroke volume, i.e. more blood per beat ejected into the aorta and pulmonary artery, than for untrained persons.

In pathological circumstances the volume of the ventricles may indeed be changed, with consequences predictable from Starling's Law. If the valves are imperfect, for instance, contraction of the ventricles squeezes some blood backwards into the atria; the atria and ventricles become overfull and enlarged, and the beat becomes more forcible. In shock or haemorrhage the venous return to the heart is inadequate, the ventricles fail to fill adequately at diastole, their fibres are *not* stretched and the beat becomes weak. However, although Starling's Law is of importance to the pathologist and is interesting in illustrating a parallel with a property of striated muscle, in the normal function of the heart its significance is overridden by the much greater effect of nerve reflexes.

Cardiac output

The cardiac output is defined as the volume of blood leaving each ventricle per minute. (It is also called the minute volume.) In an adult man at rest it is about

5 litres/min; if his heart rate is 70 beats/min, about 72 ml of blood are ejected at each stroke. Output per beat is called stroke volume. The cardiac output could be raised by increasing either the rate (number of beats per minute) with a constant stroke volume, or the stroke volume, or both.

Heart rate

The resting heart rate is determined partly by the inherent rhythm of the fastest beating portion of the myocardium, the SA node or pacemaker, which imposes its rhythm on the remainder of the myocardium; and partly by two sets of efferent nerve fibres of the autonomic nervous system, running from the central nervous system (CNS) and terminating at the pacemaker tissue in the SA node (see Chapter 10). One set of fibres, parasympathetic fibres in the vagus (cranial X) nerves, carries impulses which slow down the beat; the other set, the sympathetic nervi accelerantes emerging from the first thoracic nerve pairs (T_1) in the spinal cord, quickens the heart beat. Both sets of nerves are carrying impulses all the time; that is, they are tonically active. If one set, say the vagus, is cut in an experimental animal, the tonic activity of the nervi accelerantes is unopposed, and the heart rate speeds up; conversely, if nervi accelerantes are cut, the heart beat slows, by unopposed action of the vagus. If both sets of fibres are cut, the heart rate, now dependent simply on the pacemaker's own rhythm, is almost normal, though perhaps slightly faster than in the intact animal— say 90 instead of 70 beats/min. This suggests that in the normal animal at rest the tonic activity of the vagus is somewhat stronger than that of the nervi accelerantes.

The impulses in both sets of nerves are dependent on neurones in the medulla oblongata in the brain stem, below the brain and above the spinal cord. This area of the medulla receives afferent impulses from all over the body as well as from other parts of the CNS, especially the hypothalamus. Indeed almost any afferent nerve if stimulated strongly enough can have an effect on the heart rate: a sudden sharp pain such as a bang on the shin can slow the heart rate for a beat or two by increasing vagal tone. Input to this medullary region from other regions of the CNS could arise from the psychological states of fear or excitement, which quicken the heart beat by increasing the impulse rate in the (sympathetic) nervi accelerantes. But not all changes in the heart rate are as dramatic as this. It is probable that all the time the rate of the heart is being slightly modified by small changes in vagal and sympathetic tone, in response to the many inputs.

There are three sensory organs (or sensory regions) which are particularly important in sending to the CNS impulses that modify heart rate (Fig. 5.2). These are stretch receptors (also called baroreceptors) lying in the circular smooth muscle of the wall of certain main arteries; they are found in the carotid sinus region, where the common carotid arteries—one each side—bifurcate into internal and external carotids; and in the aortic arch, where the aorta, emerging from the left ventricle, curves sharply and turns downward caudally (see Fig. 5.2). The carotid sinus baroreceptors send impulses up afferent fibres in the glossopharyngeal (cranial IX) nerves, left and right. The aortic arch receptors transmit via afferent fibres in the left vagus nerve. In some species of animals including the rabbit this group of afferent

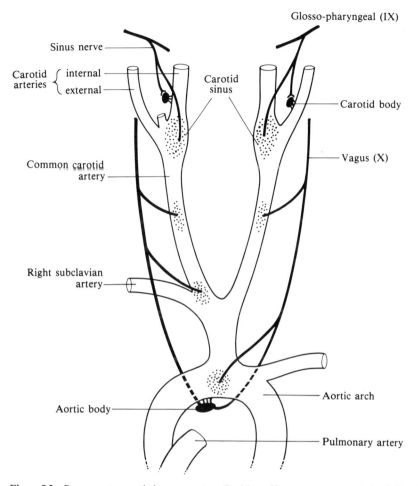

Figure 5.2 Baroreceptors and chemoreceptors. Position of baroreceptor areas (stippled) and chemoreceptors (solid black), and their afferent innervation, in the arteries near the heart.

fibres forms a separate bundle of axons, not in the same sheath as the vagus; it is then called the 'vagus depressor'.

The stretch receptors are tonically active, so impulses are being carried up these afferent nerves to the CNS all the time. But their frequency is much increased when these regions of the arteries are stretched or dilated by an extra-large volume of blood within them. If, for instance, the outflow of blood from the main arteries into arterioles in the head or trunk is slowed down (say by a partial obstruction or external pressure on a small artery), blood tends to be dammed back into the arteries, the walls of the carotids or aorta become stretched, and more impulses are carried up to the medulla. The response is an increase of (parasympathetic) vagus impulses and a reduction of impulses in the (sympathetic) nervi accelerantes, so that heart rate slows down, and there is a lower cardiac output for a few beats; this gives time for the excess blood in the arteries to be accommodated in arterioles, and prevents overstretching of arterial walls. Conversely, if the arterial walls become too flaccid—say by a sudden, severe haemorrhage reducing the whole blood volume—the lessening of stretch on the arterial walls has the opposite effect: fewer afferent impulses, less vagal tone and increased sympathetic tone; so the heart rate quickens. Once again, though extreme instances have been described, there are certainly small moment-to-moment fluctuations of input up these afferent nerves. These slight variations in impulse frequency, caused perhaps merely by movements of the head or the chest, could initiate small transient fluctuations of heart rate.

The reflexes described above, from the arterial stretch receptors, are known collectively as baroreceptor reflexes. Baroreceptors do occur elsewhere in the cardiovascular system, though it is the carotid and aortic sets which have most effect on heart rate. One other group also seem to affect heart rate: the stretch receptors in the wall of the left atrium, close to the point where the pulmonary vein from the lungs enters it. A stretch of this region, say by a slight increase of volume of blood entering the left side of the heart from the lungs, has the effect of *quickening* the heart beat. The receptors send impulses to the cardiac centre via afferent fibres in the vagus (cranial X), and the centre responds by decreasing the tonic impulses in the efferent vagal fibres to the pacemaker. The slightly quicker heart beat and greater cardiac output will help to eject the additional blood from the left side of the heart.

Apart from the vagus and sympathetic nerves the pacemaker at the SA node can be affected by the temperature and composition of the blood entering the heart. As expected, an increase in temperature quickens and a reduction slows the heart beat. This can easily be seen in reptiles and amphibia, but is observable in birds and mammals also. The heart rate increases in a fever; and in hibernating mammals in which body temperature falls, the heart rate slows. An important chemical effect on the heart is produced by the hormone adrenaline, secreted from the adrenal medulla in conditions of excitement, stress, fear and exercise, and circulating by the blood to the heart. It quickens the heart, in much the same way as the sympathetic nervi accelerantes, and thus raises cardiac output. Several inorganic substances affect the heart beat. Calcium and K^+ ions are always present at a precise concentration in the blood plasma; if this concentration alters, the pacemaker rhythm is disturbed and the whole myocardium can be damaged. Potassium ions entering the plasma from cells during dehydration, as in diarrhoea in infants, sometimes cause a cardiac disturbance. But apart from actual damage by disease, the heart, including its pacemaker, appears to be a sturdy, tough, reliable organ. It serves most humans so well that they are scarcely conscious of its activity for 60 or 70 years.

Stroke volume

Small changes in cardiac output are determined mainly by changes in heart rate with little alteration in stroke volume. Changes in stroke volume do occur, however. As we have seen, a sudden increase of volume of blood in one or both ventricles, by stretching the myocardial fibres, causes the next beat to be more forcible (Starling effect), and thus gives a greater stroke volume. A more frequent increase in stroke volume is brought about by a more nearly complete emptying of the ventricles at the end of systole—the end-systolic volume is smaller than before. This happens in strenuous exercise and is brought about by sympathetic nerves (the same nervi accelerantes from T_1) ending in the myocardium, not just at the SA and AV nodes but among the ventricular fibres. This production of a vigorous beat giving an increase in stroke volume by a greater emptying of the ventricles is called the *inotropic* effect of the sympathetic nerves. 'Inotropic effect' means that at any given initial length of the ventricular muscle fibres, the subsequent contraction is more forcible with sympathetic stimulation, or adrenaline, than without. The quickening of heart rate by sympathetic nerves to the pacemaker (or by adrenaline) is called the *chronotropic* effect. Athletic training in humans results in an increase in cardiac output, achieved mainly by increased stroke volume.

Cardiac output is thus adjustable to the varying requirements of different parts of the body, by alteration in stroke volume or rate of heart beat. This alteration may last for just a few beats or for several hours, and later in this chapter some situations will be described in which this adjustment takes place. This flexibility of function of the heart, dependent largely on varying rates of impulses along its efferent nerves, makes the cardiac output an important determinant of arterial blood pressure, through which the distribution network of the body's blood supply is maintained.

Arteries and arterioles

In man and many other species the flow of blood to the brain is extremely constant, and also extremely large in relation to the size of the organ. The brain, unlike most organs, has no available reserve of energy-supplying materials such as carbohydrate or fat, and cannot switch to an anaerobic metabolism, as can many organs during conditions of low oxygen supply. Brain cells are therefore dependent on blood-borne materials throughout their life. The stretch receptors in the walls of the carotid arteries are well placed to assist the heart in maintaining this steady flow to the brain. In other organs, notably skeletal muscle, skin and alimentary canal, the rate of blood flow varies with the prevailing state of activity. This variation is brought about mainly by variation in the lumen of the arterioles; the smooth muscle of their walls can be affected by nerve reflexes, as well as by locally produced metabolites, and by circulating adrenaline. The total volume of blood in the body is, however, limited, and although the heart can achieve an increase in its rate of output of blood—a fivefold increase is not unusual in exercise—there is no way in which a maximum supply of blood to all organs of the body could be attained simultaneously. More blood flow to one organ necessitates less blood flow to another. This manoeuvrability, brought about mainly by the reflexes controlling arterioles, is dependent on the maintenance of a steady head of hydrostatic pressure in the main arteries of the body. Here again stretch receptors in the aortic arch form an essential part of the signalling system.

Without this steady pressure at the point where blood emerges from the heart—the source or root of the blood supply—the flexibility of the system could not be achieved. Amid the varying and quickly changing demands of this or that organ, some factor of the cardiovascular system must remain fairly constant; and this factor—this 'still centre'—is the arterial blood pressure.

Arteries and arterial blood pressure

Arterial pressure means the outward pressure on the walls of the main arteries, at right angles to the direction of blood flow. The main arteries are the aorta (in the trunk), carotids (neck and head), brachials (upper limbs) and femorals (lower limbs); the pressure in all these is much the same. The SI unit of pressure is the pascal, Pa. For blood pressure measurement a conventionally used unit is the millimetre of mercury, mmHg. $1 \text{ Pa} \equiv 7.5 \times 10^{-3}$ mmHg. In a young adult human lying down, the pressure reaches a peak of about 120 mmHg during systole when the arteries have just received a load of blood from the left ventricle, and falls to about 80 mmHg during diastole when the aortic semilunar valve is shut and the blood ejected at the last beat is moving along to the arterioles. The difference between systolic and diastolic pressures is called pulse pressure (40 mmHg in this case); and the values of systolic and diastolic pressures are often written thus: 120/80. In a human standing upright the effect of gravity would increase the pressure at the feet, and this would have to be added to the effect of the heart's output. So in the legs there would be the additional hydrostatic pressure of a column of fluid of the height between legs and heart; conversely, in the head gravity would have the effect of decreasing arterial pressure, by tending to pull blood down towards the heart.

There are a number of physical, mechanical and structural properties of the circulation and blood, which influence and help to maintain arterial pressure. These properties are:

1. elasticity of the walls;
2. volume of blood, or 'filling pressure';
3. flow rate of blood and branching of blood vessels;
4. viscosity of blood;
5. speed (velocity of blood flow).

These factors will be considered in turn.

Elasticity of arterial walls

The onward movement of blood through the arteries while the ventricles are relaxing and filling and the semilunar valves are shut depends entirely on the elasticity of the arterial walls. This property allows the sudden intake of blood ejected from the ventricles; the walls then recoil, squeezing the blood along into the arterioles. This elasticity smooths out what would otherwise be enormous fluctuations in pressure at the different phases of the cardiac cycle. If the arteries resembled glass-tubing rather than rubber-tubing, there would be a great pressure on their walls at systole and a sudden drop at diastole, and consequent abrupt changes of flow rate into the arterioles. One of the pathological changes of old age in humans is that arteries tend to lose their elasticity, with resultant strain on their walls.

Volume of blood

The total volume of blood in relation to the effective capacity of the circulation at any time must obviously have some effect on arterial pressure. In extreme alterations of blood volume, say a sudden haemorrhage, the loss of volume in relation to capacity causes a fall in arterial pressure; and a blood transfusion into a healthy individual would cause a rise, as volume would be in excess of capacity. In some types of shock there is much loss of fluid from the circulation through capillary walls into the interstitial space; again, a mismatching of volume and capacity occurs, and arterial pressure falls. But the relation of arterial pressure to blood volume cannot be simple, because the effective capacity of the circulation is constantly changing with the activity of different organs: some vascular beds open up, others decrease. Clearly the heart can eject into the arteries ('resistance vessels') only what it receives from the veins. The veins can bring to the heart what they receive from the capillary bed. But the veins can also act as storage organs and can therefore in the short term supply to the heart more blood than they are currently receiving from the capillaries. The actual capacity of the circulation—if such a term has any meaning—is unmeasurable; but an indication of the 'fullness' of the circulation is conveniently obtained by measurement of the pressure in the main veins close to the heart, or the right atrium. In fact measurement of right-atrial filling pressure is useful clinically, because if it remains fairly steady, an adequate (but not excessive) amount of blood can enter the heart at each cardiac cycle, the ventricular fibres will be suitably stretched, and the strength of the beat maintained.

Flow rate of blood

The flow rate of blood through a blood vessel depends on the pressure difference ($P_0 - P_1$) between the two ends of the vessel, and on the resistance along its length. The resistance depends on the dimensions (length, l, and radius, r) of the vessel, and also on the coefficient of viscosity, η, of the blood itself. These facts have been summarized and quantified in the equation:

$$\text{Flow rate} \propto \frac{(P_0 - P_1)\pi r^4}{8\eta l}$$

a formulation known as Poiseuille's Law. This equation allows prediction of flow rate and pressure drop in various blood vessels according to their dimensions. The flow rate in arteries is large: there is not much fall in pressure along their length and, although they are long (l is large), they are also wide (r and r^4 are large). Arterioles are narrow, the smallest being almost thread-like, and they are also long. So if flow rate is to be kept constant, the pressure drop ($P_0 - P_1$) along their length must be great: typical values might be 90 mmHg at the beginning of an arteriolar bed, 20 mmHg at the end.

The Poiseuille equation also allows prediction of the effect of branching on resistance to blood flow. There may be either an increase or a decrease in resistance after the branch-point. There will be an increase in resistance (per unit length of blood vessel) unless the total cross-sectional area of the system after the branch is larger by a factor of at least 1.4 than the cross-section of the original vessel. A further deduction from the Poiseuille equation is that since the flow rate depends on the fourth power of the radius, a small change in radius will have an enormous effect on flow rate in that particular vascular bed. This is of great importance in permitting physiologically controllable changes in arteriolar lumen to bring about changes in blood flow to various organs.

Viscosity of blood

Blood is a more viscous fluid than water, and the viscosity, as we have seen, contributes to resistance and so to arterial pressure. The viscosity of blood depends partly on the plasma proteins which form a colloidal solution; and partly on the number and nature of the red cells in suspension: the more numerous the red cells per cubic millimetre of blood, the greater the viscosity. Red-cell count, though slightly different in various parts of the circulation, remains fairly constant in normal life. In severe anaemia (red-cell deficiency) viscosity and consequently arterial pressure are reduced; and in a rare disease of humans called polycythaemia, when red cells become too numerous, the blood is more viscous than normal, as well as increasing in volume, and arterial pressure increases.

The red cells do not behave like solid particles in suspension; so in terms of viscosity the flow of blood is not like, say, the flow of liquid mud containing tiny sand-grains in suspension. It is more like the flow of an emulsion—a liquid-in-liquid suspension. The red cells have their own internal viscosity, and this, together with the ease with which their membrane can be deformed and distorted, gives blood 'anomalous viscosity'— much less viscosity than would be found in a suspension of rigid spherical particles of the same diameter. This property makes possible the flow of blood through fine capillaries of diameter even less than that of the red cells.

Velocity of blood flow

The velocity of the blood and the nature of its movement through the vessels have a bearing on arterial pressure. Velocity is greatest in the large arteries close to the heart, and decreases at every branch-point of the vessels. Blood normally flows in a streamlined manner: the layer of blood close to the wall of the tubular vessel is almost stationary. The next adjacent layer moves slowly, and so on, the central core of blood moving with the greatest speed; so there is a velocity profile across the cross-sectional area of the artery. This streamlined flow causes little strain on the smooth interior walls of arteries. But in places where the velocity is very great (in large arteries near the heart) and where there is branching of vessels, or a valve, or perhaps a partial obstruction by a pathological deposit of fat on the inner wall, the flow may become turbulent instead of streamlined, and the blood moves in eddy currents near the corner or obstruction, like the eddies seen in water near boulders on a river bed.

Turbulent flow causes considerable increase in wall pressure, and the artery may actually become strained at that point.

The velocity of blood flow in the large veins close to the heart is almost as great as that in the arteries. The flow in veins is always streamlined, and the pressure on walls is far less than in arteries.

In streamlined flow the energy of the driving pressure $(P_0 - P_1)$ along the length of the tube is largely dissipated against the viscosity of the fluid. In turbulent flow it is mainly dissipated in creating the eddies. In this case the Poiseuille Law does not apply, and the resistance to flow is determined *both* by the viscosity *and* by the density of the fluid, as well as by the radius of the tube.

The critical velocity, V, at which the streamlined flow is forced to become turbulent, is calculated as

$$V = \frac{K\eta}{dr}$$

where η = viscosity (in poises), d = density (in g/ml), r = radius (in cm) and K is a constant called the Reynolds number, which is about 1000 for blood and many other fluids. (This equation means that in a fluid of rather *low* density, the velocity would have to be very high before turbulence occurs.) For the human aorta near the heart in an individual at rest, if we substitute realistic values in the equation, we obtain a critical velocity of about 40 cm/s. This velocity may actually be reached by the blood during the ejection phase at the beginning of systole; but for most of the cardiac cycle the velocity of the blood flow is well below the critical value.

Before ending this discussion of the mechanical and structural effects in the circulation, we will mention an interesting phenomenon known as 'plasma skimming'. Across the cross-section of the blood vessels there is not only a velocity profile but also a profile of red-cell concentration. The red cells are in greatest abundance in the centre of the lumen, and least near the vessel walls; red cells, for reasons not entirely clear, tend to accumulate in the fastest flowing region, forming an axial core, along the vessel's centre. At points where the vessel bifurcates in the usual manner with an angle of much less than 90° between the two limbs, the axial core of red cells also bifurcates, a roughly equal number of red cells moving down each branch (Fig. 5.3a).

At points where a branch leaves the main trunk at right angles (Fig. 5.3b), a rather large proportion of the cell-poor fluid at the periphery of the main vessel moves into the branch, and the main axial core of cell-rich fluid continues at high speed in a straight line. If, from the side-branch, another branch comes out at right angles, the blood in this contains an even lower proportion of red cells. In this way the haematocrit (volume percentage of red cells in whole blood) becomes less at each right-angle branch. This process of plasma skimming is of some importance in certain vascular beds, notably in the kidney where there are three or four right-angle branches between the renal artery and the afferent arterioles of the outer cortex.

The structural and mechanical factors affecting arterial pressure are of great importance in maintaining the normal circulatory system. In the healthy human or

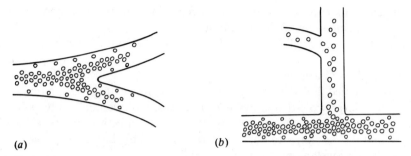

(a)

(b)

Figure 5.3 'Plasma skimming' at right-angle branches in the vascular bed. In (a), where there is an acute angle between the branches, the axial stream of erthrocytes is equally divided. In (b), where each branch is placed at a right-angle, the cell-poor peripheral stream of blood is selectively removed.

other animal such factors remain fairly steady. The structure, morphology and elasticity of arteries and arterioles do not alter much; neither does the volume or viscosity of the blood. Of the properties mentioned so far, the only ones which do vary under physiological conditions are the velocity of blood flow, which increases when the cardiac output is raised, as in exercise; and the total capacity of the circulatory system, which can be reduced when some vascular beds constrict in conditions associated with sympathetic nerve stimulation. These conditions will be discussed later in this chapter.

Arterioles

The arteries carry the blood from the heart to the main regions of the body: the head, trunk and limbs. Successive branching subdivides the blood supply and distributes it among the organs and tissues, and it is the arterioles which bring blood to the vessels of the microcirculation where there occurs the exchange of nutrients and waste products and gases with the living cells. However, the distribution of blood among the different organs can vary from hour to hour, perhaps from minute to minute. Except for the brain, organs are not equally active all the time, and it is through the work of the smooth muscle of the arterioles that the flow rate to various parts of the body can be adjusted according to activity.

Between the circular smooth-muscle fibres in arteriole walls there are numerous sympathetic nerves. The activity of these nerves depends on the medullary cardio-vascular neurones mentioned earlier in connection with control of heart rate. They are tonically active: that is, they conduct a continuous stream of nerve impulses from the CNS to the smooth muscle, the effect of which is to stimulate the circular smooth muscle, keeping the arterioles partially closed. If, for any reason, this sympathetic tone is increased—that is, there is a greater frequency of nerve impulses—the smooth muscle contracts further, and the arteriolar lumen shuts almost completely; so little or no blood can enter capillaries supplied from that arteriole. If sympathetic tone is reduced—that is, fewer impulses are transmitted—the arterioles dilate, and blood flow increases. Therefore only one set of nerves to the smooth muscle of arterioles is required to alter the blood supply in one way or the other: increased tone constricts the vessels and reduces flow, decreased tone dilates the vessels and increases flow. Since the resistance is inversely proportional to the fourth power of the radius (as indicated in Poiseuille's equation), for a given pressure a fairly small change in radius makes a great difference to the resistance, and consequently to the flow rate into the arteriole. So the tonic action of the sympathetic nerves, adjusting the radius (and thus the lumen) of the arterioles, has a very significant role in the distribution of blood according to the varying needs of the body's systems.

There is never a physiological state in which all arterioles are simultaneously *dilated*, and the usual situation is that more blood in one area or organ means less in another. However, it does sometimes happen that very many arterioles are simultaneously *constricted*. During conditions of excitement, or at the start of exercise, the sympathetic tone to arterioles in the skin and the splanchnic region (intestines, kidneys, liver, spleen) is greatly increased, and these arterioles constrict. The blood flow in these regions is much reduced, blood is dammed back towards the arteries, and arterial pressure temporarily increases. This sympathetic activity associated with excitement must be initiated in the so-called 'higher centres' of the brain. A widespread change in sympathetic vasoconstriction tone can also arise from a reflex, originating in the baroreceptors of the carotid sinus and aortic arch: the same baroreceptors as affect heart rate. These work as follows: a sudden increase of stretch in these main arteries makes the receptors increase the impulse frequency in the sensory nerves (glossopharyngeal, cranial IX; and vagus, cranial X); these impulses affect the neurones in the medulla of the brain stem, in such a way as to cause them to reduce the sympathetic vasomotor tone to arterioles; the arterioles then dilate, the blood which has stretched the arteries is accommodated in them and the stretch is lessened. Conversely, a reduction of stretch of the main arterial walls, by the opposite processes, increases vasomotor tone to arterioles, which causes damming back of blood towards arteries. These reflexes thus iron out violent fluctuations of pressure in the main arteries by altering the resistance of the outflow from arteries into arterioles.

This stabilizing effect of the baroreceptor reflexes is constantly at work, adjusting vasomotor tone and arterial pressure to small alterations in activity or position of the body or limbs. An extreme example involving the same set of reflexes occurs in a pathological condition, a haemorrhage. A sudden loss of blood reduces arterial pressure, and the baroreceptors respond, initiating a massive prolonged arteriolar constriction in many regions (and incidentally there is constriction of venules and veins, also). The consequence is a great reduction of the total capacity of the circulation; the remaining blood in the body is shunted away from the abdominal organs and limbs, and towards the heart, lungs and brain. This dramatic case is a reminder of an activity which is continuously occurring in less extreme form throughout life.

It should be mentioned here that the arterioles in certain body organs—notably those of skeletal muscle of the limbs, and of the myocardium of the heart—are thought to have in their sympathetic innervation some fibres that operate somewhat differently from those described above. These sympathetic fibres (called sympathetic vasodilators) carry impulses which initiate a dilatation, *not* constriction, of those particular arterioles. Sympathetic vasodilators, incidentally, release at their endings a different chemical transmitter (acetylcholine) from that released by most other sympathetic fibres (noradrenaline). These fibres will be mentioned again when the cardiovascular effects of exercise are considered.

Capillaries and microcirculation

The capillaries are totally different in structure from all other blood vessels. Their walls consist of a single layer of endothelial cells, lying on a thin basement membrane of connective tissue, and there are no smooth muscle or elastic fibres. The endothelial cell layer is continuous with the innermost cell layer of the smaller arterioles and venules. In many places the cells are rather loosely joined; the junctions may be quite leaky. The intercellular cement is constantly being removed and replaced.

The term 'microcirculation' usually includes the smallest arterioles and venules as well as the true capillaries. The microcirculation in an area of tissue consists of a network of capillaries supplied from a small arteriole (metarteriole) through a sphincter (ring of smooth muscle) called the precapillary sphincter. The sphincters are under sympathetic control. Tonic impulses shut the sphincter and prevent arteriolar blood from entering that capillary bed. In this case, blood from arterioles reaches the venules through the arteriovenous anastomoses (Fig. 5.4). Conversely, a reduction in sympathetic tone allows relaxation of the sphincter and entry of blood into the

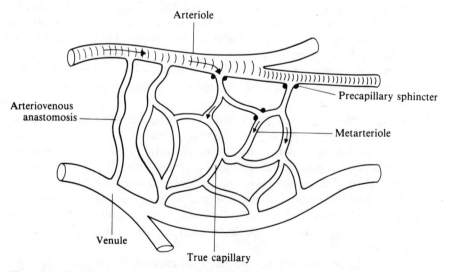

Figure 5.4 Capillary bed and arteriovenous anastomosis.

capillary bed. So the sphincters constitute another point at which distribution of the blood flow can be controlled.

It is by way of capillary beds ('exchange vessels') that nutrients, gases and waste products enter and leave all cells of the body. The movement of water, dissolved gases, and small solutes is by means of diffusion gradients, which make the exchange in both directions extremely rapid. The exchange through and between the cells of the capillary walls and basement membrane is so rapid that interstitial fluid is virtually indistinguishable from plasma minus protein. The main barrier to diffusion, the steepest concentration difference, is that between interstitial fluid and cell contents.

The rate of diffusion obviously depends on the surface area of the capillaries, and therefore on the number of open vessels in the given portion of tissue. The rate depends also on the permeability of the capillary to the particular chemical substance, and on the diffusion gradient. A steep gradient could be achieved either by rapid uptake into the tissue cells from interstitial fluid: this would be the case, say, for oxygen and glucose in an active muscle; or by rapid flow of blood bringing more material into the vessel. Diffusion exchanges are very sensitive to flow rate of the blood; and for most substances it is only at very high blood flow rates that diffusion rate is limited by the permeability of the membrane of the tissue cell.

There is a second process by which material can be moved out of capillaries. This is called bulk flow, and it probably occurs via small fluid-filled pores between but not through the capillary endothelial cells. Bulk flow would take water and all materials dissolved in it of appropriate dimensions for the pores. The movement of material by bulk flow is trivial compared with the enormous diffusion rates in both directions across the capillary wall, and has no bearing on the main function of the microcirculation—the supply of nutrients and oxygen to the tissue cells. It has, however, been studied in some detail, partly because of its clinical importance in connection with oedema, an accumulation of excess interstitial fluid symptomatic of several diseases.

The mechanism of bulk flow depends on the relative hydrostatic and osmotic pressures inside the blood vessel and immediately outside it. (These pressures are called Starling forces, after the physiologist who first drew attention to them.) In an open capillary through which blood is flowing briskly, there would be a hydrostatic gradient outwards, vessel → interstitium. But there would be an oncotic gradient inwards, interstitium → vessel, because the oncotic pressure due to plasma proteins is always greater than that due to the large colloidal molecules (including traces of protein) in the interstitial fluid.

Assuming that there is no movement of the colloids, the bulk flow rate per unit surface area of vessel wall, F, is given by

$$F = L_p[(P_v - P_i) - (\pi_v - \pi_i)]$$

P_v and P_i are hydrostatic pressures in vessel and interstitium, and π_v and π_i are the corresponding oncotic pressures. L_p is a factor called hydraulic conductivity, related to the number and dimensions of the pores. It differs in value in different microvascular beds; in the liver, for instance, L_p is large—the capillaries here are rather leaky. Realistic figures for actual values of hydrostatic and oncotic pressures, say in the microcirculation of a muscle, would be $P_v = 36$ mmHg, $P_i = 2$ mmHg, $\pi_v = 25$ mmHg, $\pi_i = 3$ mmHg. So bulk flow rate would be proportional to $(34 - 22) = 12$ mmHg. (Note that the figure 25 mmHg given for π_v relates to *oncotic* pressure of the plasma in the blood vessel, and is extremely small compared with total osmotic pressure of the plasma.)

Rate of bulk flow is obviously related to hydrostatic pressure within the microcirculation. But unlike diffusion rate, it is not directly related to the rate of blood flow through it. Direct measurement of hydrostatic pressures within small blood vessels has given evidence that the smallest arterioles and venules as well as the true capillaries may participate in bulk flow. Hydrostatic pressure within the microcirculation depends on the resistance of the vessels immediately upstream (arteriolar side) and downstream (venule side). Constriction of arterioles would lower the capillaries' hydrostatic pressure by reducing the flow of blood into them; constriction of venules would raise it, by damming back the flow out of them. Such constrictions could result from sympathetic nerve stimulation. There could also occur a *vasodilatory* effect of adrenaline (as would be released in conditions such as haemorrhage or hypoxia), working directly on β-receptors of small arterioles (described in Chapter 10, p. 204); and this too would lead to increase of capillary hydrostatic pressure.

It is easy to demonstrate bulk flow *out of* the microcirculation in normal physiological conditions; it is much more difficult to demonstrate bulk flow back *into* the microcirculation from the interstitium; but this is not to say that it does not occur. What is certain is that much of the water and solute including all the protein forced out into the interstitial space by bulk flow is returned to the circulation via the lymphatic vessels. Small thin-walled lymph capillaries run among the cells of nearly all organs of the body, and join up into larger lymph vessels which empty their contents via two large lymph trunks into main veins close to the heart. If disease alters one or other of the components of the Starling forces—say there is a reduction of plasma protein level and therefore of plasma oncotic pressure—an excess of interstitial fluid (oedema) could occur; and the same symptom could result from a blockage of a main lymph duct, such as happens in the condition of elephantiasis, as there would be an obstruction to the return of interstitial fluid into the circulation.

The microcirculation is very labile. Metabolites such as carbon dioxide and H^+ ions open up the small vessels; this is very noticeable in exercising limb muscles, where before exercise less than 10 per cent of the capillaries may be perfused with blood, and during exercise, 100 per cent. Other chemicals producing vasodilatation of the microcirculation are bradykinin, a short-lived hormone (chemical messenger) produced locally in some glands during activity and dilating their blood vessels; and vasoactive intestinal polypeptide in the alimentary canal, which contributes to the opening of intestinal blood vessels in the postprandial state. The blood gases are of much importance in the control of the brain's microcirculation: carbon dioxide opens it up, excess oxygen shuts it down. (Although oxygen excess does not occur in normal life, it could happen in humans breathing oxygen under pressure.) Sympathetic vasoconstriction of arterioles upstream of any particular microvascular bed would obviously reduce flow rate of blood through it; but adrenaline, released in plenty into the circulation in conditions such as haemorrhage and hypoxia, would cause vasodilatation, by a directly relaxing effect at β-receptors on small arterioles.

The microcirculation shows some degree of 'autoregulation'*—that is, control of its own hydrostatic pressure independent of the general arterial pressure; and this 'autoregulation', by minimizing the variations of bulk flow, could maintain a fairly steady fluid balance across the walls of exchange vessels. An experimentally produced example of 'autoregulation' was obtained by perfusing a dog's leg muscle: when the perfusion pressure was increased threefold, there was only a 15 per cent increase in the exchange-vessel pressure in the muscle at rest, and 30 per cent in the exercising muscle. The precise mechanism of 'autoregulation' is still being investigated.

Venules and veins

The veins have thinner walls, a wider lumen, and less elastic tissue than the corresponding arteries (Fig. 5.5). Blood flow in them depends of course on entry of blood from capillaries, but the propulsion along veins is produced very largely by the pressure or 'milking' effect of the tissues through which the veins run, squeezing on the thin-walled vessels and forcing the blood forward and onward to the heart. The valves, made of flaps of endothelial lining, prevent backward flow of the blood, so the external tissues pressing on the walls of veins can move blood in one direction only. Isotonic muscular movements of the limbs, which cause rhythmic swelling and narrowing of muscles, are particularly effective in assisting the onward movement of blood in veins, and also of the lymph in the even thinner-walled lymphatic vessels which drain excess interstitial fluid and return it to the circulation. In the trunk the rhythmic movements of respiration have a similar effect: at inspiration (inflation of lungs) the diaphragm moves towards the abdomen and presses on the abdominal contents including the inferior vena cava; at the same time the negative (subatmospheric) pressure in the thorax helps to pull blood from the abdomen into the thoracic cavity, towards the heart. At the next expiration intra-abdominal pressure is reduced, as the diaphragm relaxes, allowing rapid refilling of the main abdominal veins from their venules and capillary beds. Venous pressure in the venae cavae near the heart is about -1 mmHg, (below atmospheric) and in the thoracic cavity during inspiration -5 mmHg so the total effective pressure for filling the right side of the heart during inspiration would be -6 mmHg.

The mechanical properties of the walls of the venules and veins mean that they can increase their volume without much change in pressure. If they fail to empty into the heart as quickly as they are being filled from the capillary end, they become engorged and distend, with little change in pressure on their walls; the limit to distensibility may be reached quite suddenly, when the elastic tissue can stretch no further or when the

---

* The term *autoregulation* usually refers to the process by which *blood flow rate* through an organ remains fairly steady despite fluctuations in arterial pressure. In this instance the term has been used in the sense of maintenance of a fairly steady *hydrostatic pressure* in the microcirculation, and for this reason the word has been put in quotation marks in the text.

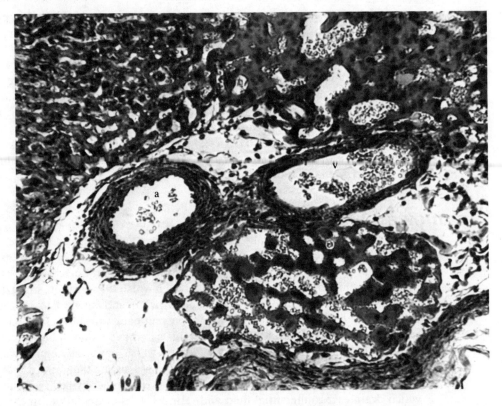

Figure 5.5 Small artery (a) and adjacent vein (v). Note thicker wall and more circular cross-section of artery. Placenta (guinea-pig). ×95. (Courtesy of P. Harris and P. Taylor.)

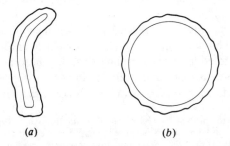

(*a*)   (*b*)

Figure 5.6   Cross-section of veins. (*a*) Flaccid and partially empty. (*b*) Full during venous storage of blood.

surrounding muscle or skin presses on the vein wall (Fig. 5.6). Readers must be aware of the distensibility of the superficial veins of their own limbs, when the body becomes heated, with consequent large skin blood flow. The distensibility of veins gives the venous side of the circulation a large capacity, and venous blood can be used in a sense as a reserve. The main veins, like the arteries, have a sympathetic innervation, which is tonically active (venomotor tone). If the tone of all venous sympathetic nerves increases simultaneously, a considerable volume of blood could be squeezed out from the now-constricted veins into the remainder of the circulation. Under conditions of stress, which increase venomotor tone, many tissues including liver, intestine, skin and muscle contribute 30–50 per cent of their 'resident' blood volume to the total blood reservoir.

Cardiovascular adjustments under various conditions

After considering the general properties and functions of each section of the cardiovascular system, we now study the manner in which the blood circulation as a whole adjusts itself in certain of the occurrences of daily life.

Gravity and posture

The hydrostatic pressure of the blood becomes especially important during changes of posture. For quadrupeds the head, heart, lungs and main vessels of the trunk are all on much the same horizontal level, whether the animal is lying or standing, so alterations in hydrostatic pressure during postural change may not cause much problem (though the hydrostatic pressure at the base of the neck of a giraffe browsing on high leaves must be considerable). With man and other bipeds the case is different, and considerable cardiovascular adjustments take place when a man lying supine suddenly stands. Gravity opposes the flow of blood up the main carotid arteries from the heart, and enhances the blood flow down the descending aorta towards the abdomen and legs. The region of the carotid sinus and aortic arch will thus be less stretched than when he was supine. The arterial wall baroreceptors reduce their sensory impulse traffic to the cardiovascular controlling regions of the CNS. In this way sympathetic tone to the heart and blood vessels is increased, the heart quickens, arterial pressure rises, and the main veins expel blood towards the heart. For the standing human the heart rate is always slightly greater and arterial pressure slightly higher than when he is recumbent. Should the baroreceptor reflexes work rather slowly, the small consequent reduction of blood flow up to the brain may cause a slight transient sensation of dizziness—a sensation experienced by many people who rise quickly from a stooping position.

A further problem may arise if a man stands still for several minutes without moving his legs. There will be pooling of blood by gravity in his feet. The pressure in the veins of the feet is about 100 mmHg: the hydrostatic pressure of an aqueous column from feet to right atrium. The lack of muscular pressure on the leg veins will mean that there is inadequate force for raising the column of blood in the veins back towards the heart. The inadequacy of the venous return may even cause a reduction of stroke volume of the heart (Starling effect) and the person may become faint. Some movement of muscles of the legs and feet is always needed for adequate return of blood to the heart when one is in the upright position.

Exercise

The response of the cardiovascular system to exercise such as running or swimming is of great interest, and of practical importance to those concerned with physical training and athletics. In nearly all conditions the period of exercise is preceded by some kind of emotional excitement, whether the exercise is that of the predator running to make a kill, the prey escaping, or the human preparing for a race or running for a bus. Emotional excitement causes a generalized stimulation of sympathetic nerves, and release of adrenaline from the adrenal glands. The sympathetic stimulation

1. quickens the heart rate and makes the heart beat more forcibly—effects enhanced by the adrenaline;
2. increases arteriole constriction in most organs;
3. increases venomotor tone, moving blood from venous reservoirs towards the heart;
4. perhaps *dilates* the coronary vessels supplying the myocardium.

If the excitement does not in fact lead on to physical exercise, sympathetic tone returns slowly to resting level, and the adrenaline is rapidly destroyed in the body; heart rate and arterial pressure return to their original levels.

If physical exercise starts, however, these sympathetic effects continue, and also some further vascular changes occur:

1. The microcirculation of the actively working muscles dilates, and many formerly empty capillaries become filled—an effect of 'metabolites' such as carbon dioxide, lactic and pyruvic acids, and possibly potassium ions and ADP, leaking from the active muscle cells.
2. The venous return is increased by the pumping action of contracting and relaxing limb muscles squeezing blood at a great rate towards the heart, and is also enhanced by the quick and deep respiratory movements accompanying exercise, increasing the negative pressure on blood in the inferior vena cava in the thorax.

From these changes, initiated partly by the preceding excitement, and partly by the activity of the muscles themselves, there follow various effects on the circulation:

1. Cardiac output is increased, by the chronotropic effect (increased rate of heart beat) and inotropic effect (more vigorous beat, lower end-systolic volume) of the sympathetic and adrenaline stimulation—in adult man, the cardiac output may rise from about 5 litres/min at rest to 25 litres/min in hard exercise.
2. Venous return is increased, partly by the increased venomotor tone but mainly by the muscle-pump effect.
3. The systolic arterial pressure increases slightly (diastolic pressure may be hardly changed).

4. The blood is shunted away from the abdominal organs, in which arterioles are constricted, and towards muscles.

5. In numerous well-filled muscle capillaries, blood is brought into close contact with active cells.

For mechanical reasons the muscle blood flow may occur in spurts—almost stopped by pressure of the fibres when muscle contracts, then flowing rapidly during the relaxed phase.

The increased cardiac output occurs simultaneously with (or even slightly before) the increased venous return, and there is no stage at which the ventricular muscle fibres are stretched. The Starling effect therefore cannot be invoked to explain the increased stroke volume of exercise. This increase of stroke volume must be due to the effect of sympathetic stimulation and of circulating adrenaline on the myocardium, giving a more vigorous beat and more complete emptying of the ventricles at the end of systole. In excessively severe exercise, when the heart rate is so fast that the time of diastole is cut short, there may be too little time for adequate filling of the ventricles, so both end-diastolic and end-systolic volumes are small, and stroke volume is reduced.

The consequence of these circulatory changes of exercise is of course that blood is shifted from the abdominal organs and venous plexus in the basal layer of the skin, and shunted towards the active muscles. The actively working skeletal muscles of the limbs are thus supplied with glucose, fatty acids and oxygen by the well filled capillaries in which blood comes into close proximity to the muscle fibres; and lactic and pyruvic acids and carbon dioxide are removed.

If the exercise is prolonged, a further circulatory change takes place. The heat generated in the actively working muscles causes dilatation of the skin blood vessels. The mechanism is as follows: warm blood from the active muscles affects temperature-sensitive cells in the hypothalamus at the base of the brain. Impulses from this region affect vasomotor tone, overriding the initial constriction of the skin blood vessels, and allowing these vessels to relax. The consequence is that a large blood flow in the superficial vessels permits cooling of the blood, and the body is saved from the overheating which might otherwise occur. Deep body temperature is always slightly raised in prolonged exercise, but not as much as it would be without this hypothalamic temperature-controlling mechanism.

A limit to the capability of the circulation may be reached in severe or prolonged exercise. If many blood vessels of skeletal muscle *and* skin are dilated simultaneously, the capacity of the circulation may become too much for the volume of circulating blood. Right atrial pressure decreases, the heart fails to fill adequately, and the heart beat weakens. This is a possible cause of collapse in long-distance runners.

Appendix 5 describes some changes caused by physical training in man.

Diving

Aquatic and semiaquatic mammals and birds (seals, ducks, porpoises) show an interesting cardiovascular adjustment during diving and underwater swimming.

There is a marked slowing of the heart ('diving bradycardia') and an intense vasoconstriction of arterioles or small arteries in the muscles of the limbs and splanchnic area. The blood supply to many body organs is thus reduced, and during the dive the muscles use anaerobic glycolysis as their energy source. After the dive large quantities of lactic acid, which have been accumulating in the muscles, come flooding into the general circulation. Humans show diving bradycardia, but in a less marked degree; however, humans can enhance the bradycardia by training. Table 5.1 illustrates diving bradycardia.

Table 5.1 Heart rate (beats per minute) before and during a dive

	Before	During
Man (trained)	80	30
Beaver	130	10
Penguin	240	40
Seal	120	10
Porpoise	120	40

The consequence of these circulatory adjustments is that little oxygen is used by most of the body during the period when lung ventilation cannot operate. Brain blood flow is unaltered. Arterial pressure does not rise excessively in spite of the intense arteriolar constriction, because cardiac output is reduced by the bradycardia.

The slowing of the heart is achieved by an increase in vagal tone to the pacemaker; the arteriolar constriction is presumably achieved by increased sympathetic tone to arterioles. The cardiovascular responses occur very quickly at the time of the dive and are therefore presumed to be brought about by a reflex, but the afferent input is uncertain; the touch of water on nasal receptors has been suggested. Interpretation of experiments on diving bradycardia is complicated because many semiaquatic animals such as seals, which slip into or under water when startled, show 'fear bradycardia'—a slowing of the heart (by increase of vagal tone) whenever they are frightened. (This contrasts with the majority of land species in which the heart *quickens*, by sympathetic stimulation, during fright.) So such experimental manipulations as placing the head of a seal or a duck under water in a bath in a laboratory ('forced diving') may elicit a bradycardia due to fear rather than submersion.

There are sense organs termed chemoreceptors which are responsive to the tension of dissolved oxygen (Po_2) in the blood perfusing them; these are the carotid bodies, visible as small spherical red objects lying between the internal and external carotid arteries each side; and the aortic body, lying just outside (and very close to) the wall of the aortic arch. From these, sensory nerves, in which impulse frequency is increased by a lowering of the blood Po_2, run in the glossopharyngeal (cranial IX) and vagus (cranial X) nerves to the respiratory and cardiovascular integrating neurones in the medulla (and possibly elsewhere in the CNS). These impulses have a considerable effect on respiratory rhythm, and a *much* slighter effect on the cardiovascular system, increasing vagal tone, slowing heart rate, and increasing peripheral resistance. There has been some speculation that these chemoreceptor reflexes might contribute to diving bradycardia; a mammal or bird under water without lung ventilation would show a lowered arterial P_{O_2}, which might initiate the reflex. However, the P_{O_2} fall is neither quick enough nor severe enough to explain the instantaneous bradycardia which seems to occur at the very moment of diving. If these chemoreceptors have any role in diving, it might be as a signal to an animal swimming under water that it is time to resurface. Experimental support for this idea is that in ducks diving spontaneously, those in which the chemoreceptor fibres have been cut (to put the carotid bodies out of action) remain under water for longer than intact or sham-operated birds. It has been suggested that in humans and perhaps other mammals chemoreceptor effects on the circulation are of help to the fetus during birth, at the intermediate stage when the placental circulation is shutting down but the lungs are not yet functioning. Clearly in these conditions the arterial blood would become hypoxic (deficient in oxygen). There is evidence that muscle blood flow of a fetus while in the vaginal canal is small; and bradycardia in the infant can be observed during a difficult birth when the hypoxic stage may be prolonged. The elucidation of the mechanism and interpretation of cardiovascular effects from the arterial chemoreceptors await further study.

Summary and problems

This chapter has given an account of the function and control of the main parts of the cardiovascular system. The heart is not a particularly efficient pump; it generates much heat, and its efficiency expressed as the percentage

$$\frac{\text{useful work}}{\text{work + heat}} \times 100$$

is only about 5 per cent in the body at rest, and about 15 per cent during exercise. However, it is extremely sturdy and durable, and though the beat is myogenic, nerves can alter both its rate and its contractility under various conditions. The main arteries maintain on the blood within them a fairly steady pressure. Arterial blood pressure does vary to some extent, being slightly higher in exercise, and lower during sleep. But its variations are less than those of either the cardiac output or the resistance of the arterioles; thus the arteries maintain a steady head of pressure, allowing manoeuvrability of the blood supply among the body organs.

These adjustments in the distribution of the blood supply during the changing activities of the body are carried out by the arterioles and by the rich sympathetic nerve supply to their smooth muscle. The arteries and arterioles together are the 'resistance vessels' of the circulation. The capillaries together with the smallest arterioles and venules are the 'exchange vessels', through the walls of which the cells of the body are supplied with nutrients and oxygen. The venules and veins are the 'capacitance vessels', by means of which blood can be withdrawn from or released into the general circulation. The manner in which the components of the circulation are adjusted in various real situations—the standing of a man, the taking of exercise, the diving of animals—has been used as a practical illustration of circulatory functions.

Much has been omitted from this account. The nature and place of the medullary centres controlling the heart and blood vessels have not been discussed. All that can be said for certain is that damage to the medulla of an animal causes a fall in blood pressure, and that in this region there appear to be neurones of which the function is to integrate the cardiovascular responses to afferents from all over the body, and from 'higher centres'. Indeed no mention has been made of many afferent inputs into this medullary region. The baroreceptors (and the chemoreceptors) and their afferents have been described but almost any afferent nerve in the body if stimulated sufficiently has an effect (a raising or a lowering) on arterial blood pressure.

Again, the account given above of the cardiovascular response to exercise may create the impression that all is known. This is erroneous. How does it come about that though the systolic arterial pressure is raised at the start of exercise, the heart is not slowed by a consequential baroreceptor reflex? How much of the additional venous return to the heart during exercise is due to passive emptying of the veins (elastic recoil of walls), how much to venomotor nerves, and how much to the squeezing of skeletal muscle? Trying to quantify the effects which are already familiar in general qualitative terms has proved extremely difficult. In short there are many omissions and simplifications in this chapter, and though much is known about the function of the cardiovascular system, very much still awaits discovery.

6 Respiration

Introduction

Respiration consists of the process of entry of oxygen into the body and the removal of carbon dioxide formed during oxidation of organic molecules in the body's metabolism. The main route of entry and removal for land vertebrates is by the trachea and lungs. (For some amphibia, oxygen may also enter directly through the moist skin.) The movement of gases and exchange of gases at the lung surface, where the thin-walled alveoli of the lungs come into close contact with the walls of the lung capillaries, is called external respiration. The distribution of oxygen and its entry into cells all over the body, together with the movement of carbon dioxide in the reverse direction from cells to lung surface, is called internal respiration. The rhythmic set of muscular movements involved in moving air in and out of the trachea, bronchi and lungs is called breathing, the inward and outward movements being termed inspiration and expiration respectively.

The movements of respiration and the inflation of the lungs will be described first. Next comes an account of the control of the respiratory rhythm and its modification under various physiological conditions. Finally, there is a description of the carriage of the respiratory gases between the lungs and the other body organs and of the part played by the haemoglobin of the red cells in this gas transport.

The mechanics of breathing

Respiratory movements

The thoracic cavity of mammals is surrounded by the rib cage and sternum on the dorsal and ventral sides, by the diaphragm below (caudal side) and by the clavicle and muscles of the neck above (rostral side). The cavity is divided longitudinally by a thick structure of connective tissue, the mediastinum. The two portions of the cavity (left and right) thus formed are each lined by two thin films of connective tissue, the pleurae. The parietal pleura lies closely against the inner surface of the thoracic muscles, ribs and diaphragm; and the pulmonary pleura closely surrounds the lungs. The two pleural surfaces are well lubricated, separated by a thin film of moisture and are normally in close contact; they slide over each other during breathing. (If the pleural surfaces become inflamed as in the disease pleurisy, the sliding is disturbed and each breath becomes painful.)

The diaphragm is a dome-shaped sheet of striated muscle fixed at its perimeter to the body wall, and with a connective-tissue tendon (central tendon) at the apex of the dome. The muscle fibres are arranged more or less radially and when they contract during inspiration the central tendon is pulled down towards the abdomen and the dome becomes less curved. This enlarges the thoracic cavity in the rostrocaudal axis (top to bottom).

Intercostal muscles lie obliquely between the ribs, as shown in Fig. 6.1a.

Several pairs of ribs (the third to the sixth, in man), as shown for the adult human in the figure, slope steeply downwards from their hinged articulation with the vertebrae at the back. The first pair of ribs is fixed by ligaments to the sternum and clavicle and is also stabilized by the pull of the neck muscles. Shortening of the external intercostal muscle fibres during inspiration pulls the ribs closer to each other and, since the top pair of ribs is fixed, each rib is thereby drawn closer to the one above it, moving on its hinged articulation with the vertebra. The consequence of this raising of the ribs into a more nearly horizontal position (for man) is that the thoracic cavity is enlarged in its dorsoventral axis (back to front) (Fig. 6.1b). The ribs of corresponding left and right pairs also move apart from each other, so the thoracic cavity is slightly enlarged during inspiration in the left to right axis.

This enlargement in all three planes of the closed thoracic cavity pulls the pleurae outwards and creates a subatmospheric pressure in the lungs. In consequence, air rushes down the trachea into the lungs. In quiet breathing the subsequent expiration is a passive process, consisting of the elastic recoil of the lungs and thoracic wall as the respiratory muscles (diaphragm and intercostals) relax. In deep breathing or forced expiration or coughing, expiration is an active process. Muscles of the abdominal wall

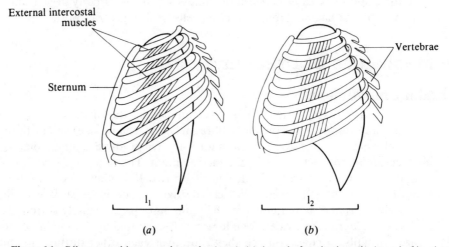

Figure 6.1 Rib cage and intercostal muscles (man). (a) At end of expiration. (b) At end of inspiration. As the external intercostal muscles contract, lifting the ribs to a more nearly horizontal position, the dorsoventral diameter of the chest increases such that $l_2 > l_1$.

contract and force the diaphragm upwards (in the rostral direction) and expiration may be helped by the contraction of another set of intercostal muscle fibres running obliquely in the other direction from rib to rib, in such a way that their contraction pulls the rib cage downwards (in dorsal and caudal direction).

Different species (indeed different individuals) differ in the extent to which they use the diaphragm and the intercostals during breathing. It is only in mammals that the thoracic cavity is completely closed off by the diaphragm below; the mechanism of breathing in birds, reptiles and amphibia is quite different from that of mammals. In young human infants the chest is barrel-shaped with the ribs arranged more nearly horizontally. So rib movements would have little effect in enlarging the thoracic cavity and the infant breathes mainly by diaphragm movement. Singers and performers on wind instruments develop good control of their respiratory muscles and the muscles themselves may show hypertrophy (enlargement) through these activities.

The airways

Figure 6.2 illustrates the bronchial tree and its terminal branches. The trachea divides into right and left bronchi, each of which bifurcates repeatedly (some 20 times in the human lung), giving smaller and smaller branches. Each of the bronchioles so formed terminates in an alveolar duct, and alveoli.

During inspiration, as explained, atmospheric air enters the lungs by reason of the subatmospheric pressure induced in the thoracic cavity by contraction of the

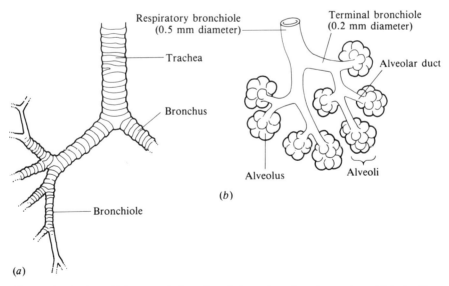

Figure 6.2   (*a*) Bronchial tree, main branches. (*b*) Branches of respiratory bronchioles leading to alveoli.

respiratory muscles. This air first passes through the nasal passage where it is warmed and saturated with water vapour and where hairs filter out any particles larger than 10 μm in diameter. Then it passes down the trachea and to the two bronchi, one to each lung. The walls of the trachea and bronchi contain incomplete rings of cartilage which give them some degree of rigidity; and these walls contain also elastic and smooth-muscle fibres. On the inner surface are goblet cells secreting mucus, and ciliated cells whose cilia waft material outwards towards the nasal passage. The cilia provide an effective way of removing small particles (not filtered in the nose) which enter with the atmospheric air; it has been found that active cilia can move the mucous layer with the particles embedded in it, at the rate of 1 cm/min. Irritation of the trachea and bronchi, by cigarette smoke for example, has the effect of increasing the number of goblet cells and decreasing the number of ciliated cells; so there is more mucus (a common finding among smokers) but less ability to move it, and the bronchi may become blocked. Certain carcinogenic substances paralyse the cilia, so particles may become embedded in the walls of the bronchi.

If all is well, the atmospheric air, now warmed to body temperature, moist and particle-free, passes through the bronchi, to enter the bronchioles, which by repeated bifurcation become gradually narrower. The walls of the bronchioles have an abundance of smooth muscle, longitudinal and circular, which is under the control of sympathetic and parasympathetic nerves. Sympathetic activity dilates the bronchioles by relaxing the circular smooth muscle (so also does adrenaline from the adrenal glands, which in many parts of the body has an effect resembling that of sympathetic nerves). Parasympathetic activity constricts the bronchioles. These two sets of efferent nerves can be activated by several reflexes; for instance a reflex starting at cold receptors in the nose causes bronchiole constriction by parasympathetic action and irritants have the same effect. Deep breaths (presumably via stimulation of bronchiole stretch receptors) lead to dilatation of the bronchioles by sympathetic action. These sympathetic nerves also participate in the general widespread sympathetic activity which occurs all over the body during emotional excitement, the so-called 'fight or flight' reaction.

Part of the work of breathing is involved in overcoming the elasticity of the thoracic wall and lungs and in expanding the alveoli; and the other part is done in overcoming frictional resistance to air flow, most of which is the resistance of the air passages (the trachea, bronchi and bronchioles). When breathing is slow and deep, the frictional resistance is low. In man, at 10 breaths per minute, less than 25 per cent of work done is due to the overcoming of frictional resistance; at 40 breaths per minute, quick shallow breathing, though the total work done is almost the same, about 60 per cent is used in overcoming resistance. The flow of air through the tubes is not entirely streamlined: there is turbulence, especially at bifurcations. But (as in capillaries) in streamlined flow the resistance is markedly dependent on the diameter of the tubes: the narrower the tube, the greater the resistance. In the disease asthma the airways are narrowed and their resistance is greatly increased because the circular smooth muscle of the bronchioles is abnormally contracted; so the work of the respiratory muscles in the effort of adequately ventilating the lung alveoli is made much greater than normal.

Expansion of the lungs

It is in the thin-walled almost spherical alveoli at the termination of each bronchiole that the actual exchange of gases occurs between the lungs and the blood. The diffusion barrier is only the thin epithelial cells lining the alveolus and the thin endothelial cells of the capillary wall.

During quiet breathing each breath of atmospheric air enters the lungs by way of the trachea, bronchi and bronchioles and at the end of inspiration some of this air is still present in these air passages, through the walls of which no gaseous exchange occurs. This volume of air is called respiratory dead-space. The remainder of the air reaches the alveolar surfaces through which exchange is possible; this volume is called alveolar ventilation. In an adult human a normal quiet breath might consist of 450 ml atmospheric air; of this, about 150 ml would be dead-space air and 300 ml alveolar ventilation.

The alveoli are almost spherical, so the lungs resemble millions of tiny (but intercommunicating) bubbles which enlarge during inspiration and contract during expiration; but once a newborn animal or infant has taken its first breath, the alveoli never empty completely, even after a forced expiration. It is possible to measure the pressure required to inflate, to a given volume, the lungs of an animal, excised after death. If the lungs are then filled with physiological saline instead of air and inflated to the same volume, it is found that much *less* pressure is required. The difference is due to the presence, in air-filled lungs, of an air–water interface between the alveolar air and the film of extracellular fluid lining the alveolar surface. Surface tension is constantly pulling the circumference of the spherical alveolar air-bubble inwards, the surface tending to shrink to its smallest possible area. Therefore the pressure required to inflate the lungs has to overcome not only the elasticity of the tissue of the lungs and thoracic cavity but also this surface tension. If the lungs are filled with fluid, there is no air–water interface and no surface-tension effect, so inflation pressure now is simply overcoming the elastic resistance, and thus the required pressure is much lower.

Lung surfactant

In the living mammal, inflation of the alveoli during inspiration is greatly helped by the presence, at the air–water interface, of a lipoprotein mixture called lung surfactant, the lipid components of which are several different phospholipids. This has the effect of reducing by about tenfold the surface tension of the interface. Therefore a much smaller (negative) pressure change is required to inflate the alveoli to a given size than would be needed if there were only a pure extracellular fluid film on the alveolar surface; and the work of the respiratory muscles is thereby lessened.

The presence of lung surfactant is useful in other ways. One is to maintain the relative sizes of the alveoli, preventing the smaller ones from collapsing into the larger ones and overinflating them. This collapse and hyperinflation would normally occur whenever the air within two air-bubbles of different sizes is in contact, as shown in Fig. 6.3. The power of lung surfactant to lower surface tension obviates this danger,

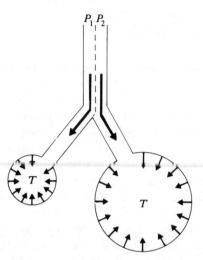

Figure 6.3 Small and large alveoli and the Laplace Law. By the Laplace Law, the pressure of inflation, P, within a spherical bubble of radius r is equal to (opposed by) $2T/r$, T being surface tension, an inherent property of the material of the bubble, 'pulling' the wall of the bubble inwards. In the diagram, P_1 and P_2 are the pressures applied at the top of the vertically partitioned tube keeping the bubbles inflated, and T is the same for both bubbles. If $r = 5$ units for the left bubble and $r = 10$ units for the right bubble, $P_1 = 2T/5$ and $P_2 = 2T/10$. So $P_1 > P_2$. If the two bubbles are joined by removal of partition, the two pressures will tend to equalize by passage of air from left to right, so the small bubble will empty into the large one.

because of the curious ability of the surfactant to alter its effectiveness according to the area over which it is spread. This ability is shown in the experiment illustrated in Fig. 6.4.

In the experiment a trough is filled with water and a movable barrier is placed across the surface. The surface tension can be measured by a platinum strip and force transducer (Fig. 6.4a). For pure water the surface tension is about 70 dynes/cm (0.07 N/m); it does not alter if the barrier is moved (Fig. 6.4b). Addition of a detergent to the water causes a fall of surface tension to about 30 dynes/cm; again as the barrier is moved there is no change. If surfactant derived by washing out an animal's lung is spread on the water surface to the left of the barrier, the surface tension of the water is greatly reduced, perhaps to about 5 dynes/cm; furthermore the surface tension varies as the barrier is moved: it is minimal when the barrier is near the left-hand end of the trough and the area is small and presumably the layer of surfactant molecules is thick. It is increased along the path shown by the arrow as the barrier is moved to the right; it is decreased as the barrier is moved back to the left (but the decrease does not follow the reverse path of the increase; it takes the path shown by the double arrow). If surfactant in the body behaves as it does in this experiment, and if it is assumed that each alveolus produces the same amount of surfactant, this amount would presumably form a thicker layer in a small alveolus than a large one, and therefore have a greater lowering effect on surface tension, so reducing the tendency of small alveoli to squeeze their contents into neighbouring large ones.

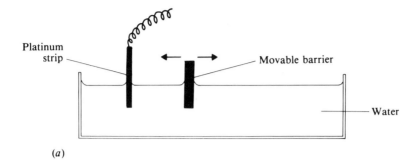

(a)

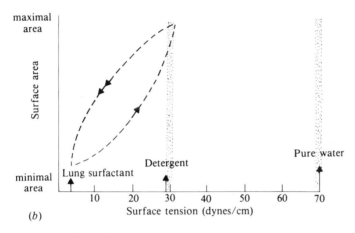

(b)

Figure 6.4 Surface tension and area. (a) Trough, movable barrier and platinum-strip recorder used for illustrating change in surface tension with area under different conditions. (b) Plot of surface tension against area. Arrows on abscissa at 70 and 28 dynes/cm (0.07 and 0.028 N/m) show surface tension of pure water and of water with added detergent. Vertical dotted lines show that there is no effect of moving barrier (altering area) in these cases. With surfactant, surface tension is very low (approximately 5 dynes/cm i.e. 0.005 N/m) and it alters as area is changed (dashed lines and arrows). (Adapted from West, J. B. (ed.), *Best and Taylor's Physiological Basis of Medical Practice*, 11th edn, Williams and Wilkins, Baltimore, 1985.)

(See Appendix 4 for a note on lung compliance and hysteresis.)

Another role of lung surfactant is assisting the first breath taken by the newborn animal or infant directly after birth. Before birth the lung alveoli are collapsed and the thin film of moisture within them makes their opening up quite a difficult process (like opening a plastic bag which has a layer of water in it). The first breath requires a considerable muscular effort; but without surfactant the effort would be greater still. After the first few breaths, when all the alveoli are inflated, they never again collapse completely in normal life; there always remains some residual air, even after the most vigorous forced expiration. In consequence the lungs of a dead creature that has once breathed will float in water. (This point is useful in determining whether a dead infant was stillborn or was born alive and died subsequently.)

Lung surfactant is derived from certain types of cells, called type 2 cells, which are found in the alveolar lining, and which can extrude the surfactant in the form of flat sheets (lamellar bodies) which are able to spread quickly and evenly over an aqueous surface.

There has been speculation as to the molecular mechanisms by which lung surfactant functions to stabilize the volume of alveoli, both when at their minimum size at the end of expiration and at their maximum size at the end of inspiration. Observations have been made on mixtures of two pure phospholipids, phosphatidyl glycerol (PG) and dipalmitoyl phosphatidyl choline (DPPC), both of which are components of natural lung surfactant. These observations indicate that a 3:7 mixture of PG:DPPD spreads rapidly and evenly in a film over the surface of water at 37 °C (body temperature). Repeated cycles of compression and expansion of such a film cause a gradual depletion of the PG component; the remaining DPPC is solid at 37 °C and forms rigid 'rafts' floating on the aqueous surface. One may therefore picture some such solid incompressible structures in the lung, separating the aqueous lining film of the alveolus from the air space, and preventing the small alveoli at expiration from collapsing in on themselves and filling up with fluid.

The tasks of lung surfactant then are:

1. reducing the amount of muscular effort required to inflate the lungs at each inspiration;
2. equilibrating the pressure within the lungs among the alveoli of various sizes;
3. assisting in the initial inflation of the lungs at birth;
4. keeping the alveoli dry.

The type 2 cells lining the alveoli in which the surfactant is synthesized come to maturity only in the last few weeks of prenatal life. So premature infants may have an inadequate supply of the surfactant in their alveoli at birth. Not only will the first breath be extra difficult, but also after that first breath the alveoli will tend to collapse and fill with fluid, and the next and each subsequent breath may require the same effort again. This leads to a condition called 'respiratory distress syndrome' to which premature infants are very susceptible in the first hours or days after birth. Natural surfactant or a dry powder mixture of the effective lipid compounds PG and DPPC can be placed by intubation straight into the trachea of a premature infant, whence it will move into the alveoli as the lungs expand. Such treatment has proved successful in either preventing the respiratory distress or making the condition less severe, and the mortality in these newborn infants has been thereby reduced.

There is constant turnover of surfactant. Continued manufacture of the lipoprotein requires a continuous blood supply to the alveolar surface. If the blood supply to a patch of lung becomes blocked (say by a small clot or embolus), surfactant supply and manufacture in that group of alveoli will diminish and the alveoli will collapse. If the blood supply is re-established, surfactant can be made again and the alveoli can be reopened.

Bulk flow and diffusion

Like movement of material in and out of capillaries, movement of gases in the respiratory system is partly by bulk flow and partly by diffusion. In the upper respiratory tract—through the nose, trachea and so on, down to the alveoli—the movement is by bulk flow, and the pressure difference causing the movement is the (negative) pressure created by expansion of the thoracic cavity. In the alveoli, movement of gases occurs by diffusion through the alveolar and capillary walls due to the effect of chemical diffusion gradients, partial pressures of the gases in the gas mixture of alveolar air and tension of dissolved gases in the plasma.

The *partial pressure* of a given gas in a gas mixture is that proportion of the total gas pressure which corresponds to the percentage by volume of the particular gas: if, in a gas mixture at 760 mmHg, there is 21 per cent oxygen by volume, the partial pressure of oxygen is:

$$\frac{21}{100} \times 760 = 160 \text{ mmHg}$$

The *tension* of a gas *in solution* is that pressure (in mmHg) in the gas phase in contact with the solution which is just sufficient to prevent the given amount of gas from coming out or to force more into solution. Thus if the tension of a certain gas in solution is *lower* than the partial pressure of that *same* gas in the ambient gas phase, more of the gas will go into solution; and vice versa.

The *amount* of gas held in solution depends not only on its partial pressure in the ambient gas phase but also on the solubility of the particular gas, in the particular solvent.

The symbol 'P' is used as an abbreviation both for partial pressure and for tension: so 'PO_2' and 'PCO_2' can refer either to the alveolar air or to blood plasma.

The values of partial pressure of respiratory gases in atmospheric and alveolar air and tension of gases in mixed venous blood in a typical mammal at rest are shown in Table 6.1. It is clear that there is a gradient of about 66 mmHg forcing oxygen into the blood, and about 6 mmHg forcing carbon dioxide into the alveolar air. Yet about the same volumes of the gases move (in opposite directions) across the alveolar membrane, in the same brief time, 0.3 s. It can be said at once that the gradients are maintained constant, and steep, partly by the speed with which the gases, once past the diffusion barrier, enter into chemical reactions; and partly by the velocity of the blood flow through the alveoli.

Table 6.1 Partial pressure and tension of respiratory gases

| | Partial pressure/tension (mmHg) | |
	Oxygen	Carbon dioxide
Atmospheric air	160	0.3
Alveolar air	106	40
Mixed venous blood	40	46

Control of respiratory rhythm

Efferent nerves and medullary neurones

As we have seen, the mechanism of breathing depends primarily on contraction of respiratory muscles which enlarge the thoracic cavity; air is thus pulled into the airways, moistened, and warmed to body temperature. The stream of air, overcoming airway resistance, reaches the alveoli, the expansion of which is aided by surfactant; and the exchange of gases with the dissolved and chemically combined gas of plasma in the lung capillaries can occur. Our next consideration is the initiation of the whole process: how do the respiratory muscles, diaphragm and intercostals contract and then relax in a continuous, rhythmical sequence throughout life?

The striated muscle fibres of the diaphragm and intercostals are quite different from the cardiac muscle fibres of the heart. Unlike cardiac fibres, they have no inherent rhythmicity and their contraction is entirely dependent on the impulses coming along nerve fibres supplying them. If the extrinsic nerves to the heart were to be cut, the heart would still beat rhythmically. If the nerves to the respiratory muscles were to be cut (or damaged as in the disease poliomyelitis), breathing would cease.

The innervation of the intercostal muscles is, as one might expect, by the intercostal nerves, motor fibres issuing from the spinal cord in the upper thoracic region. The diaphragm is innervated by the pair of left and right phrenic nerves, the roots of which are in the cervical (neck) region, C_{3-5}. The nerves pass down the neck, then through the thoracic cavity alongside the mediastinum (the central partition) and so reach the diaphragm. It seems somewhat surprising that the diaphragm is innervated by nerves originating so high in the spinal cord; the explanation lies in embryological development. The developing embryo in early prenatal life has such a marked flexure in the body that the lower part of the thorax is quite close to the neck; at a later stage the flexure straightens out, the diaphragm is distanced from the neck and the phrenic nerves of necessity lengthen greatly.

In normal quiet breathing both sets of nerve fibres show rhythmic bursts of activity, consisting of trains of impulses starting slowly, building up to a maximum frequency, then rather quickly dying away until another burst of impulses starts. This causes the rhythmic muscular contractions and passive relaxations of inspiration and expiration. This rhythmic activity is controlled from groups of nerve cell bodies in the brain stem sometimes collectively known as the respiratory 'centre'. The respiratory centre is situated along most of the length of the medulla oblongata and the lower part of the pons. Sensitive electrodes placed on this region of the brain of an animal will record rhythmic bursts of activity from the simultaneous discharge of many neurones. Rhythmic activity of the respiratory region of the brain in fact was one of the first inherent rhythms of the central nervous system to be detected. (Electrodes placed on the brain of a goldfish picked up bursts of electric discharge in time with the movements of the operculum, the gill-cover whose movement forces oxygenated water across the gill surfaces.) The precise mechanism causing rhythmic bursts of activity of groups of neurones of the central nervous system has not yet been discovered. It is not known, either, how the medullary respiratory neurones suddenly start their rhythmic activity at the birth of a mammal. A fetus in the uterus, late in gestation, can make only a few slight irregular and uncoordinated movements of its respiratory muscles; and yet suddenly within a few minutes after birth the regular rhythmic movements start and continue throughout life. Experimenters investigating the medullary region of mammals have tried to define and locate separate parts: 'inspiratory' and 'expiratory' centres, 'excitatory' and 'inhibitory', 'pneumotaxic' and 'apneustic'. It is doubtful whether such definitions are useful or helpful in understanding this region of the brain stem; methods of study are at present too crude and, in any case, central respiratory control seems to work somewhat differently in different mammalian species. All that can safely be said is that from birth onwards, bursts of activity in the general region of the medulla and lower pons give rise to bursts of increased impulse frequency in the phrenic and intercostal nerves and thus to activity in the respiratory muscles.

Factors affecting medullary respiratory neurones

The inherent rhythmicity of the medullary respiratory neurones can be influenced by input of afferent nerve impulses from many sources. Indeed almost any group of afferent nerves in the body, if stimulated sufficiently, have some effect on respiration: for instance a sudden pain such as a bang on the shin, or a sudden cold stimulus such as a plunge into cold water, causes a quick inspiratory gasp. Obviously there is some voluntary control over respiration. The making of sounds (speech included) involves this control; for singers and performers of wind instruments, breath control is an important part of the training. In addition there are several reflexes (besides those already mentioned in connection with pain and cold) which involve respiration: coughing and sneezing originate in touch receptors in the larynx and trachea and in the nose, respectively. The result of irritation in these regions is an abrupt explosive expiration, through the mouth (cough) or nose and mouth together (sneeze); this could be a protective device forcibly blowing out the source of the irritation and thus freeing the airways. A hiccough or momentary spasm of the diaphragm sometimes results from a temporary blockage at the lower end of the oesophagus. The swallowing reflex, initiated by touch at the back of the tongue, is associated with complete inhibition of the respiratory rhythm during the act of swallowing. (Closure of the trachea by the epiglottis during swallowing ensures that the bolus does not enter the trachea and lungs; see Chapter 4.)

Two factors of particular importance in the control of the normal respiratory rhythm—one mechanical and one chemical—will now be described. The first of these is the Hering–Breuer reflex. This reflex originates in stretch receptors in the walls of the small bronchioles, which are stimulated increasingly as the lungs inflate during inspiration. This stimulation generates a train of impulses of gradually increasing frequency in afferent nerve fibres in the vagus nerves (cranial X). These impulses impinge on the medullary respiratory neurones, which are inhibited (when a certain frequency of vagal input is attained), thereby allowing relaxation of the diaphragm, passive elastic recoil and expiration. The subsequent expiratory phase in the respiratory centre is also shortened and inspiration then restarts. The effect is to make the respiratory rhythm slightly quicker and each breath slightly less deep than it otherwise would be. Different species differ in the extent to which the Hering–Breuer reflex operates in controlling the observed rhythm of normal quiet breathing. In many species, cutting of the vagal afferent fibres results in a rhythm which is slower and deeper than the normal; this implies that the build-up of vagal input cuts short each inspiratory effort, leading to deflation of the lungs and thus to the normal rhythm. In other species (probably including man) the vagal afferents from the bronchiole stretch receptors do not seem to operate at every breath but may work during forced overinflation, acting more as a defence mechanism in protecting the lungs against ruptures by accidental overinflation.

The second important factor influencing the medullary respiratory neurones is the precise chemical composition of the arterial blood and the cerebrospinal fluid (CSF). Any increase in P_{CO_2}, even a slight one, has the effect of quickening and deepening the breathing, thus increasing the ventilation of the alveoli; the quicker breathing means a greater rate of changeover of alveoli air and the deeper breathing means that at each breath there is a larger percentage of alveolar ventilation (and proportionally less dead-space).

Alveolar air normally has a P_{CO_2} of about 40 mmHg (in man). (This is considerably greater than that of atmospheric air, about 0.3 mmHg.) If the alveolar P_{CO_2} were to rise to, say, 40.5 mmHg, respiratory rate would be enormously increased and the person would make quick deep gasps. If the P_{CO_2} were to fall to 39 mmHg, respiration could be completely inhibited for about half a minute, until the venous blood bringing carbon dioxide to the lungs and diffusion of this gas into the alveolar air space produces sufficient accumulation of alveolar carbon dioxide to allow the arterial blood going to the brain to stimulate the medullary respiratory neurones and re-establish the rhythm. Most of the changes, however, would not be as extreme as this; there is not normally either violent gasping or complete cessation of breathing. Small momentary changes in alveolar P_{CO_2} are going on all the time and causing slight transient fluctuations in pulmonary ventilation, superimposed on the steady rhythm. One can observe this simply by watching the thoracic movements of a sleeping animal or human for about 10 minutes: the movements are unlikely to be completely regular. The arterial blood normally equilibrates quickly with whatever gas mixture is available to it in the alveoli; and the respiratory neurones respond quickly to the precise level of P_{CO_2} of arterial blood; so the influence of composition of alveolar air on respiratory rhythm takes only a few seconds—certainly no more than a couple of breaths.

The chemosensitive nerve cells are not those of the respiratory neurones themselves but cells in specialized areas on the surface of the brain stem, in the medulla oblongata close to the roots of the glossopharyngeal (nerves cranial IX and X) and vagus (see Fig. 6.5). There must be very short connections between these cells, known as central chemoreceptors, and those of the respiratory neurones, so rapid is the response. This surface of the brain stem is normally surrounded by CSF, the fluid which fills the four ventricles of the brain and is present *outside* the brain stem and spinal cord.

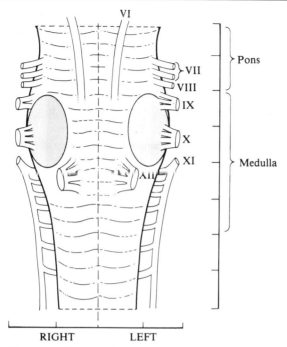

Figure 6.5 Position of central chemoreceptor areas on ventral surface of brain (cat). Roots of cranial nerves in roman numerals. (Adapted from Severinghaus, J. W., R. A. Mitchell, B. W. Richardson and M. M. Singer, *Journal of Applied Physiology*, **18**, 1155–1166, 1963.)

If a slight excess of carbon dioxide is present in alveolar air, one may envisage the following series of events: arterial blood in equilibrating with alveolar air in the lungs now has a P_{CO_2} of (say) 40.2 mmHg, a higher than normal tension. This blood quickly reaches the choroid plexuses of the brain, the tufts of capillaries in the ventricles from which the CSF is derived. The carbon dioxide diffuses into the CSF and reaches the chemosensitive tissue on the medullary surface, where it causes stimulation of the respiratory neurones and increase in ventilation, thus reducing blood P_{CO_2} back to normal. The converse changes occur when arterial P_{CO_2} decreases: CSF P_{CO_2} level falls and respiration is inhibited, allowing arterial P_{CO_2} to rise to normal.

An excess of H^+ ions in the plasma has a similar effect on the CSF, the central chemoreceptors and the respiratory centre. Metabolic acids (lactic and pyruvic) may accumulate in the blood, particularly after prolonged muscular exercise; and in several diseases (notably untreated diabetes mellitus) there is a build-up of organic acids in the blood. Such situations lead to a reduction in blood bicarbonate, a condition called 'metabolic acidosis'. In metabolic acidosis, breathing is stimulated by the increased H^+ ion level (lowered pH) in the blood and CSF. But the respiratory response is slower and smaller than the response to a rise in blood P_{CO_2}. This difference suggests that the action of carbon dioxide at the central chemoreceptors is not simply due to its acidifying effect on CSF. The CSF has less buffering capacity than the blood, and the dissolved carbon dioxide would indeed increase its H^+ ion concentration considerably. But a given increase of $[H^+]$ in CSF and in medullary extracellular fluid has been shown to produce a far greater effect on respiration (or at least on phrenic-nerve action potentials) if this increase is produced by carbon dioxide than if the same increase is produced by a 'fixed acid' such as HCl (Eldridge *et al.*, 1985a). We do not yet know whether the difference can be explained by the existence on the cells of central chemoreceptors of separate receptor groups for carbon dioxide and H^+; or whether the stimulus to the chemoreceptor cells is a change in their *intra*cellular pH, and that the carbon dioxide is more effective simply because it is able to cross the cell membrane and reach the intracellular fluid more rapidly than H^+ ions.

There is no doubt that for mammals and birds and indeed all land vertebrates the precise level of arterial P_{CO_2} is a fundamental controlling factor in determining the alveolar ventilation: a raised P_{CO_2} (hypercapnia) stimulates it and a lowered P_{CO_2} (hypocapnia) decreases it. In contrast, the precise level of oxygen in arterial blood seems to have much less effect on normal breathing. Atmospheric air has 21 per cent of oxygen by volume and alveolar air (in man) about 14 per cent by volume, which means an alveolar partial pressure of $(14/100) \times 760 = 106$ mmHg. This is sufficient to cause (almost) full saturation of arterial blood leaving the lungs. There are several areas of chemoreceptor tissue (Fig. 6.6): two carotid glomera and two or three aortic glomera, which are close to but separate from the baroreceptor organs in the main arteries near the heart, being located at the bifurcation of the common carotid and under the aortic arch. These chemoreceptor areas are known as *peripheral* chemoreceptors, in contrast with the *central* chemoreceptors already described on the surface of the medulla oblongata. They are small spherical bodies richly supplied with blood vessels; they contain thin-walled epithelial cells and are innervated by afferent fibres in the glossopharyngeal nerve (cranial IX) from the carotid glomera and afferents running the vagus nerve (cranial X) from the aortic glomera. The chemoreceptor cells are stimulated by a marked fall in P_{O_2} (hypoxia) in arterial blood; the impulse discharge along the afferent fibres increases in frequency and the effect on the respiratory centre in the medulla is such as to cause increase in the rate and depth of breathing (conversely, in some animals and in newborn infants, though not in adult man, there is a *reduction* in respiration rate if they are made to breathe 100 per cent oxygen instead of normal atmospheric air, a procedure which raises their arterial P_{O_2}). Recordings of nerve impulses made directly from the chemoreceptor afferents of animals reveal that even when the animal is breathing normal air there is some impulse traffic; so presumably the medullary respiratory neurones are constantly receiving some chemoreceptor drive from these oxygen-sensitive glomera. But in hypoxia the chemoreceptors are not really very effective in stimulating respiration and so enabling the body to gain adequate oxygen in this adverse condition. The chemoreceptors in fact do not start increasing their discharge until alveolar P_{O_2} level has fallen to about 60 per cent of its normal value and even then the additional ventilation caused by increased chemoreceptor drive is not very great. In most real (non-experimental) situations where the alveolar P_{O_2} decreases, the P_{CO_2} also *increases*, and this P_{CO_2} rise stimulates breathing and thus acts as the protective

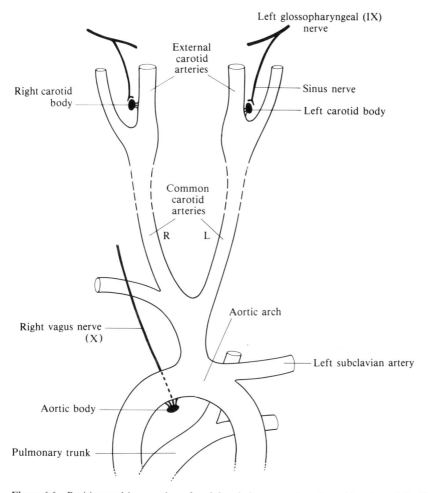

Figure 6.6   Position and innervation of peripheral chemoreceptors (carotid and aortic bodies).

mechanism of the body. This happens, for example, in the disease pneumonia where exchanges between alveolar air and blood are impaired by accumulation of fluid. The unusual situation when both Po_2 *and* Pco_2 decrease simultaneously—in the lowered atmospheric pressure of high altitudes—will be discussed later.

Although hypoxia is undoubtedly the main factor stimulating the peripheral chemoreceptors, there is some evidence that they are sensitive to hypercapnia (raised Pco_2) also. This sensitivity is worth mentioning because it has been invoked to help to explain the mystery of the immediate hyperventilation at the start of exercise. If an animal breathing normal atmospheric air at a low steady rate is made to breathe a gas mixture containing high Pco_2 *for one breath only*, and then returned to normal air breathing, it will briefly hyperventilate, within 2–5 s. This effect is almost certainly due to the arrival at the peripheral chemoreceptors of a short column of CO_2-enriched air from the lungs. The time-interval is not long enough for blood from the lungs containing the raised P_{CO_2} to have reached the central chemoreceptors via the choroid plexus and CSF, and the minute addition of carbon dioxide would have an infinitesimal effect on the general level of P_{CO_2} in arterial blood. The effect of the raised carbon dioxide is so rapid and so transient that it must be peripheral chemoreceptors operating here.

It may surprise biologists that it is the carbon dioxide level in the body rather than the oxygen which is the precise determinant of ventilation rate. Comparative studies have shown that this is true for land animals only. Gill-breathing aquatic animals, whether marine or fresh water, are very sensitive to the P_{O_2} level of the water and hardly at all to the P_{CO_2} level. Respiratory movements in many species of fish (movements of operculum or gill-cover) increase as the P_{O_2} of their surrounding water falls; but rise of P_{CO_2} in the water (with constant P_{O_2}) has no effect. A certain species of lungfish comes to the surface from time to time and takes in a gasp of atmospheric air; the frequency with which it does this increases if the P_{O_2} of the air above the water is (experimentally) reduced. In amphibia the respiration rate of the entirely aquatic tadpole is P_{O_2}-determined and that of the terrestrial adult is P_{CO_2}-determined. A suggested interpretation of these differences between land and water animals is based on the fact that carbon dioxide forms acid in solution. The carbon dioxide (and thus carbonic acid, H_2CO_3) formed from metabolism in aquatic creatures on leaving the body is at once diluted in the vast volume of the surrounding medium and wafted away from the body surface by currents, so there is no danger of accumulation of H^+ ions in the animal's vicinity. Oxygen is not abundant in water because of its limited solubility (only 2 per cent in water at 15 °C). So it is not surprising that in aquatic creatures it is oxygen lack, rather than carbon dioxide excess, that is the main respiratory stimulant. For land animals the amount of water available is always severely limited. The carbon dioxide formed in their metabolism must be accommodated, until removal from the body, by solution in the restricted volume of their own body water, which is thereby made more acid. For many animal tissues a short period of hypoxia is not disastrous: the tissue survives by continuing to take up oxygen, depleting more than usual the oxygen supply in the blood flowing through it. Acid accumulation might perhaps be more damaging to cells; the extreme sensitivity of medullary cells to carbon dioxide and H^+ ion excess, with consequent stimulation of respiratory rate and maintenance of a steady arterial P_{CO_2}, helps in stabilizing the pH of the body fluids of the terrestrial species. This somewhat speculative interpretation of the differences of respiratory control between land and water animals is so satisfying that one hopes it is correct.

Respiratory experiments in man

Human subjects are not entirely suitable for experimental study of the control of ventilation. Although the experimenter may rely on the conscious cooperation of the subject, almost inevitably a person who knows that his breathing is under observation

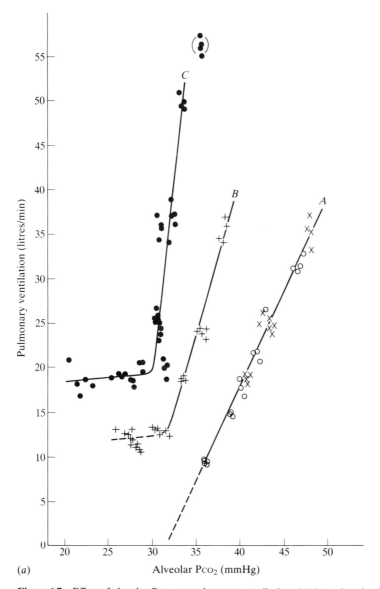

Figure 6.7 Effect of alveolar P_{CO_2} on pulmonary ventilation. (*a*) At various levels of P_{O_2}. *A*: 100 mmHg. *B*: 47 mmHg. *C*: 37 mmHg. (Reproduced by permission from Nielsen, M. and H. Smith, *Acta physiologica Scandinavica*, **24**, 293–313, 1951.)   (*continued*)

unconsciously makes slight alterations in his respiratory rhythm. The experimenter must try to fix the subject's attention on something else (such as reading a book) during the course of the experiment. A series of ingenious experiments was carried out on humans in the 1950s, to elucidate on interrelationship of four factors known to

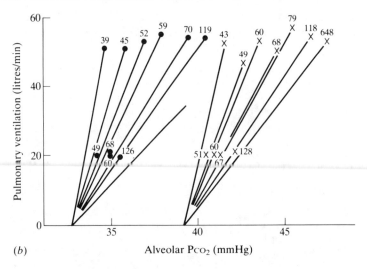

(b)

Figure 6.7 (b) During metabolic acidosis. Lines on right: at normal plasma pH; lines on left: during acidosis induced by ammonium chloride ingestion. Small numbers on lines show P_{O_2} at these points. 'Fan' of response-lines shifts down the x-axis during acidosis. (Reproduced by permission from Cunningham, D. J. C., D. G. Shaw, S. Lahiri and B. B. Lloyd, *Quarterly Journal of Experimental Physiology*, **46**, 323–334, 1961.)

have an important effect on ventilation in man: arterial P_{CO_2}, arterial P_{O_2}, metabolic acidosis and raised body temperature. In the first experiment, ventilation (in litres/min) was measured as the subject was given different known levels of carbon dioxide in the inspired air, but with normal inspired P_{O_2}, 100 mmHg. The ventilation was plotted against inspired P_{CO_2}; the result was the straight line, A, shown in Fig. 6.7a, indicating that ventilation was directly proportional to inspired P_{CO_2}, at normal P_{O_2} (or above) and that this relationship continues right down to zero ventilation at about 32 mmHg P_{CO_2}, when breathing would stop. The experiment was repeated using lower levels (below normal) of oxygen in the inspired air; in these cases (B and C on the graph) the ventilation was even more sensitive to P_{CO_2} (the slopes of the straight lines are steeper); but at some (low) level of P_{CO_2}, ventilation became insensitive to P_{CO_2}, and became proportional to P_{O_2} deficiency, as shown by the horizontal parts of B and C. If the slopes of all three lines are extrapolated to the x-axis, they reach it at points in the range 28–32 mmHg; at this level of inspired P_{CO_2}, ventilation would cease. The slope of the lines (sensitivity of ventilation to P_{CO_2}) and their intercept on the x-axis vary with different subjects.

Similar experiments were carried out on human subjects first before and then after they had produced in their blood a metabolic acidosis, by taking for some days doses of ammonium chloride; this has the effect of lowering the normal level of blood bicarbonate. The effect of the metabolic acidosis (Fig. 6.7b) was that the entire set of graphs was shifted down the x-axis. For one subject (Fig. 6.7b) at normal blood pH the intercept on the x-axis was 39 mmHg P_{CO_2}, and at lowered blood pH it was

32 mmHg. Presumably the metabolic acidosis lowered both blood and CSF pH, therefore maintaining a respiratory stimulus at the central chemoreceptors, in spite of the low carbon dioxide in the inspired air. A similar set of experiments carried out, not with acidosis but with experimentally raised body temperature, revealed that this stimulus had the effect of steepening the slopes of all the ventilation–Pco_2 lines, indicating an even greater sensitivity of ventilation to carbon dioxide level, at all oxygen levels. In this case the input into the medullary respiratory neurones would have come from temperature-sensitive neurones in the hypothalamus, in the floor of the third ventricle of the brain.

These experiments on man have been helpful in disentangling the interrelated effects of various stimuli on a single set of effector organs, the respiratory muscles; and this is clearly of use in understanding the control of respiration in real everyday situations. In prolonged exercise, for instance, body temperature rises, and this effect might be responsible for increasing the sensitivity of the respiration to very small fluctuations of arterial Pco_2.

Respiration in special circumstances

Exercise

Exercise, particularly isotonic exercise such as running and swimming (sometimes called 'dynamic exercise') where the limbs move rhythmically, increases both rate and depth of breathing with the result that pulmonary ventilation is enormously increased. For instance a man at rest, breathing air in and out of his lungs at about 5 litres/min, might breathe about 25 litres/min in and out while on a steady run. This of course results in removal of the large quantities of carbon dioxide generated during the rapid metabolism of the muscles and in making available an abundance of oxygen, arterializing the quickly flowing blood in the lung capillaries. Isometric exercise ('static exercise') such as weight-lifting and pulling a heavy load—exercise in which work is done against gravity and the muscles of the limbs and trunk may maintain a rigid position for several seconds at a time—is much less effective in increasing respiration. Indeed breath-holding may occur during the exercise and a short period of overbreathing (hyperventilation) would follow when the exercise is finished.

The observable facts about respiration in dynamic exercise are well established. There is an immediate increase in pulmonary ventilation at the start of exercise; then a sustained high level during steady running or swimming. At the end of the exercise, breathing rate and depth fall sharply and then more gradually and it may be several minutes before the resting level of respiration is re-established. It must be said at once that there is no fully satisfactory and generally agreed explanation of the mechanisms which bring about these changes. A feature which is particularly hard to explain is the accurate matching (during steady-state exercise) of the rate of work and the rate of the body's overall oxygen consumption. This quantitative relationship between work rate and oxygen consumption is so precise that rate of oxygen intake can be used as an indicator for comparing amounts of work done in different types of exercise—say comparing running and swimming; and oxygen intake during maximal effort in humans is used as an indicator of improved performance during physical training. These facts about respiration in exercise are not in dispute but aspects of their interpretation still puzzles us.

One idea recently proposed to explain the simultaneous starting of hyperventilation and rise of blood pressure with exercise is that all three responses arise from a single stimulus: activation of a 'locomotor area' in the hypothalamus. The basis of this hypothesis is a series of observations made on decorticate or decerebrate cats in which a well-localized region of the hypothalamus was stimulated chemically, by an inhibitor of γ-aminobutyric acid, one of the naturally occurring inhibitory transmitters (see Chapter 13, p. 292). By this stimulation, movements of the animals' limbs were initiated at the same instant as an increase in action potentials in the phrenic nerve to the diaphragm and a rise in arterial pressure; and clearly the motor cortex of the brain was not necessary for the effect (Eldridge *et al.*, 1985b). The authors who reported these experiments named the action of the hypothalamus a 'central command' or 'feed-forward signal'. The hypothalamus is anatomically quite close to the pons and medulla through which the respiratory rhythm and many cardio-vascular responses are controlled, so the idea is plausible in that respect: only short connections would be needed between the hypothalamus and pontine-medullary region. The hypothesis is ingenious and might help to explain not only the simultaneity of the start of exercise and the respiratory effect but also the matching of oxygen consumption to work output. We may hope for confirmatory experiments, perhaps under more physiological conditions.

Whether the peripheral chemoreceptors of some animals are involved in the start of the hyperventilation of exercise by responding to small transient within-breath fluctuations of arterial P_{CO_2} is still in question. Another mechanism postulated for the initiation of the hyperventilation is an afferent input to the medullary neurones from receptors in the joints during rapid movements. This idea is supported by the finding that even passive movement (for instance movement by an experimenter of the limbs of an anaesthetized animal, or movement of the legs of a person seated on a bicycle with mechanically driven wheels) can cause a considerable increase in pulmonary ventilation. This hypothesis is also supported by the observation that isotonic exercise such as running, in which the joints move, stimulates considerable hyperventilation, whereas isometric exercise such as weight-lifting, in which the joints are almost immobile, does not produce hyperventilation while in progress.

During sustained exercise the actively working muscles generate large amounts of carbon dioxide, which is taken to the lungs in venous blood and blown off from the body by increased respiratory activity. The muscles also use large quantities of oxygen; fully saturated arterial blood leaving the lungs reaches the muscles at a rapid rate of flow; and because of the high ambient P_{CO_2} the muscles extract much more oxygen from each litre of blood than they do at rest. So the venous blood leaving the muscles now carries almost no oxygen. During exercise, however, there is no observable change in the P_{CO_2} or P_{O_2} of the blood in the main *arteries*. This means that whatever else affects the respiratory neurones, the mechanism does not (at least initially) involve either the central chemoreceptor tissue on the medullary surface or the hypoxia-driven response of the peripheral chemoreceptors.

During sustained exercise, however, two other factors—temperature increase and pH decrease in arterial blood—might affect the respiratory medullary neurones and maintain the hyperventilation. Warmed blood heated in the working muscles could quicken the respiratory rhythm; and increased acidity, as we have seen, stimulates the medullary respiratory neurones. Additional acid enters the blood from the muscles in sustained exercise because lactic and pyruvic acids are formed at a high rate from glycolytic (anaerobic) breakdown of muscle glycogen. This process goes on continuously and the acids are normally built back into glycogen in the liver or used in metabolism by cardiac muscle or excreted. If they are generated in working muscles more quickly than they can be removed by the liver, heart or kidney, some may remain in arterial blood and very slightly lower its pH; buffering by the bicarbonate system of the plasma means that the corresponding amount of carbonic acid is generated and this, via the choroid plexus and central chemoreceptor tissue, will stimulate respiration as already explained.

Much of the increased muscle activity of isotonic exercise, such as running, involves muscles containing a high proportion of white ('fast twitch') fibres. These fibres show little or no aerobic respiration. They have few mitochondria, and their energy supply is almost entirely anaerobic, leading to lactic and pyruvic acid production and later to carbon dioxide production in the body when these acids leak into the blood and undergo buffering. In consequence, there is during exercise considerable carbon dioxide production for no corresponding oxygen uptake. The respiratory quotient (RQ) defined as

$$\frac{CO_2 \text{ output in unit time}}{O_2 \text{ intake in unit time}}$$

is determined in the long term by the types of food undergoing oxidation in the body. Pure carbohydrate oxidation produces an RQ of 1.0, fat oxidation an RQ of 0.7, and protein an RQ of about 0.8. On a mixed diet the RQ is normally about 0.85. Since the metabolic acidosis occurring during prolonged exercise generates carbon dioxide (by blood buffering, see Chapter 8) not directly related to oxygen intake, the RQ tends to rise. Mainly because of this additional carbon dioxide production, the RQ may rise transiently as high as 1.5. The RQ and the overbreathing are not reduced to resting levels for several minutes after the end of exercise as the excess of organic acids takes some time to be removed from the circulation.

Low atmospheric pressure

Mountain climbing and high-altitude flying present respiratory problems for man, because of the lower atmospheric pressure at higher altitude. At 3000 m the atmospheric pressure is only 520 mmHg and the P_{O_2} in the atmosphere 104 mmHg, giving an alveolar P_{O_2} of only 70 mmHg: insufficient to cause complete saturation of haemoglobin in the blood leaving the lung capillaries. This hypoxia is immediately apparent to a person who moves quickly from near sea level to an altitude of, say, 2000 m. He feels 'breathless' on very minor exertion and his lips may have a slight tinge of blue, the colour of incompletely saturated haemoglobin. The carotid and to a lesser extent aortic chemoreceptors are stimulated by the hypoxia and initiate an increase in ventilation; but this, after a few deep breaths, reduces the alveolar carbon dioxide and the consequent *lowering* of P_{CO_2} in arterial blood will tend to inhibit or reduce respiration. Then after a few minutes the combined effect of the hypoxia and a build-up of alveolar carbon dioxide (as more carbon dioxide is brought to the lungs in venous blood) restarts respiration with the result that the alveolar carbon dioxide is again washed out, respiration is inhibited and so on. The man or animal suddenly transferred to high altitude undergoes 'periodic breathing'—a short series of deep breaths alternating with a cessation of breathing. The body is presented with the difficulty of a simultaneous reduction of atmospheric and alveolar P_{O_2} and P_{CO_2}. Carbon dioxide is being produced at the usual rate but the lowered atmospheric pressure gives a steep gradient for the removal of carbon dioxide entering the lungs in the venous blood and so a few breaths will cause enough washout of carbon dioxide to cause a mild alkalosis of arterial blood with consequent respiratory inhibition. As explained in Chapter 17, there is eventually (after some days of acclimatization) an active transport of bicarbonate ions, $(HCO_3)'$, out of the CSF—or possibly of H^+ into it—at the choroid plexus. Thus the CSF is permitted to remain at its normal pH, or even slightly below it, even though the plasma is showing a slight alkalosis, and so the hypoxic drive from peripheral chemoreceptors dominates respiratory control.

After acclimatization at altitude transport of oxygen also improves. Erythrocyte production is stimulated by an increase in erythropoietin (see p. 171), so circulating red cells increase in number. There is an increase in erythrocyte 2,3-diphosphoglycerate (DPG), which favours release of oxygen from haemoglobin in the tissues. The supply of oxygen to the tissues is also enhanced by an initial increase of cardiac output of some 20–50 per cent. This is not maintained, but there is an increased number of capillaries in the muscle, heart and brain. In muscle, especially heart muscle, there is increased myoglobin and numbers of mitochondria. All these adaptive changes are seen in people moving from low levels to high altitudes, but it must be remembered that over 10 million people live permanently at an altitude above 3000 m and some can work at a level of 5700 m.

Few animals live permanently above 5500 m, but birds can fly as high as 9000 m. This is made possible by the special structure of the bird's lung which allows arterial blood leaving the lung to be 80 per cent oxygenated whereas mammals' blood would be only 24 per cent saturated at this altitude. In the bird's lung the alveoli are replaced by air-capillaries radiating from a system of air-tubes or parabronchi; air flow through this system is unidirectional as compared with the tidal air flow of mammals. The operation of the system depends on non-respiratory air-sacs connected with the lungs which act as reservoirs.

Underwater swimming and diving

Mammals and birds cannot of course breathe when swimming under water. While breathing ceases and carbon dioxide continues to be brought to the lungs in venous blood, the build-up of carbon dioxide in alveolar air will give the usual respiratory drive and eventually forces the underwater swimmer to the surface to breathe. Many species of mammals (otter, beaver, seal, whale) show adaptations which permit them to stay under water for a longer or shorter period of time. A spectacular example is that of of the sperm whale, which is reported to go as deep as 1000 m and to remain under water for an hour or more without encountering any obvious problems. One of the oxygen-saving mechanisms during a dive is the slowing of the heart (diving bradycardia), which is accompanied by a fall in the blood flow to the muscles, skin and viscera, so the flow to the brain and heart is maintained. In some mammals stimulation by water of receptors in the nasal region triggers the cardiac slowing. Diving vertebrates also have a relatively large blood volume, and this may be accompanied by development of large venous reservoirs. Certain species show anatomical specializations such as several pairs of floating ribs, not attached to the sternum; during a deep dive the high pressure of water surrounding the chest is transmitted to the air space of the lungs, which partially collapse and restrict capillary circulation in the alveoli, thereby preventing solution of excessive amounts of air in the blood.

Human divers working at depth are faced with several physiological problems. A major one is the high ambient pressure which increases by 1 atm for every 10 m (30 ft). Air must be supplied at the pressure of the surroundings, otherwise the lungs would collapse. But oxygen and nitrogen under high pressure are hazardous. Hyperbaric oxygen may cause damage to the lung and the nervous system; nitrogen under pressure dissolves in membranes and other lipid structures causing nitrogen narcosis, a state resembling anaesthesia. In diving bells (described in Chapter 17) and helmets, nitrogen of the air is replaced by helium which has little effect. Another danger is the expansion of the gas and its release from solution if the diver ascends too rapidly. This results in decompression sickness. The bubbles will form emboli in pulmonary, myocardial or cerebral circulations or become lodged in joints. To overcome this problem, decompression chambers are employed so that pressure can be reduced slowly.

Humans swimming at shallow depths can lengthen their underwater swimming by training. However, disasters can occur if the would-be underwater swimmer precedes his swimming by a period of overbreathing, thereby washing out much carbon dioxide from his lung alveoli. This will indeed delay the onset of the CO_2-respiratory drive and the sensation of the 'need' to breathe. But meanwhile oxygen is being used as alveolar P_{O_2} is falling. As we saw, the P_{O_2}-sensitive chemoreceptors are not in fact very sensitive, and do not stimulate respiration until rather low P_{O_2} levels are reached. By this time the unfortunate swimmer may have become unconscious through oxygen lack, and is thus unable to surface and so drowns.

Birds and mammals—man included—have spread out over the globe, in earth, in air and in water. All species can take exercise and can make the respiratory adjustments which enable the alteration in their rate of movement. But man unaided makes a poor showing on high mountains or in the water. He is limited by his respiratory physiology, and it is only his technology that enables him to accompany the soaring bird and the diving whale.

Carriage of gases in the blood

The respiratory movements described above maintain in the lung alveoli a gas mixture of fairly steady composition: about 14 per cent oxygen and 5 per cent carbon dioxide, the remainder being nitrogen and water vapour. There are slight fluctuations during the respiratory cycle, the lowest oxygen level and highest carbon dioxide level coming near the start of an inspiration. In a large mammal such as the elephant, which breathes only about three times per minute, or in diving animals such as seals, there would be so much time between each breath for loss of oxygen into arterial blood and gain of carbon dioxide from venous blood that the fluctuations in composition of alveolar air may be considerable. For convenience, we will consider alveolar air in humans fairly stable at 13.9 per cent (about 106 mmHg) oxygen and 5.2 per cent (40 mmHg) carbon dioxide.

Carriage of oxygen

Exchange of gases by diffusion in lung alveoli is extremely rapid because the surface area is large, the barrier to diffusion—capillary and alveoli walls—is thin, and the pressure gradient is steep. Mixed venous blood with Po_2 about 40 mmHg is exposed to a partial pressure difference of $(106 - 40) = 66$ mmHg, driving oxygen into solution in the blood (Table 6.1). The oxygen in solution in plasma diffuses into the red cells (erythrocytes) where it immediately reacts with haemoglobin, the red pigment within the erythrocytes, in its deoxygenated form, termed deoxyhaemoglobin. Haemoglobin, a protein of molecular weight about 68 000, contains four peptide chains and four haem rings carrying Fe^{++} in the centre of each ring. One molecule of oxygen combines loosely with each of the four haem units of haemoglobin. This chemical reaction, by removing oxygen from solution, maintains a steep diffusion gradient, so more oxygen diffuses into the blood and more is available for combination with deoxyhaemoglobin and so on until the haemoglobin is (almost) saturated, becoming oxyhaemoglobin. This is achieved when the Po_2 tension in the plasma is about 90 mmHg. The blood spends less than a second in the resting (human) lung capillary but only 0.3 s is necessary for all these processes, and blood normally leaves the lungs and enters the left ventricle of the heart with (nearly) all the haemoglobin oxygenated and plasma fully oxygen-saturated. Arterial blood, which is bright scarlet in colour, contains (per 100 ml in man) about 20 ml oxygen combined with haemoglobin and 0.3 ml dissolved in the plasma. The blood moves from the left ventricle of the heart to all parts of the body where in the peripheral capillaries it is close to interstitial fluid with a much lower oxygen tension. Here it gives up its oxygen; haemoglobin releases oxygen from the loose combination and becomes partially desaturated, deoxyhaemoglobin. The precise degree of desaturation is different in different organs. In an actively working muscle the Po_2 of interstitial fluid may be as low as 5 mmHg and the blood of the venous outflow contains almost no oxygen. Such blood has the dark-purple colour of deoxyhaemoglobin. The blood returning from the brain, however, has lost very little oxygen per unit volume and is still bright scarlet in colour. The brain's active metabolism and great oxygen requirement is supplied by an extremely high rate of blood flow per gram of tissue.

The combination of oxygen (uptake and release) with haemoglobin is not directly proportional to the tension; the relationship is not a straight line but an S-shaped curve. Figure 6.8a shows the oxygen-dissociation curve. It is seen, on the flat portion at the upper end of the haemoglobin curve, that haemoglobin is 97 per cent saturated at 90 mmHg and any increase in partial pressure will make little difference to its saturation. In the range of 35–44 mmHg, the slope of the curve is steep and nearly straight. This is the range of Po_2 in the interstitial fluid of most normally active tissues; so here the haemoglobin is becoming desaturated and oxygen is being given up to the tissues. (Again, at the base, the curve tends to flatten out, showing that at these very low oxygen tensions a somewhat larger change in tension is needed to make a difference to the saturation). The precise characteristic S-shape of the dissociation

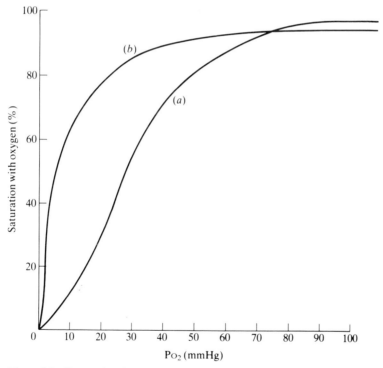

Figure 6.8 Curves showing percentage saturation with oxygen (oxygen-dissociation curves) at various Po_2 levels. (a) Haemoglobin in whole blood. (b) Myoglobin solution. (Adapted from Horrobin, D. F., *Medical Physiology and Biochemistry*, Arnold, London, 1968.)

curve is due to the uptake of the four oxygen molecules at differing affinities, the addition of the first altering the affinity of haemoglobin for other oxygen molecules.

In the fibres of red muscles there occurs the pigment myoglobin, a protein of molecular weight 16 700, containing one (not four) haem unit. This pigment also takes up oxygen in loose combination. The dissociation curve of myoglobin (Fig. 6.8b) indicates that this compound remains oxygenated until quite low levels of Po_2 are reached in the surrounding fluid. These low Po_2 levels might occur in a muscle during long sustained activity. At, say, 20 mmHg, the haemoglobin in the blood is about 30 per cent saturated; but the myoglobin within the muscle cells is nearly 80 per cent saturated even at this level. So the myoglobin can act as a short-term oxygen store within the muscle fibres, where it maintains oxygen level and thus the energy supply during prolonged activity. This short-term oxygen storage is particularly important in cardiac muscle where ventricular contraction obliterates the lumen of the coronary artery briefly at every systole and thus cuts off the blood supply to the heart muscle itself.

The mixed venous blood entering the right atrium of the heart is never completely emptied of oxygen. The content of oxygen (or proportion of oxygenated haemoglobin to deoxyhaemoglobin) varies according to the activity in different parts of the body, to the flow rate of blood through these various organs and thus to the contribution each organ makes to the total venous return. Obviously minimal oxygen in mixed venous blood would be present after hard muscular exercise, when the muscles are removing much oxygen and a large proportion of the venous return has come from these active muscles. Even so, the Po_2 of a man's mixed venous blood after exercise may still be about 35 mmHg, equivalent to about 60 per cent saturation of the haemoglobin.

Carriage of carbon dioxide

Carbon dioxide, like oxygen, is present in both venous and arterial blood and is carried in three forms:

1. dissolved and combined with water as carbonic acid, (H_2CO_3);
2. as the bicarbonate ion, (HCO_3)';
3. as a carbamino compound combined with —NH_2 groups on side-chains of certain amino acids of haemoglobin (and to a much lesser extent of plasma protein).

Carbamino-haemoglobin might be produced thus:

$$(Hb—NH_2) + CO_2 = HbNH \cdot COOH = HbNH \cdot COO + H^+$$

Uptake of carbon dioxide takes place in the capillaries and the presence of the enzyme carbonic anhydrase in the red cells ensures the sharing of the carriage of carbon dioxide between erythrocytes and plasma. From the tissue capillaries, carbon dioxide is carried to the lungs in venous blood and is lost into the alveolar air. Table 6.2 shows the proportions of carbon dioxide present in each of the three forms, in arterial blood leaving the left ventricle and in mixed venous blood entering the right atrium. We may notice first how comparatively slight is the difference in composition of arterial and

Table 6.2 Carriage of carbon dioxide in various forms in man

| | Carbon dioxide (mmol/l)* | | |
	Venous blood	Arterial blood	Difference
Plasma			
– Dissolved	0.8	0.7	0.1
– $(HCO_3)'$ ion	16.2	15.3	0.9
– *Total*	17.0	16.0	1.0
Erythrocytes			
– Dissolved	0.4	0.3	0.1
– $(HCO_3)'$ ion	4.4	4.3	0.1
– Carbamino-haemoglobin	1.4	1.0	0.4
– *Total*	6.2	5.6	0.6
Total in blood	23.2	21.6	1.6

* For any gas 1 mmol occupies 22.4 ml (= 44 mg for carbon dioxide).

venous blood in respect of carbon dioxide; secondly, that in the plasma of both, the ratio of $(HCO_3)'$ ions to dissolved carbon dioxide is about the same, approximately 20:1; and thirdly, that even in arterial blood there is some carbon dioxide combined as carbamino-haemoglobin and that about a quarter of the carbon dioxide *change*, as arterial blood becomes venous, is due to the formation of more of the carbamino compound. The human body, even at rest, is losing about 300 ml/min (about 13 mmol) of carbon dioxide and is taking in about the same volume of oxygen. But the table reveals that the carbon dioxide exchanges in lungs and tissues cause only very slight changes in chemical composition of the blood; a fact of some importance in the maintenance of the body's chemical stability. A later chapter (Chapter 8) shows the importance of the constancy of the 20:1 ratio of bicarbonate to carbonic acid in the control of plasma pH.

The diffusion gradient for carbon dioxide in actively metabolizing tissues forces carbon dioxide from the tissue into the blood where it produces carbonic acid, giving H^+ ions and $(HCO_3)'$ ions:

$$CO_2 + H_2O \rightarrow H_2CO_3 \rightarrow H^+ + (HCO_3)'$$

This reaction occurs in both the plasma and the erythrocytes but much more quickly within the erythrocytes because of the presence there of a specific enzyme, carbonic anhydrase, catalysing the reaction between carbon dioxide and water; a reaction which uncatalysed is rather slow. The consequence is that far more H^+ and $(HCO_3)'$ ions are generated within the red cells than in the plasma. The H^+ ions are quickly taken up onto deoxyhaemoglobin in the cells, as will be explained; but for the $(HCO_3)'$ ions a diffusion gradient, from the cells into the plasma, is rapidly established. Bicarbonate ions diffuse out, but the requirement of electrical equilibrium means that loss of these anions from the cells would necessitate either loss of the same number of cations or gain of another type of anion into the cell. Chloride ions diffuse more rapidly across the erythrocyte membrane than either K^+ or Na^+ ions;

thus as the $(HCO_3)'$ ions leave the cells Cl' ions enter and electrical equivalence is maintained. The diffusion of $(HCO_3)'$ ions from the erythrocytes results in the CO_2-carrying power of the blood (in bicarbonate form) being shared out between cells and plasma.

The H^+ ions generated in the reaction of carbon dioxide with water are taken up in the plasma by the buffering action of the plasma proteins, and in the erythrocytes by that of haemoglobin. This removal of free H^+ pushes the reaction to the right. On the haemoglobin the H^+ is taken up by amino-acid side-chains on the globin, displacing K^+. In fact (as will be explained), the deoxyhaemoglobin, which is formed in the passage of blood through metabolizing tissues, is a better buffer (proton acceptor) than oxyhaemoglobin, so more H^+ can be carried from the tissues. Within the erythrocytes some of the carbon dioxide forms carbamino-haemoglobin. This reaction takes place much more readily with deoxy- than with oxyhaemoglobin. It is here in the tissues that haemoglobin loses its oxygen simultaneously with carbon dioxide uptake, so a larger amount of deoxyhaemoglobin conveniently becomes available for combination with carbon dioxide. If for any reason the body's P_{O_2} is kept artificially high, say by breathing oxygen under pressure, this will seriously interfere with removal of carbon dioxide from the tissues because there will be a lesser amount of deoxyhaemoglobin available.

In the lungs, where the venous blood encounters in alveolar air a lower P_{CO_2} than its own (say, 40 mmHg as compared with 46 mmHg), all these reactions are reversed. The carbon dioxide is released into the alveoli, carbonic anhydrase catalyses the $CO_2 + H_2O$ reaction in the reverse direction, many $(HCO_3)'$ ions are lost from the erythrocytes and some enter cells from the plasma, again by exchange with Cl' ions. Meanwhile, the simultaneous oxygenation of haemoglobin aids the release of carbon dioxide from its combination as the carbamino compound. Although the partial-pressure gradient for carbon dioxide across the alveolar capillary membrane is much less than that for oxygen (Table 6.1), movement of carbon dioxide into the alveoli from the blood is as rapid as that for oxygen, because of the greater solubility of carbon dioxide in body fluids and membranes (20 times greater). Therefore equilibration for both gases occurs within 0.3 s.

Haemoglobin

The unique chemical properties of the haemoglobin molecule enable it to play a special role in the combined operation of carrying the two respiratory gases, oxygen and carbon dioxide. One of the properties has already been mentioned: the fact that oxygenation and deoxygenation of the haemoglobin molecule help in the break-up and formation of carbamino-haemoglobin in the lungs and tissues, respectively. Some other physiologically useful aspects of haemoglobin chemistry will now be described.

The S-shaped dissociation curve relating percentage saturation of haemoglobin to ambient P_{O_2} has been shown in Fig. 6.8. Figure 6.9 shows the curves obtained experimentally by measuring percentage oxygen saturation in relation to P_{O_2} at different ambient P_{CO_2} levels. It is seen that at the higher P_{CO_2} (90 mmHg) the curve is

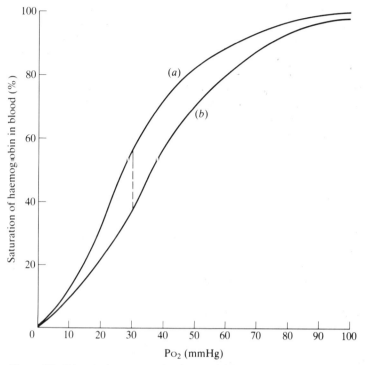

Figure 6.9 Dissociation curves for haemoglobin in blood at two ambient P_{CO_2} levels. (a) P_{CO_2} = 40 mmHg. (b) P_{CO_2} = 90 mmHg. Dotted line indicates release of oxygen at a given P_{O_2} as blood reaches a region of high P_{CO_2} in a working muscle.

shifted to the right. Curve *a* corresponds with the P_{CO_2} found in arterial blood leaving normal alveoli, and curve *b* with the P_{CO_2} found in the interstitial fluid of exercising muscle. Thus the haemoglobin leaving the lungs starts on curve *a* but in flowing through the muscle (where the tension of oxygen is, say, 30 mmHg) it comes onto curve *b*. So the presence of the high P_{CO_2} in muscle enables the haemoglobin, at an ambient P_{O_2} 30 mmHg, to give up an additional amount of oxygen to the tissues, as shown by a fall in oxygen saturation from 58 per cent to 38 per cent; clearly an advantage in this active tissue.

The shift to the right of the oxygen-dissociation curve with an increasing ambient P_{CO_2} is known as the Bohr effect. If a similar series of oxygen-dissociation curves is obtained at different pH values, instead of at different P_{CO_2} values, precisely the same result is obtained: the more acid the solution, the further to the right the dissociation curve is shifted. The P_{CO_2} effect is due to the release of H^+ by carbonic acid in solution. As we shall see, the H^+ ions (protons), known in this connection as the 'Bohr protons', become attached to groups on the globin subunits of deoxyhaemoglobin.

Haemoglobin, like all weakly acidic proteins, acts as a part of a buffer system, binding H^+ ions provided by any acid stronger than itself. Deoxyhaemoglobin is in fact a more efficient buffer than oxyhaemoglobin: that means that during conversion of oxygenated haemoglobin to the reduced form in the tissues, the haemoglobin becomes a weaker acid, and so a more efficient acceptor of H^+ ions. At this moment, and especially within the red cells because of the carbonic anhydrase there, large amounts of H^+ and $(HCO_3)'$ are being formed via carbonic acid. Many of the H^+ ions are accepted by the haemoglobin (probably on side-chains of histidines in the globin chains). So there is little change in (free) H^+ ion concentration. Venous blood flowing out of the tissues is a little more acidic than arterial blood but only very slightly. It has been calculated that if the change in pH between arterial and venous blood were from pH 7.4 to pH 7.3, 1 mM H^+ per mM haemoglobin could be taken up; but if, during this pH change, the haemoglobin *remained* in the form of oxyhaemoglobin, only 0.25 mM H^+ per mM haemoglobin could be taken up. In the lungs the converse change will occur: the formation of the more acidic oxyhaemoglobin donates H^+ to the formation of carbonic acid, immediately dissociated by carbonic anhydrase to carbon dioxide and water, and the carbon dioxide is given out into the alveolar air. In this way the uptake and release of each of the respiratory gases ensure the efficient release and uptake of the other.

These cooperative effects of the respiratory gases have been known for many decades and their advantage in the distribution of oxygen and removal of carbon dioxide is apparent. Understanding the processes at the molecular level is only now becoming possible. The structure of the haemoglobin molecule, including the amino-acid sequence of the four polypeptide chains which make up the globin part of the molecule, has been unravelled by a series of brilliant studies in protein chemistry. The four peptide-chain subunits are known as α, α', β and β' and the four haem groups, each one containing an iron atom at its centre (Fig. 6.10a), fit into cavities in the four much-folded chains. Each haemoglobin molecule carries four oxygen molecules (one associated with each of the Fe^{++}) on oxygenation. The four molecules of oxygen are added to the haemoglobin almost simultaneously; the addition of the first oxygen apparently rearranges the globin subunits in such a way as to increase the affinity for oxygen in the other haem rings. The rearrangement of the globin subunits has been detected by x-ray crystallography: the two β-chains are slightly closer to each other in oxyhaemoglobin than in deoxyhaemoglobin (Fig. 6.10b).

In deoxyhaemoglobin, a haem group in its cavity within the globin subunit may be visualized as having its central iron atom 'pulled' up out of the plane of the porphyrin ring by salt-bridges on the globin units. The iron is at the apex of a pyramid, the corners of the base of which are the four nitrogen atoms of the pyrrol rings of the porphyrin, and the Fe—N bonds are stretched out to their maximum length. This arrangement, in which the iron is under *tension*, pulled by the groups on the globin chain surrounding it, is called the T-structure of the haem (Fig. 6.11a). In oxyhaemoglobin the iron comes into the plane of the porphyrin, the pyramid is flattened out and the Fe—N bonds shorten. This is called the *relaxed* or R-structure of the haem (Fig. 6.11b). (The movement of iron involves the breaking of salt-bridges, and twice as many bridges are broken by the addition of the first oxygen molecules as by the next two; addition of the fourth involves no breaking of bridges and it happens

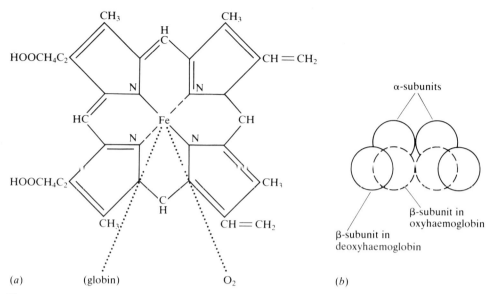

Figure 6.10 (a) Structure of haem; atom of iron is placed centrally in haem ring formed by adjoining of four pyrrol rings by methene (—CH=) bridges. (b) Two α- and two β-subunits forming the haemoglobin molecule. The β-subunits move closer together as haemoglobin becomes oxygenated.

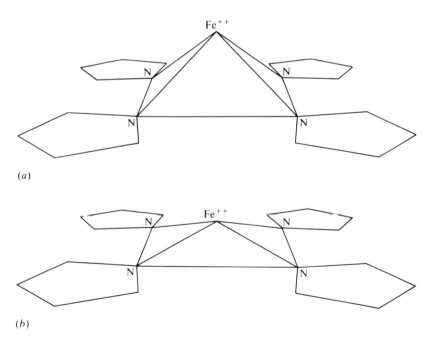

Figure 6.11 Three dimensional structure of haem in (a) the T-state ('tense'), and (b) the R-state ('relaxed'). In both states the five-sided pyrrol rings lie all in the same plane, their nitrogen atom towards the centre of the haem. In the T-state the Fe^{++} is drawn out of the plane of the pyrrols.

easily; there is thus a successive cooperative 'binding' of the molecules.) In any haemoglobin solution, or in the blood, the T- and R-structures are both present and there is an equilibrium between them, $T \rightleftharpoons R$. In the R-structure there is less stearic hindrance to the addition of the oxygen and in conditions of high Po_2, an increasing proportion of the haem groups will 'relax' and equilibrium will come towards the R-state. The T-state, on the other hand, is favoured by the presence around the haemoglobin molecule of organic phosphates, including DPG. The organic phosphates may be visualized as binding the haemoglobin molecule between the two β-chains and keeping them apart, as they are in the T-state; so in the presence of abundant DPG, oxygen affinity is decreased (haemoglobin dissociation curve shifted to the right). There is some evidence that mountain dwellers permanently exposed to low atmospheric Po_2 develop a high level of DPG in their erythrocytes (Chapter 17). This ensures that though the haemoglobin may never become fully saturated with oxygen in the lungs, at least oxygen can be readily released in the tissues. In addition to the organic phosphates the Bohr protons bind to certain specific parts of the globin chains on the cavity containing the haem; and these, too, help to stabilize the T-state of low oxygen affinity. These great advances in the understanding of haemoglobin at the molecular level have gone far towards explaining its unique properties as the respiratory pigment of vertebrates.

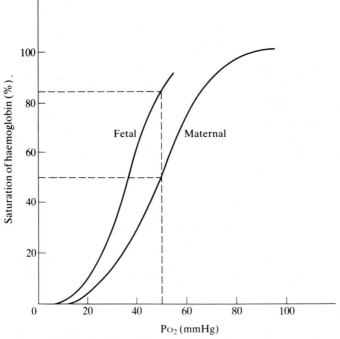

Figure 6.12   Discussion curves for fetal and maternal haemoglobin. Vertical dotted line at Po_2 50 mmHg indicates conditions in placenta. At this level, fetal blood is about 85 per cent saturated but maternal blood only about 52 per cent saturated.

The form of haemoglobin synthesized before birth in the mammalian fetus is slightly different from that of the adult (see Chapter 15 under Fetus). Consequently fetal haemoglobin has a slightly different oxygen-dissociation curve from the adult form: it is displaced to the left (Fig. 6.12). In the fetal form the globin chains are α, α', γ and γ', and the presence of γ (instead of β) reduces the ability of DPG to bind to haemoglobin. The shift to the left in fetal haemoglobin facilitates oxygen exchange in the placenta. If the ambient Po_2 of the placental tissue is, say, 50 mmHg, the maternal blood entering the placenta will lose oxygen to the point of being only 50 per cent saturated, whereas the fetal haemoglobin at this ambient Po_2 could become 85 per cent saturated. But diffusion of gases across the placental barrier is much slower than that between lung alveoli and pulmonary blood, and the fetal (umbilical cord) blood always has a lower Po_2 than maternal placental blood.

Erythrocytes

The red cells are formed and removed from the circulation continually throughout life. In the fetus this process occurs in the liver and spleen as well as in the bone marrow of many bones. The amount of erythropoietic (red-cell forming) tissue is gradually restricted during growth and in the adult human it occurs only in the marrow of the sternum, ribs and vertebrae. When red cells are removed from the circulation (largely by the spleen), the iron of the haemoglobin is retained (mainly in the liver) and re-used in haemoglobin synthesis; and the amino acids of the globin can be re-used, but the porphyrin ring structure, which surrounds the iron in haemoglobin, is excreted from the body as bilirubin and biliverdin of the bile and new porphyrin rings are synthesized.

There are some advantages in having the haemoglobin of the blood packed inside red cells. If the same amount of haemoglobin were to be free in solution in plasma, this would necessarily give the plasma an inconveniently high viscosity as well as a large oncotic pressure. Also the molecular volume of haemoglobin is such that it is able to pass through some of the small pores at the glomerulus of the kidney and would thus be lost little by little in the urine. Indeed, in some diseases where haemoglobin becomes free in plasma, the pigment or its derivatives soon show up in the urine. (This may happen in the disease malaria in which the red cells are invaded and rapidly destroyed by the organism *Plasmodium*.)

Red cells of many mammalian species take the form of a biconcave disc. This shape has a large surface area per unit volume, an advantage in the role of gas exchange with the surrounding plasma. In many species the mature red cell has no nucleus, mitochondria or any other organelles: the entire cell contents are haemoglobin and other proteins including many enzymes, and salts. The surface membrane is flexible and elastic: the erythrocyte can be squeezed or distorted as it passes through narrow capillaries and around corners of the vascular system, and then can resume its normal shape on coming to a wider vessel. Like the haemoglobin molecules within it, the red cell itself is well adapted to its role as a transporter of the respiratory gases between lungs and the tissues throughout the body.

Summary

This chapter on the respiratory processes of mammals has described the mechanism by which atmospheric air enters the lungs. The rhythmic movements of the respiratory muscles are controlled by the respiratory centre in the brain stem which is itself affected by afferent nerve impulses, including those from central chemoreceptors sensitive to the P_{CO_2} and pH of the CSF. The control of the respiratory rhythm is modified under various conditions, notably during muscular exercise. A description of the mechanisms by which oxygen intake into the body in exercise is closely related to the work rate still awaits a full explanation. Red cells contribute to gas exchange in lungs and tissues. The haemoglobin in the erythrocytes is a highly efficient carrier by which oxygen is taken from the lungs to all organs of the body, and the same substance helps in the movement of carbon dioxide from all tissues to the lungs. The interpretation of the role of haemoglobin in the carriage of the respiratory gases is a striking instance of the help given by molecular biology to the study of physiological processes.

7 Body fluids and the kidney

Body fluids

Fluid balance and volume

The bodies of most land vertebrates include about 65 per cent by weight of water at the adult stage and a somewhat greater percentage at the juvenile stage. Over a period of time, say a day or so, water intake must be equal in volume to water loss in an adult remaining at constant weight. A child or any young growing animal is in positive water balance: that is, over a period of time there is a greater intake than loss of water—as of energy, nitrogen and indeed of all tissue components.

The only route of fluid intake for land vertebrates is by way of intestinal absorption of the water of food and drink. There is in addition a small production of so-called 'metabolic water' within the body during oxidation of carbohydrate and fatty acids. Some desert animals never drink but manage to maintain fluid equilibrium entirely on metabolic water together with the sparse moisture of the desert vegetation on which they feed. However, most species of terrestrial birds and mammals can maintain their fluid equilibrium only by drinking at least once a day. Marine mammals and birds do not drink fresh water; some of these species have specialized mechanisms which excrete the excess NaCl inevitably ingested with the food of the marine environment.

In contrast to the single route of water intake, there are several routes of water output from the body: via the skin, lung surface, faeces and urine. The skin is not completely waterproof and even when the sweat glands are not active there is a small amount of evaporation of water from the skin surface. This together with the loss from the lungs is called 'insensible water loss'. There is some loss of water in the moisture of the faeces; the amount differs among species and individuals. There is a loss of water through the skin in sweat; this may be considerable when body heat is increased in exercise, and also in those few species (including man) which sweat in a hot environment. Much the largest daily water loss (in temperate conditions) occurs via the urine. In an adult human in a temperate climate a daily 2-litre net water intake would be balanced by an output of one and a half litres in the urine plus half a litre by all the other routes together—skin, lungs and faeces. Water loss in urine is physiologically controllable, but the body has little or no control over the other routes of fluid loss.

Not only is there an overall balance between the fluid intake and output of the body as a whole, but also there is some degree of balance in the exchange of water across the membrane of all cells of the body; and this internal balance is a prerequisite of healthy cellular function. The cells of many tissues do swell or shrink slightly as water moves into or out of them by osmotic effects; but these movements are slight and are perfectly compatible with healthy existence.

Much of the internal fluid balance takes place by osmotic water movement. Osmolarity is now defined and the measurement of this property of solutions described.

Osmolarity

The osmotic pressure of a solution depends on the number of osmotically active particles within it, whether ions or undissociated molecules. The units of measurement of osmolarity are osmoles per litre, osm/l. A molar solution of a substance un-dissociated in solution, such as glucose, would contain 1 osm/l. A molar solution of, say, NaCl (if we assume that it is completely dissociated into its two ions) would contain 2 osm/l. Most biological fluids are more dilute than this and so are more conveniently measured in millimoles (and correspondingly, milliosmoles, mosm/l).

Osmolarity and molarity are defined as the number of osmoles and moles, respectively, contained in 1 litre of solution. Students may also come across the terms osmolality and molality. These are defined in terms of the number of osmoles and moles, respectively, added to 1 kg of water.

Blood plasma contains a mixture of:

1. salts, partly dissociated into ions;
2. undissociated crystalloids such as glucose and urea;
3. colloids such as proteins, which exert a small but significant osmotic pressure.

Osmotic pressure due to colloids is known as oncotic pressure. The whole solution has a total osmolar concentration (TOC) of about 300 mosm/l. This value of the plasma TOC is found in nearly all vertebrates, whether on land, in fresh water or in the sea. Extracellular osmolarity is in fact one of the most stable of the body's properties, strictly controlled by homeostatic mechanisms.

Much the greatest part of the plasma osmolarity is due to NaCl, and sodium bicarbonate ($NaHCO_3$). The concentration of Na^+ ions in mammalian plasma is about 145 mM, that of Cl' ions is approximately 100 mM, and that of bicarbonate ions ($HCO_3)'$, 27 mM, so these three components together provide 272 mosm/l out of the total of 300 mosm/l. Figure 7.1 illustrates the osmotically active components of plasma, both inorganic and organic.

It is seen that the total osmolarity (sum of ions and non-ionized molecules) will come to about 300 mosm/l. It is worth stressing that the TOC of the plasma can be maintained if, and only if, the concentrations of the Na^+, Cl' and $(HCO_3)'$ ions are kept at a fairly steady level. The wellbeing of every cell of the body depends upon the plasma concentration of these ions.

Total osmolar concentration can be measured directly, most conveniently by making use of one of the colligative properties of solutions, such as freezing-point

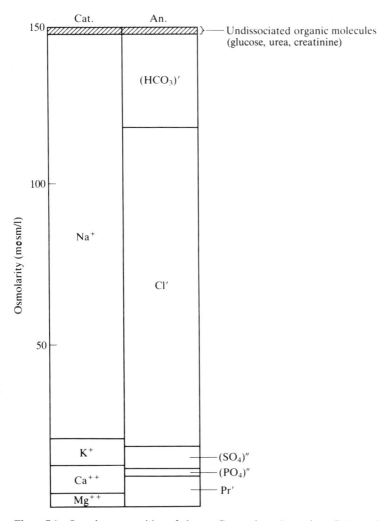

Figure 7.1 Osmolar composition of plasma. Cat.: cations; An.: anions; Pr′: protein anions. Undissociated molecules are shown across both columns.

depression. A molar solution (1000 mM) of an undissociated solute depresses the freezing point of water by 1.86 °C. Human plasma freezes at about −0.54 °C, corresponding with an osmolarity of

$$\frac{0.54}{1.86} \times 1000 = 290 \text{ mosm/l}$$

Osmolarity could also be calculated if the concentration of all solutes present, and the degree of dissociation of the salts, were known.

Fluid compartments and their measurements

The total body water (65 per cent or so by weight in terrestrial species) is divided among various compartments of the body. Well over half of the water is within the tissue cells: the aqueous solution of salts, small organic molecules and colloids known as intracellular fluid. The remainder comprises the various extracellular fluids, the main ones being:

1. blood plasma;
2. lymph;
3. interstitial fluid—fluid which is outside the cell walls and also outside the circulatory and lymphatic systems.

In addition there is a small group of fluids called transcellular fluids, which include cerebrospinal fluid and intraocular fluids, and the fluids within the abdominal and thoracic cavities. Figure 7.2 shows the percentages by weight of these various fluid compartments.

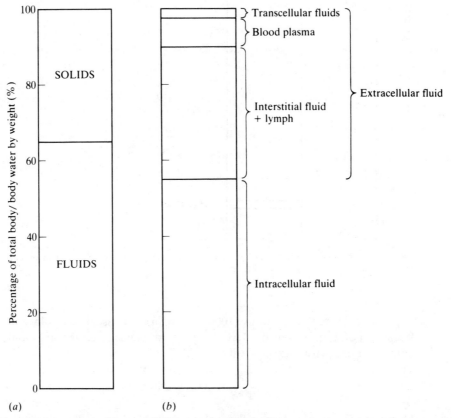

Figure 7.2 (a) Percentage by weight of solids and fluids in body of an adult mammal. (b) Percentage by weight of the components of the body fluids.

The volumes of the fluids in these compartments—extracellular, intracellular and so on—can be measured by dilution methods: that is, by placing in one or other compartment the precise weight of a substance which is known to be distributed in that compartment and excluded from others. After a period of equilibration the concentration of the substance is measured, and a simple calculation indicates the volume of fluid required to achieve that concentration. (For example if 3 g of the dye Evans Blue is injected into the blood plasma and if after equilibration the dye has a plasma concentration of 1.2 g/l, there are 3/1.2 = 2.5 litres plasma.) Measurement of intracellular fluid is usually performed by finding the total fluid volume of the body (say by dilution of a known amount of tritiated water), then subtracting extracellular fluid volume.

Some extracellular fluids

Blood plasma, interstitial fluid, lymph and cerebrospinal fluid are broadly similar in composition, at least in respect of their inorganic constituents. Cerebrospinal fluid, derived from tufts of capillaries (choroid plexuses) in the cavities of the brain, is not a simple ultrafiltrate of plasma: certain ionic constituents are in higher or lower concentration than in plasma, suggesting at least some active transport in the choroid plexuses. Blood and lymph will now be described in more detail. The maintenance of plasma volume, as we shall see, is assisted by the plasma proteins themselves, and by the flow of lymph which returns excess interstitial fluid to the vascular compartment. Both mechanisms thus contribute to volume homeostasis.

Constituents of blood

Blood plasma, a clear pale-yellow fluid, is an aqueous solution in which are suspended the formed elements:

1. erythrocytes (red cells);
2. leucocytes (white cells)—of which the main types are granulocytes, monocytes and lymphocytes;
3. platelets—small disc-shaped particles of cytoplasm budded off from large cells (megakaryocytes) in the bone marrow.

The function of erythrocytes is described in Chapter 6, and the roles of the various types of leucocytes and of the platelets in the body's defence mechanisms are discussed in Chapter 16. The formed elements comprise somewhat less than half by volume of the blood; for man 45 per cent by volume would be a typical figure; for some other species the proportion is less (for instance, approximately 35 per cent in the pig). Erythrocytes are by far the most abundant of the formed elements; when blood is centrifuged, red cells are packed into the base of the tube and the white cells and platelets are often visible as a thin layer or 'skin' above the red cells.

The main components of plasma are shown in Fig. 7.1. The pale-yellow colour is due to one of the organic molecules, bilirubin, formed from breakdown of the haem part of the haemoglobin of red cells and excreted in the bile. Proteins form about 7 per cent by weight of the plasma. Of the three main proteins—serum albumin, globulins and fibrinogen—albumin and fibrinogen are manufactured in the liver and globulins in the macrophage system of the body. The roles of globulin in defence against infections, and of fibrinogen, which is essential for blood clotting, are described in detail in Chapter 16.

In general the proteins have a role in transport. Fats, divalent ions, hormones and vitamins, for instance, are circulated in the body attached to plasma proteins. The proteins, moreover, together with the formed elements, give the blood its viscosity, an important property in the maintenance of blood pressure (Chapter 5). Albumin, the smallest molecule of the three main proteins and in the highest concentration in plasma, is particularly important in its contribution to the oncotic pressure of the plasma. Since there is only minimal leakage of protein into interstitial space, the oncotic pressure of plasma is always greater than that of interstitial fluid; and this difference of oncotic pressure, when it exceeds capillary hydrostatic pressure, enables the withdrawal of interstitial fluid back into the circulation (see Chapter 5 under Capillaries). In some diseases excessive loss of plasma albumin via the kidney, or failure to manufacture it in the liver, causes accumulation of interstitial fluid (oedema).

Lymph and lymphatics

Lymph is a clear colourless fluid flowing in thin-walled vessels (lymphatics), the smallest of which end blindly. Lymphatics lie among all tissues of the body except bone and the central nervous system. The smallest lymphatics are transparent, their walls being one-cell thick. They are loosely attached to the surrounding connective tissue by slender anchoring filaments. Small lymphatics join and merge to form larger and larger vessels. The large lymphatics have muscle and elastic tissue in their walls, and like veins are provided with valves which ensure one-way flow. The largest lymph trunks are:

1. the thoracic duct, which drains lymph from the whole of the left side of the body, the alimentary canal and the lower limbs;
2. the right lymphatic duct, which drains the upper right part of the body.

These two main ducts open into the main veins close to the heart, and valves prevent flow of venous blood back into the lymph trunks.

An important function of the lymph is to return to the blood the fluid and traces of protein inevitably lost through the capillaries of the cardiovascular system. As described in Chapter 5, most of the fluid lost from capillaries by hydrostatic pressure is regained by the oncotic pressure of the plasma proteins in conditions where this pressure exceeds the hydrostatic pressure. But there is always a slight net loss of fluid, and this loss is greatly increased during vigorous activity of any organ (say in limb muscles during running), causing lymph flow to become brisk and copious.

Entry of interstitial fluid into lymphatics is thought to take place between the thin flattened cells of the smallest lymphatics (Fig. 7.3). The overlaps at the edges of

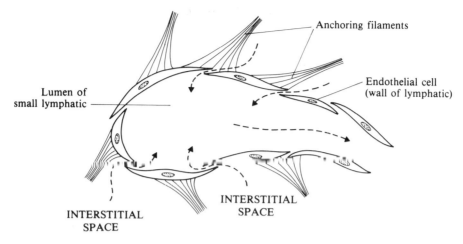

Anchoring filaments

Lumen of
small lymphatic

Endothelial cell
(wall of lymphatic)

INTERSTITIAL
SPACE

INTERSTITIAL
SPACE

Figure 7.3 Terminal lymphatic, to show entry of fluid from interstitial space, between flattened cells of endothelium.

the endothelial cells act as one-way valves: increase in hydrostatic pressure within the lymphatic could not squeeze out fluid which had already entered. Once within the lymphatic the onward flow of lymph is maintained by pressure from surrounding tissue cells, particularly from active skeletal muscle, and by valves in the main trunks.

The importance of lymph drainage is emphasized by observation of the symptoms of a rare tropical disease in which filarial worms invade lymphatics and cause mechanical blockage of some of the main lymph trunks: the affected limb becomes grossly swollen by accumulated interstitial fluid unable to drain back into the circulation.

A second important function of lymph is the absorption of fat from the small intestine (Chapter 4). The lymphatics draining the intestinal wall become packed with tiny fat droplets during absorption of a fatty meal, and the white milky appearance of these lymphatics has led to the name 'lacteals'.

A third function of lymph is the uptake and removal of foreign particles including bacteria from the tissue spaces. The main lymph trunks are interrupted by lymph nodes—small capsules of connective tissue packed with lymphocytes and macrophages. As the lymph slowly percolates through the node the phagocytic macrophages take up the foreign bodies and thus prevent the entry of bacteria into the circulation, and consequent widespread infection. Chapter 16 describes the role of macrophages and lymphocytes in the body's defence mechanism.

Movement of fluids

Movement of fluid between the compartments takes place by pressure gradients and by osmotic gradients. Hydrostatic pressure forces fluid from the plasma into the interstitial compartment and from there into the lymph. Mechanical pressure of muscle contractions squeezes the lymph along the lymphatics and eventually back to the blood. Colloid osmotic pressure brings fluid from the interstitial space into the blood. Capillary hydrostatic pressure initiates urine formation by ultrafiltering plasma at the renal glomerulus. Osmotic gradients created by active transport of sodium and other solutes move a vast amount of fluid (about 6 litres a day, in man) from the alimentary canal into portal blood.

Exchanges between extra- and intracellular fluids must also take place by osmosis but the details of the exchange mechanism are somewhat obscure. There is some controversy about whether the 'typical' tissue cell is in osmotic equilibrium with, or slightly hypertonic to, the interstitial fluid around it. Certainly it is very close to osmotic equilibrium and there is a rapid exchange of small solutes, presumably accompanied by water, in both directions across the cell membrane. Most cells are able to swell and shrink to some extent under perfectly normal (not pathological) conditions, and in severe dehydration of the whole body there is loss of cell water as well as of the extracellular fluid. Clearly there is some sort of equilibrium between intracellular and extracellular compartments. In summary, it appears that the only ways in which water moves between the fluid compartments of the body are by the 'pushing' of hydrostatic and mechanical pressure and by the 'pulling' of osmotic pressure, which in turn is largely dependent on the movement and relative concentrations of Na^+ ions.

In these exchanges of fluids between compartments, the blood plasma has a central role. It moves quickly to and among all parts of the body. It accepts fluid from the intestines and major lymph ducts, and gives it to interstitial spaces and small lymphatics and renal nephrons. The confining of the plasma proteins within the vascular system allows oncotic pressure to limit fluid loss into the interstitial space. The continuous movement of blood provides a mixing effect which prevents undue accumulation of solute in any tissue or organ. If the blood plasma can be maintained at a steady osmolarity, volume and composition, this stability will be passed on to the other fluid compartments. Herein lies the role of the kidney, and the significance of the enormous renal blood flow, some 25 per cent of the resting cardiac output. If the plasma is in a satisfactory condition, all the other body fluids are likewise, or will very soon become so.

The kidney

Most land vertebrates eat and drink at irregular intervals, depending on hunger, thirst and the availability of food and fluid, and the diurnal cycle. One important role of the kidney is the maintenance of the total fluid volume of the body, minimizing the inevitable fluctuations associated with feeding, drinking and sleeping. Another important renal function is to help in the maintenance of a constant osmolarity. As we have seen, movements of water between fluid compartments depend largely on the movement and relative concentrations of Na^+ ions. So it is not surprising that the kidney exerts its effect on total body osmolarity and volume largely by adjusting the amount of sodium as well as water conserved or excreted.

The first part of this section describes in a general way the structure and methods of study of the various regions of the nephron, and our current picture of nephron function. This description is used to illustrate the role of the kidney in the plasma osmolarity and volume. There follows an account of the kidney as an excretory organ, and as an endocrine organ. Finally, there is a summary of the chapter and a note on some of the properties of the kidney which are not yet fully explained.

The role of the kidney in the control of plasma pH is considered in detail in Chapter 8.

Structure of regions of the nephron

Nephrons, of which the kidney is mainly composed, are long coiled tubes with walls one-cell thick, closed at the end where plasma filtrate is formed and open at the end where the urine leaves. Two nephrons, one short-looped and the other long-looped, are shown in Fig. 7.4a. The closed end, Bowman's capsule, is cup-shaped, and the space within the cup is occupied by a tuft of capillaries, the glomerulus. Blood flows through the glomerular capillaries at a rather high hydrostatic pressure, and some fluid is forced through the capillary walls and into the lumen of Bowman's capsule, the walls of which are very thin. The arrangement of glomerulus plus Bowman's capsule is thus an 'ultrafilter': all components of plasma are filtered, except the proteins, the molecules of which are too large to be passed out. The fluid thus forced into Bowman's capsule is the raw material which is modified to form the urine as the fluid passes along the nephron. Almost all the modifying processes consist of removing substances from the fluid back into the blood. Only very few substances (apart from drugs) are actually added to the fluid by the cells of the nephron; H^+ and K^+ ions are two such substances. Of the filtered load entering Bowman's capsule, about 99 per cent of water and solute is returned to the blood during passage along the nephron.

After Bowman's capsule the first section of the nephron is the proximal convoluted tubule (PCT), which is highly coiled and twisted (Fig. 7.4b). The epithelial cells of the PCT have a brush-border at the luminal surface, and mitochondria lined up along the basal surface—features suggesting active Na^+ transport, through the base. Next comes a straight section, the pars recta, leading to a thin-walled straight part, the loop of Henle's descending limb; this runs down into the renal medulla, and then, as the ascending limb, turns back on itself and runs back into the cortex (Fig. 7.4a). Some nephrons have long loops of Henle which run down to the innermost part of the renal medullary tissue (renal papilla); in other nephrons the loops are much shorter, running no further than the outermost strip of the medulla, adjacent to the cortex. The proportions of short-looped and long-looped nephrons vary in different species of mammals; in most species the short-looped type predominate, and in man only about 14 per cent of the nephrons are long-looped. After the loops of Henle there follows the distal convoluted tubule (DCT), also highly coiled, but shorter than the PCT. The first portion of the DCT lies close to the glomerulus of that nephron. The DCT leads to the

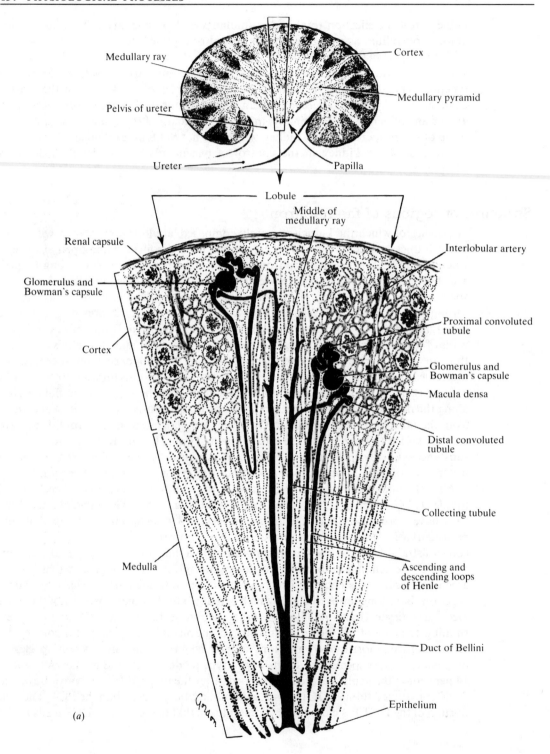

Medullary ray

Cortex

Pelvis of ureter

Medullary pyramid

Ureter

Papilla

Lobule

Middle of
medullary ray

Renal capsule

Interlobular artery

Glomerulus and
Bowman's capsule

Proximal convoluted
tubule

Cortex

Glomerulus and
Bowman's capsule

Macula densa

Distal convoluted
tubule

Collecting tubule

Ascending and
descending loops
of Henle

Medulla

Duct of Bellini

Epithelium

(a)

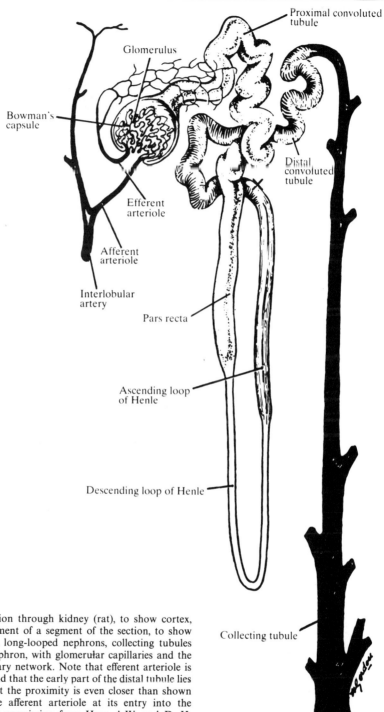

Figure 7.4 (*a*) Longitudinal section through kidney (rat), to show cortex, medulla and papilla; and enlargement of a segment of the section, to show arrangement of short-looped and long-looped nephrons, collecting tubules and ducts of Bellini. (*b*) Single nephron, with glomerular capillaries and the first part of the peritubular capillary network. Note that efferent arteriole is narrower than afferent arteriole; and that the early part of the distal tubule lies close to Bowman's capsule. In fact the proximity is even closer than shown here: point X is adjacent to the afferent arteriole at its entry into the glomerulus. (*a*, *b*: Reproduced by permission from Ham, A.W. and D. H. Cormack, *Histology*, 8th edn, J. B. Lippincott, Philadelphia, 1979.)

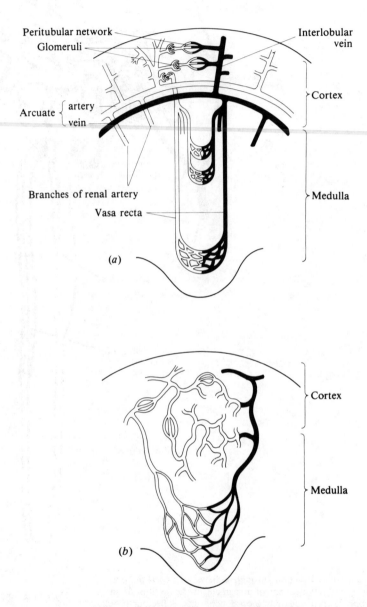

Figure 7.5 (a) Vascular arrangement in kidney of typical mammal. Arterioles, white; venules, black. Efferent arterioles of the glomeruli close to the border between cortex and medulla divide to form the descending limbs of the vasa recta in the medulla; other efferent arterioles form the peritubular network in the cortex. (b) Vascular arrangement in beaver and other semiaquatic mammals where the layout of the vessels is more random and the corticomedullary boundary is not clearly defined.

collecting duct, a straight section running down through the cortex and into the medulla. Fluid from a number of collecting ducts flows down into a single large collecting duct (duct of Bellini), which opens out near the papillary tip into the renal pelvis, an extension of the ureter into the substance of the kidney. The urine in the renal pelvis then moves by peristaltic waves down the ureter to the urinary bladder.

Renal structure and blood supply are described in Chapter 2. In some species, notably mammals associated with fresh water such as the beaver, the border between the cortex and medulla of the kidney is not clearly defined, and the vascular network is more randomly distributed than in, say, the rat. Figure 7.5 shows diagrammatically two types of renal vascular arrangement.

Nephron function: methods of study

The different regions of the nephron perform different functions, and the kidney is not such a homogeneous tissue as, say, liver or muscle. This, together with its inaccessibility, has made the kidney difficult to study. However, several powerful techniques have been devised which have gone far towards elucidating nephron function.

Micropuncture

One such method is nephron micropuncture (Fig. 7.6a). Small samples of freely flowing tubular fluid can be withdrawn from the superficial nephrons of anaesthetized animals under normal or experimentally imposed conditions and analysed by ultramicrochemical techniques. The position along the nephron at which the sample is taken is marked at the time of sampling and subsequently identified on removal of the kidney after the animal's slaughter. In this way the processing of the glomerular filtrate by proximal and distal tubule cells can be revealed. This technique is particularly useful if combined with a perfusion into the animal of a marker for movement of water—a marker such as the inert non-toxic substance inulin, a polysaccharide of low molecular weight. Inulin perfused into the plasma passes into Bowman's capsule along with the other components of the plasma and is present in Bowman's capsule at the same concentration as in the plasma. It is not secreted or reabsorbed by the walls of the nephron. So a comparison of its concentration in the tubular fluid at any particular point along the nephron with that in the plasma indicates how much of the filtered water has been lost (or whether any has been gained) before the filtrate reaches that point.

If, for instance, the level of inulin in the plasma (and Bowman's capsule) is 2 mg/l, and the level in a small sample of fluid taken from the end of the proximal tubule is 10 mg/l (a fivefold increase), we can deduce that only $\frac{2}{10}$ or 20 per cent of the filtered water remains at that point, i.e. 80 per cent has been reabsorbed. If at the same time we find that the plasma (and therefore glomerular filtrate) contains a concentration of 300 mg/l of urea, and the late proximal-tubule contains 1200 mg/l of urea, we can at once deduce that some of the filtered urea has been *reabsorbed* in the proximal tubule; otherwise there also would have been a fivefold increase in urea concentration, up to 1500 mg/l, simply because of removal of water. (Without the information on water

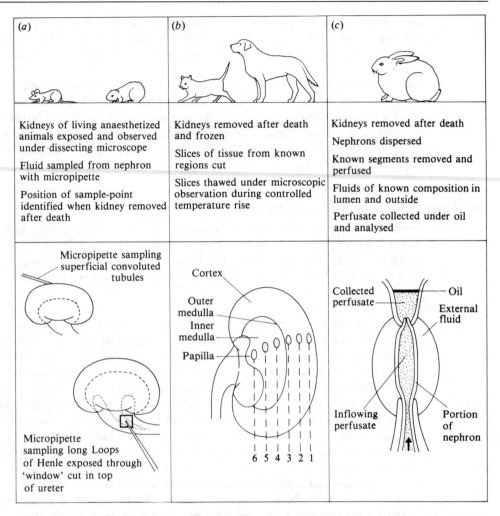

Figure 7.6 Methods of studying renal function. The animals at the top indicate species most commonly used in these types of observation. (*a*) Nephron micropuncture. (*b*) Total osmolar concentration of slices from kidney, measured by freezing-point depression. (*c*) Permeability of isolated lengths of known parts of nephron measured *in vitro*.

movement, an unwary observer might have been tempted to surmise that urea had been 'excreted' *into* the nephron.)

In most species nephron micropuncture is limited to PCT and DCT portions of nephron close to the kidney surface, but in a few species (hamsters and gerbils for instance) the very long renal papilla, extending into the upper part of the ureter, makes possible the sampling of fluid from the tips of the loops of Henle and collecting ducts, through a hole cut in the top of the ureter.

Freezing-point depression

Another way of studying medullary function is the measurement of osmolarity of whole slices of renal tissue cut from kidneys immediately after slaughter of an animal (Fig. 7.6b). Such kidneys are quick-frozen and cut into slices from the cortex, outer medulla, inner medulla and papilla. The slices are slowly thawed under microscopic observation, and the temperature of the final disappearance of ice is recorded. Total osmolarity of each slice can be calculated from the freezing-point depression of the solvent water. In this way it was established many years ago that there is a gradient of osmolarity from outer cortex (say, 300 mosm/l) to inner medulla and papilla (say, 1200 mosm/l); and that all components of the tissue—nephrons, blood vessels and interstitial fluid—appear to participate in the gradient.

Passive permeability

A third method of study of nephrons, which has been of great help particularly with those parts of the nephron inaccessible to micropuncture, is measurement of the passive-permeability properties of defined portions of the nephrons (Fig. 7.6c). The nephrons of the kidney excised from an animal immediately after slaughter can be separated; portions are identified and excised, placed in dishes in solutions of known composition, and perfused with fluids of known composition, inulin being used as a marker for water movement. The loss or gain of water and solutes from or into the perfusion fluid during its passage along the portion of tube, under the experimentally produced diffusion gradients, can be used to measure the passive permeability to water and the particular solutes under observation. This technique is especially useful for straight portions of the nephrons: ascending and descending Henle loops, pars recta and collecting ducts. It has made a useful contribution to the study of nephron function.

Clearance tests

It will be noticed that none of the above three methods used on experimental animals can be used on man. Human renal function has been studied largely by means of clearance tests, which can be used in other species also (and are described in all textbooks of human physiology). The tests involve measurement of concentration of a given solute in plasma and in urine obtained simultaneously, and measurement of the flow rate of urine. This indicates the overall function of the kidney in respect of this solute, but cannot tell by itself whereabouts in the nephron the solute is processed. The clearance rate of inulin, once again, can be used as a marker of water movement, as inulin is not itself affected in the nephron. The extent to which inulin is concentrated between plasma and urine shows what proportion of the filtered load of water must have been removed in achieving this concentration. Since inulin is unaffected in passage along the nephrons, in a steady state, the amount (in mg) of inulin leaving the body in urine in a known time (say a minute) must be the same as the amount entering all the Bowman's capsules of both kidneys in a minute. If the concentration of inulin in plasma and thus in Bowman's capsule is known, the amount of plasma ultrafiltered into the Bowman's capsules in a minute can readily be calculated. This is called the glomerular filtration rate (GFR).

If the plasma (Bowman's capsule) concentration of inulin is 200 mg/l, and 30 mg of inulin are lost from the body in a minute, these 30 mg must have been contained in $30/200 \times 1000 = 150$ ml plasma ultrafiltered at the glomeruli.

It is clear that current knowledge of nephron function is based on a mosaic of parts derived by several techniques from different species and different types of nephron. None the less, it is possible to piece together a coherent and self-consistent account of the role of the various parts of the two sorts of nephron (superficial short-looped and juxta-medullary long-looped) in the kidney of a typical mammal. The story thus put together, though it may not be accurate in detail, is a useful basis for further study. The following account describes the role of each portion of the nephron in turn, emphasizing in particular the function of the kidney as a whole in the control of plasma osmolarity and in conserving body water. We recall that the main solute of plasma is NaCl, and the main solute in the urine is urea; the role of the kidney in handling these solutes, and water itself, will be emphasized.

Figure 7.7 shows diagrammatically the percentage composition of protein-free

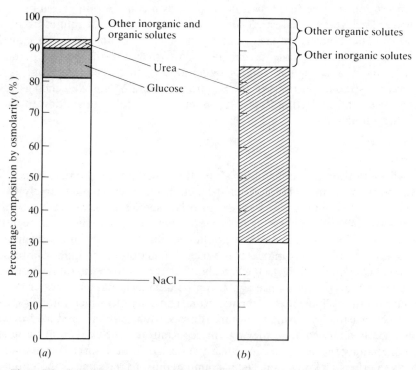

Figure 7.7 Comparison of percentage composition (in osmolarity of (*a*) glomerular filtrate and (*b*) urine. Urea (as percentage of solute) has increased and NaCl has diminished; glucose has been entirely reabsorbed.

plasma (glomerular filtrate), and of the urine of a 'typical' mammal, an adult human. It is the achievement of this difference of composition during passage along nephrons that must now be explained.

Control of osmolarity

Although it had been assumed for many years that the glomerulus and Bowman's capsule formed an ultrafiltration system at the closed end of each nephron, final proof came when micropuncture samples from Bowman's capsules and very early proximal tubule were found to have a composition almost identical with that of protein-free plasma. On entry into the PCT the fluid is subjected to sodium pumping which passes Na^+ ions from the lumen through the cells of the tubule walls and back into the blood flowing through the peritubule capillary network. Chloride ions move with the Na^+ by electrostatic attraction and water moves by osmosis. At the same time glucose undergoes active transport out of the lumen back into the blood; so too do all the amino acids present (in low concentration) in the glomerular filtrate. As in the alimentary canal the simultaneous pumping of Na^+ is necessary for glucose and amino-acid transport. The glucose reabsorption is so active and efficient that normally the entire filtered load of glucose has been removed back into the blood by the time the fluid has reached a point one-third of the way along the proximal tubule.

Water is removed isosmotically with the NaCl and other solutes, and the fluid in the lumen of the nephron is in osmotic equilibrium with the blood plasma in the surrounding peritubular capillaries. These capillaries are carrying blood which has just left the glomeruli, so its plasma protein concentration is slightly higher than that in the general circulation, because it has lost protein-free fluid into Bowman's capsule. The consequent raising of its oncotic pressure helps in the reabsorption of water from the tubular lumen. Loss of water from the tubular fluid will of course cause concentration of all remaining solutes including urea, uric acid and creatinine. This creates a concentration gradient for such solutes, a proportion of which pass back into the plasma by simple diffusion. Between one-third and one-half of the filtered load of urea, for instance, may have diffused back into the plasma by the end of the proximal tubule. (Urea, a very soluble and diffusible substance, is widely distributed in the body in both intracellular and extracellular fluids; it is completely non-toxic and its concentration is not controlled by the body.) Figure 7.8 illustrates the activity of proximal tubule cells.

By the end of the PCT, then, about 75 per cent of the filtered NaCl and water has been reabsorbed; so too have all the filtered glucose and amino acids, probably most of the filtered K^+, and bicarbonate $(HCO_3)'$, and some of the urea. The $(HCO_3)'$ ion itself does not pass through cell walls, and the mechanism of its reabsorption will be described later. The loss of the bicarbonate means that the tubular fluid has become slightly more acid. It started at Bowman's capsule at about pH 7.4, and may be pH 7.1 or 6.9 by the end of the proximal tubule. Though greatly reduced in volume, the fluid is still isosmotic with plasma, 300 mosm/l; and the main solutes still present are NaCl (say 250 mosm) and urea (say 50 mosm).

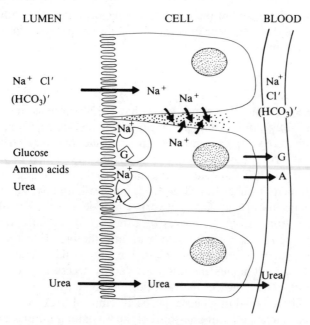

Figure 7.8 Some activities of cells of proximal tubule: absorption of ions and water; absorption of glucose (G) and amino acids (A) (carrier-assisted with Na$^+$ as symport); absorption of urea by diffusion. Long arrows denote diffusion; short arrows, active transport. All activites are present in all cells; they are shown in three different cells for clarity.

The tubular fluid now passes through the pars recta of the proximal tubule and thence to the descending limb of the loop of Henle. Some nephrons have long loops of Henle which run down to the innermost part of the renal medullary tissue (renal papilla); in other nephrons the loops are much shorter, running into the kidney no further than the outermost strip of the medulla. The proportions of long-looped and short-looped nephrons vary in different species of mammals: in most, including man, the short-looped type predominate. The function of the long loops of Henle will be described first (Fig. 7.9).

As already indicated (page 159), there is a gradation of tissue osmotic concentration from the cortex down through the medulla to its innermost tip, the papilla. The interstitial fluid at the papillary tip may be three or four times as concentrated as that in the outer cortex. If the cortical concentration is 300 mosm/l, there would thus be a gradual increase to 900 or 1200 mosm/l down the medulla to the papillary tip: a large deposit of solute in the water of the medullary interstitial fluid. This solute is not rapidly removed by the blood, because the blood itself flowing down into the medulla loses water by osmosis on the way down and regains it on the way back (see Fig. 7.9). The main blood vessels of the medulla, the vasa recta, have interconnecting capillary beds between their descending and ascending limbs. A large amount of water thus

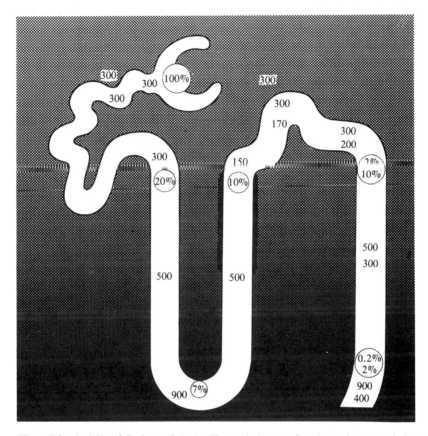

Figure 7.9 Activity of the loop of Henle. Figures in lumen of nephron show osmolarity (mosm/l) of the tubular fluid at that point. Figures in circles show the percentage of the filtered load of water which still remains, at that point. Where two figures appear one above the other, the upper one shows the condition in the normal or dehydrated animal, the lower one shows the condition during water diuresis. Note that until the middle of the DCT, conditions in the nephron are the same whether an animal is in the normal or the water-diuretic state. The darkness of the background indicates the osmolarity of the interstitium. Dark lines indicate thick section of ascending loop.

bypasses the innermost layers of the medulla, and in any case the medullary blood flow is only 1 or 2 per cent of the total renal blood flow, so interstitial solute once deposited is not quickly removed. This mechanism of the vasa recta is called countercurrent exchange.

The late proximal tubular fluid contains approximately 250 mosm/l NaCl and 50 mosm/l urea. It runs down the pars recta into the descending limb of Henle's loop, thus passing through a medium of increasing osmolar concentration. This portion of the loop is quite permeable to water, and much less permeable to NaCl and urea. The consequence is that the tubular fluid loses water by osmosis into the interstitium, and becomes concentrated, say threefold, from 300 to 900 mosm/l. (These are typical figures for a rat or dog.) There is little net gain or loss of solute, so that this threefold increase in concentration of tubular fluid has brought the NaCl level to 750 mosm/l and the urea to 150 mosm/l. However, the solute of the interstitial fluid of the innermost medullary region is about half NaCl and half urea—say, 450 mosm NaCl and 450 mosm urea, giving a total 900 mosm/l in osmotic equilibrium with the contents of the nephron at the hairpin bend at the base of the medulla (Fig. 7.9).

At this bend there is a sudden change in the permeability properties of the nephron wall. The wall, still extremely thin, made of flattened cells, is now permeable to NaCl, somewhat less permeable to urea, and much less permeable to water. There is a diffusion gradient of NaCl outwards from the tubular lumen (750 mosm/l) to the interstitium (450 mosm/l), and a gradient inwards for urea: 450 mosm/l in the interstitium, 150 mosm/l in the lumen. So in rising along Henle's loop through the inner medulla, the tubular fluid loses NaCl and gains urea, entirely by diffusion: there is no evidence of active NaCl transport, in the thin ascending limb. The fluid also regains some of the lost water. By the early distal tubule the net loss of filtered water is about 90 per cent, as compared with 75–80 per cent in the late proximal tubule.

At the thick-walled region of the ascending limb of the loop, there is yet another change in the properties of the wall. Here there is further removal of NaCl, this time by active transport out of the lumen. In fact the sodium pump of the thick ascending limb is extremely powerful; it works rapidly and is able to move Na^+ ions out of the lumen even against a considerable adverse gradient, and so to deposit yet more NaCl in the outer medullary interstitium.

The sodium pump mechanism in the thick ascending limb appears to be somewhat different from those found elsewhere, in, say, the proximal tubule and alimentary canal. Distinctive features are that:

1. The lumen in this region of the nephron is about 8 mV electro*positive* to interstitial fluid, in contrast to other regions of the nephron which are about 2 mV electro*negative*.
2. In the thick ascending limb, sodium pumping is sensitive to the precise level of K^+ present.

Furthermore some 40 per cent of Na^+ ions leaving the lumen here pass *between* not through the cells—the so-called 'paracellular shunt-path'; this movement is of course assisted by the favourable electrical gradient.

The consequence of the removal of NaCl in this region of low water permeability is that the tubular fluid has become hypotonic to the plasma and surrounding interstitial fluid. The thick ascending limb in fact is often referred to as the 'diluting segment' of the nephron. As it leaves Henle's loop and moves to the DCT in the renal cortex, the fluid is now, say, 150 mosm/l, as compared with 300 mosm/l in the plasma of the surrounding peritubular network. Furthermore a fairly large proportion (at least half) of the solute in the lumen is urea, which has been added to the tubular fluid by diffusion from the medullary interstitium.

In the case of the short loops of Henle, which do not reach the inner medulla, there is no thin ascending limb. The ascending limb is entirely of the thick-walled type, presumably actively pumping out NaCl, but water-impermeable, and therefore helping in diluting the tubular fluid, but with little opportunity of gaining urea from the interstitium.

The complicated arrangement of the flow through Henle's loop, in which the fluid becomes highly concentrated and is then diluted, finishing much more dilute than at its start, results in a deposition of solute through the medullary interstitium, gradually increasing down to the tip; and this build-up of interstitial concentration has a function at a subsequent stage of urine formation, in helping to abstract the final drops of water, minimizing water loss in urine.

The gradation of the concentration in the medulla means that the delicate thin walled cells of the loop are never required to tolerate a high concentration gradient, between lumen and interstitium. At each level the fluid within the lumen is close to osmotic equilibrium with that outside, and the actual movement of water or solute is quite small; but by a gradual build-up there is a three- or fourfold concentration difference between cortex and papillary tip, even sixfold in some mammals. The process is called countercurrent multiplication: a small gradient of osmolarity between lumen and interstitium at any one level is multiplied, in the achievement of a large gradient between the top of the loop and the hairpin bend.

By the early part of the distal tubule less than 10 per cent of the filtered load of water remains in the nephron, and the fluid is considerably hypotonic to the blood in the surrounding peritubular capillaries—say, 150 mosm/l. This situation is the same, whatever the osmotic state of the whole animal: that is, whether it is extremely dehydrated and thirsty, or whether it has just drunk a large volume of water. From this point onwards, however, the nephron functions differently according to the water balance of the whole body, as reflected in the precise osmolar concentration of the extracellular fluid. First we will describe the events when the extracellular fluid, and urine, are maximally concentrated, and urinary water loss is minimal; this is the normal state for most mammals.

The first step for the distal tubular fluid is removal of water by osmosis into the blood, so before the half-way point of the DCT is reached the distal fluid is again in osmotic equilibrium with peritubular-capillary blood, 300 mosm/l. Owing to the presence of vasopressin (antidiuretic hormone, ADH) continuously secreted from the posterior pituitary gland (pars nervosa) at the base of the brain, this part of the nephron is very water-permeable with no osmotic barrier to water movement. Thereafter there is active transport of sodium (as in the proximal tubule), together with isosmotic water removal. It seems that this part of the nephron is rather impermeable to urea and other organic solutes, which therefore become concentrated by the loss of water. Another sodium pump mechanism is also present: one which has the property of being stimulated by the circulating hormone aldosterone. This pump also has the property of exchanging intraluminal Na^+ for K^+ or H^+ ions from the circulating blood; so the tubular fluid, from which most of the filtered K^+ has been lost by re-absorption in the proximal tubule, may regain some of it in the distal tubule.

By the end of the distal tubule only 2 or 3 per cent of the filtered fluid still remains, and this contains little NaCl and a high concentration of urea. Active sodium pumping continues as the fluid runs down the cortical collecting tube, outer medullary collecting duct and finally the inner (papillary) collecting duct. This region is (in the presence of vasopressin) very water-permeable, and its highly concentrated interstitial fluid causes yet further osmotic removal of water, so the urine, as passed into the renal pelvis and ureter, has only about 0.5 per cent of its original filtered load of water.

The early parts of the collecting duct lying in the cortex and outer medulla are urea-impermeable. By contrast, the papillary collecting duct is permeable to urea, which (by water loss) has become highly concentrated in the lumen and diffuses out into the interstitium at this point, thus contributing to the high interstitial osmolarity at the papillary tip. (It is this high osmolarity which causes removal of water from the descending limb of Henle's loop, with consequent rise of NaCl level in the lumen, giving the outward diffusion gradient for NaCl in the thin ascending limb.) Some urea re-enters the lumen of Henle's loop, and recirculates through the distal tubule. Urea equilibrates across the wall of the papillary collecting duct, so urinary urea level is the same as that in the papillary interstitium. The final urine thus contains little of the filtered water, and NaCl; its main solute is urea, and the remaining solutes are other non-absorbed organic and inorganic compounds (creatinine, uric acid and ammonium salts, among others). In this way the urinary composition represented in Fig. 7.7 is finally attained.

The processes just described form the usual condition for most mammals most of the time. Animals do not normally drink more than the minimum; they drink only just enough to make good their inevitable water losses via the urine, faeces, lungs and skin. However, humans may frequently drink to excess, and in consequence may excrete more than the minimum volume water. The renal processing of an excessive water load will now be described.

If a human or other animal has just drunk a large volume of water, this is absorbed into the blood and slightly dilutes the plasma, altering its concentration from, say, 300 to 295 mOsm/l. This dilution is sensed by osmoreceptor cells (possibly in the hypothalamus), which thereby cause suppression of the secretion of vasopressin from the posterior pituitary gland. The lack of circulating vasopressin quickly reduces the water permeability of the DCT and collecting duct. So though the active transport of sodium still continues, water cannot rapidly follow solute movement, and much water remains in the tubular lumen. A large volume of dilute tubular fluid will flow rapidly through the collecting duct, there is no time for equilibration of urea at the papillary tip, and the recycling of urea will cease. In these conditions, too, the rate of blood flow through the vasa recta increases, so the osmotic gradient down through the medulla tends to disperse, as solute is carried away in the blood: instead of a threefold increase in solute interstitial osmolarity from cortex to papilla, there may now be only a twofold increase, or even less. Active sodium transport in the thick ascending limb can continue, with deposition of NaCl in the *outer* medulla, but the passive system for loss of NaCl from the thin ascending limb of the *inner* medulla would cease as there is now no means of concentrating descending-limb fluid. So at the final stage of water removal in the collecting duct, where urine equilibrates osmotically with the surrounding interstitium, the concentration attained would also be rather lower. In consequence in these conditions a large volume of fairly dilute urine is excreted. Indeed the urinary concentration may be even lower than that of blood plasma. In extreme conditions, after abundant water-drinking, tubular fluid passes so rapidly through the distal tubule and collecting duct that the dilute early-distal fluid is excreted almost unchanged. This would never happen in normal life but may occur in artificial or experimental conditions following a heavy water load.

We have described conditions at the two extremes. A raised plasma osmolarity in dehydration causes maximal vasopressin secretion and thus makes possible a steep cortico-medullary solute gradient and maximal water reabsorption; so a small volume of concentrated urine is produced, and much water is conserved. At the other extreme, dilution of plasma and extracellular fluid inhibits vasopressin output, the distal nephron becomes less permeable to water, and a large volume of dilute urine is passed. In both conditions plasma osmolarity will tend to be brought back to its normal level; though of course in severe dehydration even maximal water retention by the kidney may not achieve this normal level, and only the drinking of additional water will suffice. In normal life the extremes may never be encountered, but small hour-by-hour fluctuations of plasma osmolarity, associated with, say, mealtimes, sleep, and loss of fluid in sweat, may always occur. The brain osmoreceptors are extremely sensitive, responding to less than 5 mOsm/l fluctuation in total plasma osmolarity; and the pituitary–vasopressin secretory mechanism works rapidly. So the whole osmolar adjustment takes place within minutes—certainly in less than an hour. The vasopressin is quickly destroyed in the circulation; there is normally a low circulating level, which can be increased or decreased, according to signals from the osmo-receptors, and elsewhere.

Control of volume

The kidney, then, is able to make rapid responses to changes in the *osmolarity* of the blood, by altering the volume and concentration of the urine. It is much slower and less effective in making adjustments to changes in the total *volume* of extracellular fluid. Such changes in volume (without change in osmolarity) would rarely occur in normal life but are not infrequent in pathological conditions. In a severe hae-morrhage, for instance, there is a loss of circulating blood, and thus of both water and solute. In several diseases there is a symptom called oedema, in which there occurs excessive retention of fluid (water and solute) in interstitial spaces. Experimentally, the extracellular fluid can be increased by drinking physiological saline so that both water and salt enter the blood in proportions isosmotic with the plasma. Renal adjustments in such conditions are slow.

Excessive fluid volume

The renal processing of excessive fluid volume appears to be carried out as follows. Stretch receptors (volume receptors) in the walls of the atria, main veins near the heart, and probably elsewhere in the circulation, respond to stretching by sending more impulses up sensory nerves (including sensory fibres in the vagus, cranial X) which, via several interneurones, connect with nerve fibres of the posterior pituitary, and cause inhibition of vasopressin output. This lowering of circulating vasopressin results in less renal water reabsorption and thus a greater urinary output. It is difficult to work out the sensory paths of this reflex, partly because there seem to be numerous volume receptors in various parts of the circulation, and partly because the volume receptors seem to adapt quickly to increased stretch, and so stop responding. The renal effect is usually quite slow. It is well known that if a human drinks a litre of water, diluting the plasma, the extra fluid is lost from the body within an hour or two, whereas if he drinks a litre of saline, it may not be completely lost from the body for 24 hours; and in the meantime it reaches the interstitial fluid including that of the brain where the excess fluid may cause headache. However, the renal response to additional blood volume in the veins of the thoracic cavity may sometimes be quite rapid. Such an increase in thoracic blood volume occurs when a person lies down, and especially when he takes exercise, such as swimming, in a horizontal position. Here there is not an absolute increase in blood volume, but merely an alteration in its distribution; but the effect on the volume receptors of the thoracic cavity is the same. (One practical consequence is that on base-ships of naval or commercial scuba divers there are abundant facilities for excretion, as the divers have the need to urinate as soon as they come back on board.)

Since volume receptors are present only in walls of blood vessels, excess interstitial fluid (oedema) and excess intra-abdominal fluid (ascites) cannot be lost from the body until it has re-entered the vascular system, giving the volume receptors a chance to sense the excess. Returning interstitial fluid to the blood, or removing it by other means, often constitutes a serious medical problem.

Loss of blood volume

The converse state—a *diminution* of both water and solute—is a common pathological event. A sudden loss of blood volume, haemorrhage, is one of the most difficult conditions for the body to tolerate. The cardiovascular system itself makes adjustments—a widespread intense vasoconstriction of vessels in the skin and splanchnic area—which minimize further loss and move the remaining blood from the periphery towards the head and thorax. Urinary water loss is minimized by several mechanisms. If the haemorrhage is so severe as to cause a lowering of arterial pressure, there is so little glomerular blood flow that filtration into the nephron is small, most of the filtered fluid is reabsorbed by the proximal tubule, and the urine flow ceases. In any haemorrhage the kidney's vascular system participates in the general increase in sympathetic tone of the splanchnic area, so the blood flow in much of the renal cortex (and in consequence the glomerular filtration) is greatly reduced.

This reduction of renal blood flow is the stimulus for an interesting hormonal response. It causes the secretion from the kidney of a substance called renin, a protein of molecular weight 40 000. Renin acts as a proteolytic enzyme. On entering the general circulation it acts on a plasma protein (angiotensinogen), breaking off a decapeptide, angiotensin I, which on passing through the lungs is converted by another enzyme to an octapeptide, angiotensin II. Both angiotensins, particularly angiotensin II, have a powerful effect on vascular smooth muscle, constricting arterioles (and so helping in maintaining arterial pressure in haemorrhage). Angiotensin II also has an effect on the adrenal glands (one above each kidney), causing secretion of another hormone, aldosterone, from the adrenal cortex (zona glomerulosa). Aldosterone in turn affects the distal tubules of the kidney, stimulating sodium reabsorption, and consequently water reabsorption; so renal water and salt loss are minimized. The whole process takes some time; there may be as long as an hour between additional aldosterone secretion and additional salt and water retention; probably this is the time required for synthesis in distal tubule cells of additional enzyme molecules or sodium pumps. The long time-lag between the release of aldosterone and the renal response to it contrasts with the extremely rapid response of the kidney (within minutes) to vasopressin release. This difference helps to explain the different reactions of the human body to the drinking of a litre of water and a litre of saline.

There is some aldosterone present in the circulation all the time, maintaining distal sodium reabsorption; and there are probably other stimuli to aldosterone secretion besides the renin–angiotensin system. The source of renin within the kidney is the juxta-glomerular apparatus, a group of modified cells of the wall of the afferent arteriole taking blood to the glomerulus (Fig. 7.10).

It is likely that small amounts of renin, continuously entering the renal circulation, have a local effect at the afferent arteriole. In this case, it is suggested, the signal for

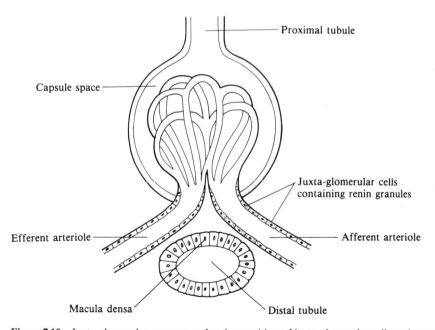

Figure 7.10 Juxta-glomerular apparatus, showing position of juxta-glomerular cells and macula densa.

renin secretion is the sodium load in the lumen of the early distal tubule, the outer wall of which is close to the glomerulus of the same nephron. If the sodium load increases (say, by increased flow rate through the proximal tubule giving inadequate time for proximal sodium pumping), renin emerges from the juxta-glomerular cells, enters the afferent arteriole, and forms angiotensins I and II, which cause a local arteriolar constriction, lowering filtration rate at that particular nephron, and thus reducing proximal tubule flow rate. This may be the basis for the phenomenon of glomerulotu-bular balance, the process by which filtration through each glomerulus remains more or less appropriate to the sodium-reabsorbing capacity of its own proximal tubule. For the kidney as a whole, GFR and renal plasma flow remain remarkably steady. In the normal adult human, for instance, sleeping and waking, during mealtimes and fasting, year after year, GFR from the two kidneys is about 125 ml/min. Deliberate ingestion of excessive amounts of salt can raise GFR, and of course a severe fall in arterial pressure would lower it. But in man in normal life a steady level of GFR prevails.

In addition to aldosterone there may be another endocrine factor influencing renal sodium excretion. This is the atrial natriuretic factor (ANF), derived from the myocardial cells in the walls of the atrial chambers of the heart. The factor is always present in the circulation in low concentration, and increased amounts appear in the plasma in response to a rise of the central vascular volume: that is, when there is additional blood in thoracic blood vessels and consequent stretch of atrial walls. The effect of ANF on the kidney is to increase the excretion of sodium and water, thus lowering the blood volume. The factor can be extracted from the atrial walls; the active principle has a slightly different chemical form in different species, but all forms are polypeptides. The human ANF is a polypeptide of 28 amino acids. The mode of action of ANF within the kidney is still under investigation. It appears to inhibit both the increased distal reabsorption of sodium caused by aldosterone, and the increased water retention in collecting ducts brought about by vasopressin; and it may have other effects in the nephron. In some species, and in isolated kidneys, ANF also increases GFR by dilating the afferent arterioles. The precise physiological role of ANF in the normal animal has still to be elucidated. It may well be one of the causes of the large urinary fluid loss following underwater swimming.

The kidney as an excretory organ

The valuable and necessary components of the ultrafiltrate formed in Bowman's capsule—water, Na^+, Cl', $(HCO_3)'$, glucose and amino acids—are reabsorbed, and excretion consists largely in the failure to reabsorb waste products of metabolism. This passive handling, an absence of reabsorption either actively or by diffusion, is true for excretion of such waste products as uric acid, creatinine, other organic acids and inactivated hormones. It is also true for a proportion of the urea; between 40 and 80 per cent of the filtered urea is present in the urine, depending on urinary flow rate: the faster the flow rate, the higher is the percentage of filtered urea excreted, as there is such a small time for diffusion back into the peritubular blood.

There are in addition a few substances which are added to the filtrate through the walls of the nephron as the fluid passes along. Hydrogen and K^+ ions are handled in this way, the amounts being dependent on their concentrations in the plasma of the peritubular blood. A few substances which do not normally occur in the body are actively excreted by the cells of the tubule. Phenol Red and p-amino-hippuric acid (PAH) are such substances; so is the iodine-containing radio-opaque substance diodrast, used clinically to show up the kidney's vascular system. p-Amino-hippuric acid is removed by the kidney quickly, both by filtration and by active secretion from the blood into the tubular lumen. This means that in an adult human an injected load of PAH is completely removed in one circulation of blood through the kidney; thus, blood emerging along the renal vein contains little or none. It seems remarkable that the tubule cells contain active pumping mechanisms for the removal of substances which the body would never normally encounter.

The kidney as an endocrine organ

As already explained, the kidney secretes renin, which, by causing formation of angiotensins I and II, affects blood vessels (constricting arterioles) and the adrenal cortex (causing aldosterone secretion). This could be considered an endocrine function: the production of a substance which via the circulating blood affects another body organ.

The kidney has a further endocrine function which has nothing to do with its role in maintaining plasma concentration and volume. The kidney secretes into the blood a hormone called erythropoietin, a glycoprotein of molecular weight 34 000, which circulates to the bone marrow and there stimulates production and maturation of red cells (erythrocytes), helping incorporation of iron into the haemoglobin. Erythropoietin seems to be produced by tubular cells throughout the length of the nephrons: phosphate-buffer extracts of either the cortex or medulla of the kidney contain the material, which can then be assayed by measurement of rate of incorporation of iron into cultures of marrow cells.

There are small amounts of erythropoietin always present in the circulation. The amount is increased in any condition which lowers the rate of delivery of oxygen to the kidney. If, for example, a human or other mammal experiences a low Po_2 (say at high altitude where barometric pressure is low), the kidney rapidly produces more erythropoietin, red-cell manufacture is quickened, and additional red cells enter the circulating blood within a few days. The same process occurs in anaemia, when the haemoglobin is fully saturated but because there are too few red cells the rate of delivery of oxygen is reduced; again, erythropoietin production is stimulated, though the hormone may not be successful in restoring cell numbers, if there is a deficiency in the marrow cells themselves. Conversely, exposure to increased atmospheric Po_2, or transfusion of excess cells into a normal animal, suppresses the level of circulating erythropoietin.

In the mature mammalian fetus, erythropoietin level and red-cell count is higher than in the adult. The fetus normally experiences some degree of hypoxia: its blood is not exposed to as high a P_{O_2} as that in the lung alveoli of the adult, and fetal haemoglobin is not fully saturated. Presumably this mild hypoxia stimulates erythropoietin production in fetal kidneys and this in turn increases red-cell production in the highly active fetal marrow. At birth the fetal blood becomes exposed for the first time to atmospheric P_{O_2} in the lungs. Within about 4 days its erythropoietin level has dropped, and in a week or two the red-cell count of the newborn creature has fallen, to approach that of the adult: in man about 5×10^6 cells/mm^3, instead of the 7×10^6 cells/mm^3 appropriate to late-fetal life. In the normal healthy human (unless he exposes himself to hypoxia by climbing a mountain above 2000 m) a steady small erythropoietin production and stable red-cell count will continue throughout life.

Summary and problems

This chapter has described the several fluid compartments of the body and the movements of solute and water between them. Movement of water can occur only by gradients of hydrostatic or osmotic pressure; the osmotic gradients are set up mainly by active pumping of sodium, and also by exclusion of plasma proteins at certain membrane barriers.

The main work of the kidney consists in maintaining plasma osmolarity and volume by reabsorbing the greater part of the protein-free filtrate of plasma formed by indiscriminate ultrafiltration at the glomerulus. During movement of filtrate along the nephrons metabolic wastes fail to be reabsorbed, and are thus removed in the urine. A few substances if present in excess in the blood are added to the filtrate through the walls of the nephrons. Such excretory products may include H^+ ions, and an important function of the kidney is participation in the control of plasma pH (Chapter 8). The later stages of the reabsorption in nephrons are alterable according to the current state of the body's water and salt balance. The appropriate stimuli reach the kidney via blood-borne hormones: vasopressin from the posterior pituitary and aldosterone from the adrenal cortex, and perhaps also a natriuretic factor.

Finally, an account has been given of the role of the kidney in maintaining red-cell manufacture in the bone marrow by the renal production of the hormone erythropoietin. It is interesting that the same organ of the body not only exerts a tight control over the composition of the fluid part of the blood, but also helps in the manufacture of its main cellular component, the erythrocytes.

Many aspects of the study of water balance and renal physiology have been omitted from this account. The renal blood supply, for instance, has hardly been mentioned. Autoregulation of the blood flow is of some physiological importance; this is the process by which the blood flow remains at a fairly steady level despite fluctuations in general arterial pressure; and this constancy in turn contributes to the steady rate of glomerular filtration. As to hormonal control of kidney function, no account has been given of the working of vasopressin at the cellular level, or of its possible effect on blood flow in the vasa recta; nor of other possible stimuli to aldosterone secretion such as depletion of body sodium, or lack of stretch at the vascular stretch receptors.

Again, no indication has been given of the important differences in kidney function between various species of animals—a fascinating aspect of comparative physiology.

Even for the topics covered, however, the perceptive reader will have noticed serious gaps in the accounts in this chapter. How much additional water is reabsorbed by the aldosterone-stimulated sodium pumping? Can this water really make any appreciable difference to the vascular volume after a haemorrhage? Is there any structural correlation with the abrupt change in permeability properties at the hairpin bend in the long loops of Henle? What is the signal to the kidney to increase output of erythropoietin? How could such a signal be sensed both in anaemia with normal Po_2 and in hypoxia with normal red-cell count? These are a few of the problems now under or awaiting investigation. The omissions in this chapter are due to lack of knowledge as well as to limitation of space.

The following chapter describes the process of maintenance of plasma pH—a process in which the kidney is only one of the several organs involved. Renal mechanisms are virtually the only means (apart from thirst and salt-appetite) by which extracellular osmolarity and total sodium level are controlled. In contrast, extracellular pH is controlled by the cooperation of two or three different organs of the body, as well as by the buffers of the plasma itself.

8 Control of the pH of plasma

Introduction

The pH of the extracellular fluid is one of the most tightly controlled of its chemical properties. Even though large quantities of H^+ ions in the form of digestion products and metabolites are entering or leaving the blood each day at irregular intervals, the plasma (of man) varies only between about pH 7.38 and 7.41. Intracellular pH is slightly lower (more acid) and varies in different tissues; in an actively working muscle cell it may be as low as pH 6.9.

The control of the pH of the extracellular fluid is carried out by several processes. One process is physicochemical: the working of the several buffer systems present in the plasma and red cells of the blood. The others are physiological or biochemical, and depend on negative feedback; that is, a drift away from the 'controlled' or 'optimum' pH sets in train a series of processes or reactions that will result in the bringing back of the pH towards its optimum. These processes take place mainly in the lungs and kidneys, and perhaps also in the liver.

Buffer systems

Buffer systems consist of two components in aqueous solution: a weak acid, and the salt formed from that acid with a strong base. (A few buffer systems are weak bases plus the salt of the base with a strong acid, but few such systems occur in animals.) Buffer systems have the effect of stabilizing the pH of a solution by mopping up or releasing H^+ ions. Since a buffer system always has two components, it is better to use the term 'buffer system', or 'buffer pair', than simply 'buffer'.

In the plasma the buffer systems are:

1. carbonic acid/sodium bicarbonate;
2. sodium dihydrogen phosphate/disodium hydrogen phosphate;
3. plasma proteins and their sodium salts.

The proteins, at the pH of the blood, are far above their isoelectric point and act as H^+ ion (or proton) donors; thus they can be considered as weak acids. These buffer systems are often abbreviated:

1. $H_2CO_3/(HCO_3)'$;
2. $(H_2PO_4)'/(HPO_4)''$;
3. HPr/Pr'.

Similar buffer systems are present in the red cell; in this case the salts are of potassium rather than sodium; and the protein buffer system is haemoglobin and its salt, HHb/KHb.

Most readers will be familiar with the theory and the practical use of buffer solutions. Such readers are reminded that:

1 Buffer systems can work to stabilize pH (for acids gained or lost by the solution) ONLY if that acid is a stronger acid than that of the buffer system itself. It is thus impossible for, say, the carbonic acid/bicarbonate system, $H_2CO_3/NaHCO_3$, to buffer additions or losses of carbonic acid itself.
2. A buffer system functions best close to the pH of half-titration, that is, close to the point where [acid component] = [salt component]; or, to put it another way, close to the pK of the buffer system.

Of the three buffer systems present in the plasma (protein, phosphate and bicarbonate), the one present in the largest amount is the bicarbonate system.

In the blood with a pH of 7.4 this system is very far on the alkaline side of its pK, which is 6.1; and the sodium bicarbonate/carbonic acid ratio in the plasma is 20:1. The phosphate system has a pK of 6.8, not very far from neutrality, and any addition of acid to the plasma will bring the phosphate system slightly closer to its pK, and thus to its most efficient region. The pK of the deoxyhaemoglobin system is 7.3, and 7.2 for oxyhaemoglobin.

The bicarbonate system cannot of course act as a buffer for its own acid component, carbonic acid, produced continuously from the carbon dioxide of metabolic oxidation. Nor is it working close to its pK, at the pH of the plasma. It is present in large concentration, however, and is in fact the main determinant of plasma pH; the abundance of the bicarbonate system, together with the fact that its acid component is volatile, not fixed, gives this system a key role in the control of plasma pH. As stated above, the two components of the bicarbonate buffer system, salt/acid, are present in the ratio 20:1, at pH 7.4:

$$pH = pK + \log 20/1 = 6.1 + 1.301 = 7.401$$

So long as the ratio remains at 20:1, the plasma remains at pH 7.4. The two (or possibly three) physiological mechanisms maintaining plasma pH work on one or other of the two components of this buffer system and have the effect of maintaining the 20:1 ratio. These mechanisms are associated with:

1. respiration;
2. renal excretion;
3. liver metabolism.

Control by respiration

Brain cells on the inner surface of the brain close to the respiratory centre in the brain stem are very sensitive to the partial pressure of carbon dioxide, P_{CO_2}, and pH of the plasma of arterial blood reaching the brain, or, more properly, to the P_{CO_2} and pH of the cerebrospinal fluid within the cerebral ventricles, which normally follow plasma P_{CO_2} and pH (see Chapter 6). If any factor raises arterial carbonic acid relative to bicarbonate (or, as usually expressed, raises the P_{CO_2} of arterial blood, to which the level of carbonic acid is directly related), these brain cells (central chemoreceptors) send signals to the respiratory centre, and respiration increases in both depth and rate. This has the effect of blowing off additional carbon dioxide from the alveolar air in the lungs. The P_{CO_2} of arterial blood, which equilibrates with alveolar air during the passage of blood through the lung capillaries, is thus reduced. This feedback process brings back to normal the arterial carbonic acid, and as a result the carbonic acid/bicarbonate ratio, and hence the arterial pH. The system is very sensitive. Alveolar and arterial P_{CO_2} are normally 40 mmHg, but if for any reason they go up to 40.5 mmHg, the effect on respiration is enormous.

The converse effect would occur if for any reason arterial sodium bicarbonate increases. The equilibrium has now moved in the other direction and the arterial pH has very slightly increased (become more alkaline). This suppresses the activity of the respiratory centre, the person or animal breathes *less* frequently, so carbon dioxide is retained in the lungs and builds up its level in alveolar air. The arterial blood then equilibrates with this higher P_{CO_2}, and so the buffer-pair ratio is brought back to 20:1 and the pH comes back to normal.

The conditions described above represent a respiratory acidosis and alkalosis, respectively. No acid or base other than the two components of the bicarbonate buffer system is involved. By this means a mild and scarcely perceptible degree of adjustment of the respiratory rhythm is probably going on all the time in daily life. The various regions of the lung are not uniformly ventilated, and additional carbon dioxide could build up in certain regions, and cause a slight increase in arterial P_{CO_2}. It may be observed for instance that the steady rhythm of the respiratory movements of a cat curled up asleep is interrupted at intervals by a much deeper breath followed by a few quick breaths, before the steady rhythm returns. A more dramatic and pathological instance of respiratory acidosis is seen in the condition of pneumonia, in which fluid accumulates in the lung and acts as a barrier to diffusion of carbon dioxide from blood to alveolus. Too little of the carbon dioxide can then diffuse from venous blood out into the lungs and too much therefore remains in the arterial blood leaving the heart. This high arterial P_{CO_2} stimulates the respiratory centre, and patients with pneumonia nearly always breathe quickly and deeply. This stimulated respiration may lower alveolar carbon dioxide and thus make the diffusion gradient from blood to alveolus as steep as possible. But the effect is rarely sufficient to bring down arterial P_{CO_2}, and so plasma pH is not restored until the diffusion path is shortened by cure of the lung disorder.

Notice that it is the P_{CO_2} of *arterial* blood which provides the stimulus to the central chemoreceptors. The raised arterial P_{CO_2} also stimulates three peripheral chemoreceptors, the pair of carotid bodies and the aortic body, which lie close to the main arteries. These receptors also stimulate the respiratory centre, via sensory nerves (the glossopharyngeal nerve (cranial IX), from the carotid bodies; and the vagus nerve (cranial X), from the aortic body). These peripheral chemoreceptors are more sensitive to lowered P_{O_2} than to raised P_{CO_2}, though the raised P_{CO_2} may have the effect of increasing the sensitivity of the bodies to lowered oxygen level.

Figure 8.1a shows the normal ionic composition of plasma. There are about 150 mmol each of cations and anions, the cations being almost entirely Na$^+$, and the anions being made up of about two-thirds Cl$'$ ions and one-third (HCO$_3$)$'$ plus protein

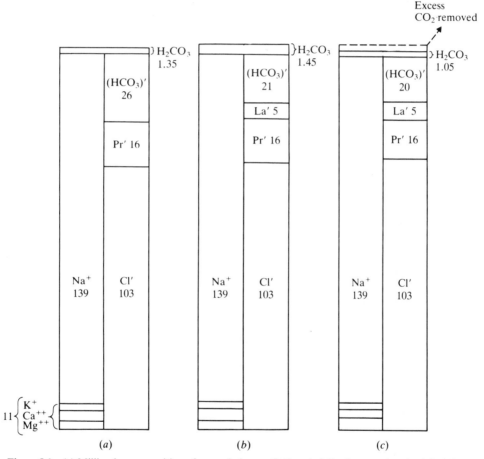

Figure 8.1 (a) Millimolar composition of normal plasma. Cations in left column, anions in right column; undissociated carbonic acid across both columns. Pr$'$: protein anions. (b) conditions after entry of lactate, buffered by the bicarbonate system: carbonic acid has increased, bicarbonate has decreased. La$'$: lactate anions. (c) Condition when hyperventilation (overbreathing) has removed excess carbon dioxide. The bicarbonate/carbonic acid ratio is again 20:1.

anions. The carbonic acid is un-ionized. From Fig. 8.1*a* it is apparent that the ratio of bicarbonate to carbonic acid is 26:1.35 or about 20:1, so the pH of the system is 7.4.

During the course of the numerous normal cellular reactions which make up the metabolism of the body, many compounds are added to the blood. These may include acids and bases. Lactic and pyruvic acids for example can pour into the blood from actively working muscles. The bicarbonate system immediately buffers them, producing the equivalent amount of, say, sodium lactate, and additional carbonic acid:

$$HLa + NaHCO_3 = NaLa + H_2CO_3$$

This brings the ionic composition to the state indicated by Fig. 8.1*b*: slightly less bicarbonate, slightly more carbonic acid. This state is sensed by the central chemoreceptors, breathing is stimulated, additional carbon dioxide is removed from the body at the alveolar surface and the 20:1 ratio is restored as seen in Fig. 8.1*c*, but with both components of the bicarbonate buffer system now at a slightly lower absolute concentration. In the converse situation of addition of metabolic base, the plasma bicarbonate would be increased relative to the carbonic acid, the respiratory centre's activity lessened, breathing reduced and carbon dioxide retained in the body, again bringing back the bicarbonate/carbonic acid ratio to 20:1. This situation is rare for normal humans in daily life; but the addition of metabolic acid is an everyday occurrence.

The cations equivalent to the total bicarbonate plus ionized protein are sometimes called 'buffer base' or 'alkali reserve'. The greater the addition of metabolic acids into the blood, the more buffer base will be used up, and the more vigorous will have to become the overbreathing, if the 20:1 ratio is to be preserved.

In certain diseases where large quantities of acids (or bases) enter the blood, the condition is called metabolic acidosis (or alkalosis). An example of metabolic acidosis is seen in the disease diabetes mellitus in which an intense fatty-acid metabolism leads to a pouring into the blood of aceto-acetic and β-hydroxybutyric acids. Metabolic alkalosis occurs pathologically after prolonged vomiting with consequent loss of gastric HCl from the body. The stomach is generating HCl from the breakdown of NaCl and of carbonic acid:

$$H_2CO_3 = H^+ + (HCO_3)'$$

and the body is left with an excess of sodium bicarbonate. The body responds by overbreathing in severe diabetes mellitus, and underbreathing in prolonged vomiting. The other mechanisms of pH control (renal and perhaps liver responses) also come into action.

Control by renal excretion

The negative feedback by which raised P_{CO_2} in arterial blood stimulates (and a raised plasma bicarbonate reduces) respiration functions very rapidly (within seconds or minutes), and stabilizes plasma pH at 7.4. However, respiratory mechanisms cannot remove base or H^+ ions from the body altogether. In the long term, excesses of metabolic acids or bases are handled by renal excretion. In man the normal mixed diet produces a small excess of acidic endproducts and the urine is slightly acid. In strict vegetarians and in herbivorous animals the diet generates more base than acid and the urine is slightly alkaline.

Bicarbonate reabsorption mechanism

At the glomerulus of the mammalian nephron all plasma components other than protein are filtered and enter the proximal tubule; this of course includes the $(HCO_3)'$ ions. It is found that by the end of the proximal tubule about 90 per cent of the filtered bicarbonate has left the filtrate. The $(HCO_3)'$ ions do not themselves cross the luminal border of the proximal tubule cell; the process of bicarbonate disappearance works as follows.

Carbon dioxide is being produced constantly in the metabolism of the tubule cell as in most cells of the body, and in the tubule cell it is rapidly hydrated by the carbonic anhydrase present in such cells:

$$CO_2 + H_2O = H_2CO_3 = H^+ + (HCO_3)'$$

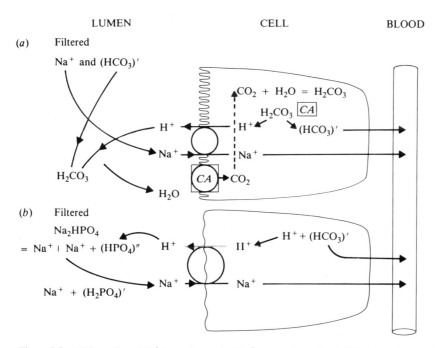

Figure 8.2 (a) Secretion of H^+ in exchange for Na^+ and reabsorption of bicarbonate in proximal tubule cell. CA: carbonic anhydrase. (b) Further reabsorption of bicarbonate, and formation of acid phosphate in lumen of distal tubule. Both processes take place in both convoluted tubules, but the phosphate mechanism predominates in the distal tubule because at this point most of the bicarbonate has already been removed from the tubular lumen.

The H^+ ion thus formed is quickly removed across the luminal border by exchange with an Na^+ ion taken into the cell. The Na^+ ion is delivered by active transport into the peritubular blood, along with the $(HCO_3)'$ ion formed as a product of the carbonic anhydrase reaction. The H^+ ion, entering the tubule lumen, meets the filtered $(HCO_3)'$ ion and with it forms carbonic acid, H_2CO_3 (Fig. 8.2a).

Carbonic anhydrase in the brush-border of the tubule catalyses dehydration of the carbonic acid to carbon dioxide and water. The carbon dioxide diffuses back into the cell and can start the process again, providing more H^+ in the cell to exchange with Na^+ as the Na^+ is absorbed. The result is that bicarbonate, with sodium, enters the bloodstream, but it is not identical with the filtered bicarbonate. However, the amount entering the blood is equivalent to the number of H^+ ions entering the tubule lumen from the cell. Thus the body secretes H^+ ions and salvages its 'buffer base'. The rate-limiting step appears to be the $Na^+ \rightleftharpoons H^+$ exchange at the luminal border.

If the carbonic anhydrase is inhibited (a process occurring as a side-effect of treatment with certain drugs), these processes cannot occur quickly enough. The consequence is that H^+ ions accumulate in the body, and the filtered bicarbonate cannot be salvaged and appears in the urine.

The consequences of the normal working of these processes is that by the end of the proximal tubule the luminal bicarbonate has fallen from 27 mmol in the filtrate to 10 mmol, and the pH has fallen from 7.4 to about 6.9. Since about 75 per cent of the volume of the filtrate has been reabsorbed at this point, it is calculated that the equivalent of 90 per cent of the filtered bicarbonate has left the filtrate.

Phosphate system

In the distal tubule this process of bicarbonate reabsorption and H^+ ion excretion continues. However, since most of the bicarbonate in the tubular fluid has been removed, the ability of the other filtered buffer pair—the phosphate system—to accept H^+ ions becomes relatively more important (Fig. 8.2b).

In this case the $Na^+ \rightleftharpoons H^+$ exchange at the luminal border results in a conversion in the tubule of $(HPO_4)''$ to $(H_2PO_4)'$, i.e. a conversion of the filtered alkaline phosphate into acid phosphate. But again, sodium bicarbonate enters the peritubular blood in an amount equivalent to the numer of H^+ ions removed; and the urine contains a larger amount of the acid phosphate than was present in the glomerular fitrate. A smaller buffering capacity is presented to the distal than to the proximal tubule because of the proximal reabsorption of most of the filtered sodium bicarbonate; so fewer H^+ ions can be secreted in this region. The processes continue in the collecting duct. This part of the nephron is able to secrete H^+ ions (in exchange for Na^+ ions) against a much steeper gradient than is possible in other parts of the nephron. When the urine has reached its maximal acidity of pH 4.5, the gradient is 1000:1. But this is rarely seen on a normal mixed diet; a urinary pH of 5.5 to 6.5 would be more usual.

The ability of the kidney to secrete more H^+ ions in mild acidosis, and thus to retain more bicarbonate, shows its responsiveness to the Pco_2 level in the peritubular blood. The excess Pco_2 of plasma and peritubular cells would provide more carbonic acid formation and consequently make more H^+ available for exchange with Na^+ in the lumen; more sodium bicarbonate is reabsorbed and the mild acidosis is corrected. In mild alkalosis there will be a slightly greater concentration of $(HCO_3)'$ ions in glomerular filtrate. Thus there will be insufficient secreted H^+ ions to combine with all the $(HCO_3)'$ ions and some sodium bicarbonate will appear in the urine. Similarly, for the phosphate buffer system, in mild alkalosis the urine will contain rather more of the alkaline phosphate Na_2HPO_4 and less of the acid phosphate NaH_2PO_4. Thus, in day-to-day living, there are fluctuations in urinary pH, related to mealtimes, type of food, overnight starvation, and so on. But the fluctuations in plasma pH, which must act as the signal for the renal cells, are so small as to be almost unmeasurable—so rapid is the greater or less H^+ loss in the urine, and the greater or less bicarbonate formation by the kidney.

Two points should be noticed in connection with this mechanism. One is that an alkalosis, if severe or prolonged, causes a drain on the body's sodium, as there is a urinary loss of both sodium bicarbonate and disodium hydrogen phosphate. This has the practical consequence that in the alkalosis associated with prolonged vomiting, the kidney cannot correct the condition unless additional sodium is given, as NaCl; and this must be given intravenously, because in such a state the alimentary canal is unable to absorb it. Another point is that in the distal tubule there is competition between H^+ and K^+ ions for exchange with sodium, during sodium reabsorption. So in any condition in which there is a simultaneous excess, or deficiency, of H^+ and K^+ ions in the blood, the kidney has difficulty in handling pH control. This would not happen in day-to-day living but does occasionally happen in pathological conditions.

Role of ammonium

A third process by which the kidney disposes of metabolic H^+ and sends $(HCO_3)'$ ions into the blood is by way of ammonium ions, $(NH_4)^+$ (Fig. 8.3). During

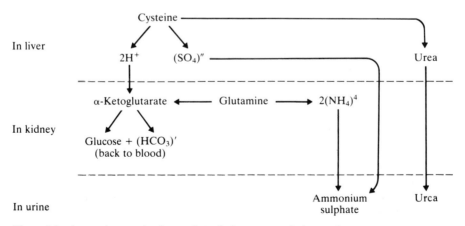

Figure 8.3 Ammonium mechanism and renal gluconeogenesis (see text).

breakdown of sulphur-containing amino acids, such as cysteine, the liver, besides forming urea, forms sulphuric acid, $2H^+$ and $(SO_4)''$. The plasma gains H^+ and $(SO_4)''$ ions in the process. In the kidney the H^+ ions combine with α-ketoglutarate, formed by deamination of the amino acid glutamine in the tubule cells, a process catalysed by the enzyme glutaminase. The products of the reaction are glucose and $(HCO_3)'$ ions, both substances being returned to the blood. (This process is called renal gluconeogenesis.) The $(NH_4)^+$ ions liberated by glutamine deamination form ammonium sulphate with the $(SO_4)''$ ions from the cysteine, and these ions are excreted in the urine.

This mechanism probably occurs to some extent all the time, but is greatly enhanced in conditions of acidosis. In fact if plasma H^+ increases, over a period of days the amount of renal glutaminase increases by a process of enzyme induction. This has the effect of making more α-ketoglutarate available for gluconeogenesis; thus more bicarbonate will be made simultaneously, and the 'buffer base' of the blood will increase; and incidentally large quantities of $(NH_4)^+$ ion come out in the urine. Indeed the urine of people in this state may smell of ammonia, so great is the concentration of ammonium salts present.

Liver metabolism

A neutral amino acid such as alanine, oxidatively deaminated in the liver, might be expected to form ammonia (NH_3), carbon dioxide and water:

$$CH_3NH_2CHCOOH + 3O_2 = NH_3 + 3CO_2 + 2H_2O$$

$$CO_2 + H_2O \rightarrow H_2CO_3 \rightarrow H^+ + (HCO_3)'$$

$$NH_4^+$$

$$urea$$

The carbon dioxide and water immediately form carbonic acid, and thence H^+ and $(HCO_3)'$ ions. But very little gaseous ammonia can exist at the pH of the cell; it at once takes up a proton to form ammonium ion, $(NH_4)^+$. So the products of the reaction are bicarbonate and ammonium, which indirectly, via the urea cycle, form urea:

$$2(NH_4)^+ + 2(HCO_3)' = (NH_2)_2C{=}O + 3H_2O + CO_2$$
$$(\text{urea})$$

$$or\ H_2CO_3 + 2H_2O$$

(So from every *pair* of equivalents of $(NH_4)^+$ and $(HCO_3)'$ the liver disposes of *both* $(NH_4)^+$ and *one* $(HCO_3)'$ ion by urea synthesis and the remaining $(HCO_3)'$ as carbonic acid.)

There is some evidence that if extracellular (and intracellular) pH is raised (i.e.

plasma is more alkaline), and thus bicarbonate is in excess, urea synthesis is increased, disposing of the surplus. If pH is lowered, urea synthesis is decreased; oxidative deamination continues as before and the $(NH_4)^+$ ion, instead of forming urea, is now disposed of by synthesis of glutamine (in the liver), with glutamic acid:

$$COOH \cdot C_2H_4 \cdot CH \cdot NH_2 \cdot COOH + NH_3 =$$
$$CONH_2 \cdot C_2H_4 \cdot CHNH_2 \cdot COOH + H_2O$$

An $(HCO_3)'$ ion is thus spared, and is added to the body's 'buffer base'. So the liver is able to switch from one synthetic process to another, according to the extracellular pH, thus disposing of more or less bicarbonate by means of more or less urea synthesis. The liver could therefore be included, with the lung and the kidney, among the organs controlling plasma pH.

The processes described above certainly occur, and are sensitive to extracellular pH in isolated liver cells and in perfused mammalian liver. It is still an open question how much those processes function in the control of pH in response to the small day-to-day fluctuations of plasma pH and bicarbonate/carbonic acid ratio.

The liver is the primary organ along the route of entry, at irregular intervals, of digested foodstuffs from the small intestine via the portal blood. One might speculate that the liver is thus well placed to act as a 'coarse-adjustment' mechanism of systemic plasma pH, whereas the renal and respiratory mechanisms might provide the 'fine adjustment'. Evidence is needed from whole-body experiments, in addition to those from isolated liver cells and the perfused organ, before such a role for the liver can be established.

Summary

The tight control of the pH of extracellular fluid is brought about by the buffer systems, physicochemical devices; by the physiological mechanism of respiratory adjustments consequent on central chemoreceptor response to small changes in P_{CO_2} of cerebrospinal fluid, either stimulating or depressing respiratory rhythm; by the mass-action effect of H^+ ions (or $(HCO_3)'$ ions) on enzymes of kidney tub   lls (and possibly liver cells); and (in chronic acidosis) by the interesting biologica of enzyme induction, generating more of one of the renal enzymes involved. physicochemical and biological processes make a contribution to the system continuously at work in the body.

9 Conduction in nerve fibres

Introduction

The nervous system and the endocrine system both play a part in coordinating the functions of a number of other organs of the body. This coordination allows some degree of ordering among the many claims on the body's energy and materials. It also allows the body to respond appropriately to events, conditions and changes in the outside world. By the endocrine system, chemical substances are carried round the body in the bloodstream from their site of production to their sites of reception; the system conveys materials (as a postal system does). The nervous system, on the other hand, conveys not materials but coded information, more like a telephone network. This chapter is concerned with the process of conduction along the peripheral nerves—the 'wires' of the nervous system. Events at the ends of the wires (neuromuscular junction, sensory endings and central nervous system) will be described in Chapters 11, 12 and 13.

Nerve cells (and muscles also) make use of the electrical charge on their cell membrane—a charge which, as explained in Chapter 3, is present on all cell membranes. Although it has been known for many years that activity in nerve fibres (nerve impulses) involves an electrical change, the precise way in which the impulse is generated and conducted could not be worked out in detail until fibres could be studied in isolation, out of the animal and cut from their own cell body. Most nerves in vertebrate animals are myelinated (see Chapter 2 under Nervous system). The thick myelin sheath of Schwann cells makes their axons less accessible to study, and also creates a process of impulse conduction peculiar to this type of nerve. Unmyelinated axons do occur in vertebrates, but they are extremely thin and fragile, and difficult to isolate. In the invertebrate species unmyelinated nerves are robust, and exist in a wide range of diameters.

One such unmyelinated nerve, the giant axon running in the mantle of the squid *Loligo*, has proved very convenient for the study of chemical and electrical events during conduction of impulses on nerves in general. Such an axon, cut from its cell body and lying in a dish of aerated sea water, can be made to conduct impulses for many hours. Its large size, nearly 1 mm in diameter, makes possible the insertion of electrical leads into the cytoplasm, the tip of the lead being arranged so that its does not touch the inner surface of the axon membrane. If this lead is connected through a sensitive voltmeter with another lead lying outside the axon in the sea water, a voltage of about $-70\,\text{mV}$ (the membrane potential) is recorded.

Subthreshold and action potentials

If the nerve axon is stimulated in some way—say by a slight tap or pinch, or a drop of some chemical, or a brief electrical pulse—a small electric change occurs in the membrane potential, and would be recorded on the voltmeter. The membrane potential moves from -70 mV to about -60 mV, and then returns to its resting level of -70 mV. This would occur only quite close to the spot on the axon where the stimulus was given. This small potential change (called a subthreshold change) is just detectable a short distance from the point of stimulation, but it dies away in both directions along the nerve and might be undetectable 5 mm away (Fig. 9.1a).

If the nerve axon is now given a more vigorous stimulus—mechanical, chemical or electrical—a different electrical response of the membrane is detected. The potential goes from -70 mV to about -50 mV, then suddenly changes, to zero, then to about $+30$ mV (that is, the inside of the membrane becomes electropositive). Then the

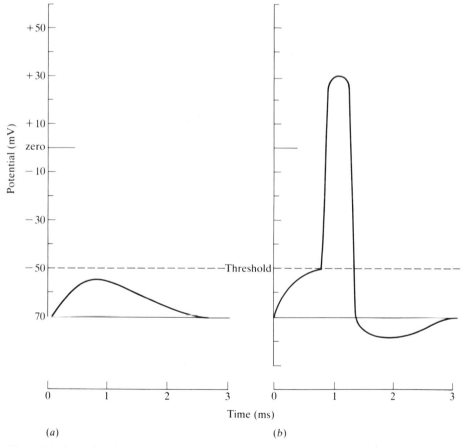

Figure 9.1 Potentials in unmyelinated nerve axon. (*a*) Subthreshold potential. (*b*) Action potential. Resting membrane potential is -70 mV and the threshold, shown by dotted line, is -50 mV.

potential rapidly returns back to -70 mV. It may show a brief 'after-potential' to -75 mV before coming back to its resting potential (Fig. 9.1b). This series of changes, called the 'action potential', is very rapid. At any one point on the membrane it would be completed in 10–20 ms, so a very rapidly reacting voltmeter, such as a cathode-ray oscilloscope, would be needed for recording it.

These potential changes are interpreted as follows. The resting membrane potential, E_m, about 70 mV, is close to the equilibrium potential, ε_K, of the K$^+$ ion, -75 mV, potassium being the ion to which the resting membrane is most permeable (see Chapter 3 under Maintenance of cellular volume). The subthreshold stimulus causes a slight rearrangement of the membrane proteins or their surface charges and consequently slight changes in the ionic permeability of the membrane. A few extra Na$^+$ ions enter, making the interior slightly more electropositive; but this change in membrane potential itself decreases sodium permeability ('inactivation of sodium current'), and is immediately followed by an increase in potassium permeability which brings back the membrane potential towards ε_K and so restores the resting potential, E_m ('rectification'). The whole system quickly restores itself to its original state by a small additional Na$^+ \rightleftharpoons$ K$^+$ interchange.

If the stimulus is large enough, it will cause a much greater disturbance in the surface membrane, leading to a change of, say, 20 mV less negative inside. This point is called the threshold. A 'large enough' stimulus means not only a certain voltage change in the membrane potential—20 mV in this example—but also a certain *rate* of change to this new voltage. If the rate of change is too slow, rectification predominates, and a much greater voltage change must be attained to reach threshold. When the threshold is reached there is a sudden alteration of the permeability properties of the membrane (possibly a massive rearrangement of surface charge). The membrane becomes for a moment very permeable to Na$^+$ ions, or, as some physiologists say, the 'sodium gates open'. This, as shown in Fig. 9.1b, depolarizes and then reverses the membrane potential as it approaches the equilibrium potential of the Na$^+$ ion, ε_{Na}, $+55$ mV (see Chapter 3). Furthermore this increased permeability has allowed Na$^+$ ions to enter the axon, and these cations, as carriers of positive charge, also make the interior less electronegative or more electropositive, shifting the potential in the same direction as that caused by the original stimulus. So the upshoot phase of the action potential is a self-reinforcing process. Long before the tip of the action-potential spike is reached, however, the sodium permeability starts to decline ('sodium gates shut') and potassium permeability has by this time become very high. When the potential spike has reached, say, $+30$ mV, the increased potassium permeability swings the membrane potential back towards the K$^+$ equilibrium potential ('rectification'); and the 'after-potential' sometimes observed shows that the membrane may actually reach ε_K transiently, before coming back to its resting level.

The action potential described above would have a voltage of -70 to $+30$ $= 100$ mV, from the resting potential to the top of the spike. The voltage of an action potential is a characteristic property of each particular axon. A mixed nerve bundle containing numerous axons might include some axons having 30-mV action potentials and some having 110-mV action potentials, and any intermediate voltage.

The size (voltage) of the action potential is in no way related to the strength of the stimulus which initiated it. The strength of the stimulus determines whether the action potential is initiated at all: that is, whether the membrane potential reaches its threshold. But once initiated, the action potential is necessarily of the voltage appropriate to that particular axon. The stimulus applied for a particular axon will either initiate an action potential or will fail to do so, and any increase of stimulus strength beyond the threshold point will have no effect on the voltage of the action potential. This fact has been called the 'All-or-none Law'.

Propagation of the nerve impulse: local circuits

The electrical changes are initiated at a particular point on the axon, the point of stimulation. From this point the action potential is conducted by a system of local circuits, starting at the stimulus point and affecting each part of the axon membrane in turn. In the experiment shown diagrammatically in Fig. 9.2 the axon is stimulated in the middle, and the effect spreads in both directions. This generation of local circuits can be explained as follows:

For a moment during the formation of the action-potential spike at the point of stimulus, the membrane must be zero potential—that is, there is no charge across it. The adjacent unstimulated parts of the membrane still carry their normal resting charge: positive outside, negative inside. So a small electrical circuit will be set up, and a current will flow, outside the axon, from unstimulated (positive) to stimulated (zero), and inside the axon from stimulated (zero) to unstimulated (negative) (Fig. 9.2). This current will itself act as the stimulus for the next adjacent portions of the membrane, shifting their voltages from resting to threshold. Thus in these places, in turn, an action potential is generated and sodium permeability rises. So the process continues, each part of the membrane in turn undergoing the brief permeability changes and reversal of the sign of its potential, and acting as the stimulus for the next adjacent part. These chemical and electrical events, invading each part of the nerve fibres in turn, constitute the nerve impulse. In the body, of course, the nerve impulse is initiated close to one end of the fibre, either at the cell body or at a sensory ending, and is conducted to the other end.

The action potential spreads an electrical effect a short distance 'ahead of itself' along the axon, a condition called 'local excitatory state' or 'local reponse potential'.

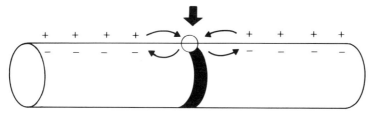

Figure 9.2 Local circuits in unmyelinated axon. Point of stimulation, thick arrow; direction of current flow in local circuits, thin arrows.

Indeed the very first part of the rising phase of the action potential as recorded at any point on an axon is due to this local excitation; and the increased sodium permeability, giving the main spike of the action potential, occurs a fraction of a millisecond later, at that point.

For a few milliseconds after passing an impulse the nerve axon is refractory; that is, it cannot be made to conduct ('absolutely refractory') or, if it can be made to respond at all, a much greater stimulus than usual is required ('relatively refractory'). In the body, as already indicated, nerves receive their stimuli close to one end of an axon or fibre, and the impulse is conducted from that point to the other end. The impulse cannot travel 'backwards' or re-excite a part of the axon through which it has just come, because that part of the axon would be refractory. As already mentioned, the voltage of an action potential is characteristic for different nerve axons. So too is the maximum frequency with which a train of impulses could follow each other in any one axon: the frequency would be determined by the refractory period of that axon.

The central nervous system (CNS) is able to interpret information about the outside world or about parts of the body, according to:

1. which nerve or group of nerves is bringing in impulses
2. how many nerves
3. with what frequency.

In general the more intense the stimulus, or the more rapid its rate of change, the greater the number of nerves involved, and the greater is the frequency with which impulses travel along each nerve.

The explanation of the conduction of an impulse in terms of local circuits was confirmed by an ingenious experiment. It was found that the resistance of the medium in which an axon is lying is an important factor in the speed of impulse conduction. If this medium is a good electrical conductor—for instance sea water, plasma or Ringer solution—the speed is rapid. If the nerve lies in olive oil, a poor electrical conductor, with only a thin film of sea water against the axon surface, the speed is low. Conversely, if an extremely good conductor such as a series of small silver plates is placed against the outer surface of the axon in which the normal (sea water) velocity of impulse conduction has been measured, the velocity is found to be even greater than normal. If impulse conduction had been simply a matter of the membrane itself and the axoplasm, the conductivity of the outside medium would not have mattered; the same speed would have been attained, whatever the outside medium (Hodgkin, 1939).

Ionic currents

A totally different type of current, not to be confused with local circuits, will now be described. This is an ionic current. Ionic currents accompany nerve action potentials; they are formed and carried by a stream of ions all of the same sign, and all moving simultaneously in the same direction. It was mentioned that during the formation of the spike of the action potential the membrane transiently becomes very permeable to sodium, and a few Na^+ ions (of which the external concentration is always higher than the internal) will therefore stream into the axon across the membrane (entering through the 'sodium gates', as the phrase goes). This increase in sodium permeability is very short-lived: the 'sodium gates' shut again rapidly. But meanwhile, the already high potassium permeability of the membrane has been increasing further, and reaches its maximum as the sodium permeability is declining. So now, with the 'potassium gates' wide open, K^+ ions stream out of the axon. During the action potential, therefore, we would expect to find two ionic currents; positive inward at first, followed by positive outward; and these minute currents can indeed be detected. After the passage of an action potential the normal $Na^+ \rightleftharpoons K^+$ exchange pump, the work rate of which is sensitive to internal sodium, does a small amount of extra work pumping back the Na^+ and K^+ ions.

The number of ions moving during one action potential is too small to allow detection by any chemical procedure, and in any case a mere chemical analysis of the axon, say, before and after impulse conduction, would not indicate at what stage during the action potential the ionic fluxes are occurring. The ionic currents caused by streams of ions passing in and out of the membrane have, however, been detected and measured, by a device called a voltage clamp. The electrical events of the action potential and impulse conduction are extremely rapid, the whole process being completed in about 30 ms, and the resting membrane potential is restored. The voltage clamp is a device for fixing the membrane potential at a certain voltage determined by the observer, and holding it there for as long as the observer wishes. (The mechanism is described in Appendix 7.) By this means the observer can fix the membrane potential at, say, the threshold voltage, at which in an *un*clamped axon the action potential would be initiated. In the clamped axon all the molecular and chemical rearrangements of surface proteins and ionic fluxes which normally occur at the threshold voltage continue unaffected, and their electrical consequences can be recorded. So with the help of fast-reacting recording equipment, it is possible to record the events which normally accompany the start of an action potential—the ionic fluxes across the membrane. Again, the membrane can be voltage-clamped at, say, the equilibrium potential of the Na^+ ion, $+55$ mV. In this condition there would be no electrochemical gradient for movement of sodium; even though the sodium 'gates' are open, no net sodium movement occurs and the corresponding ionic current is eliminated. Examples of the kind of records obtainable by the voltage clamp in a squid axon are shown in Fig. 9.3.

Using this apparatus the following facts have been found:

1. The inward stream of Na^+ ions occurs first, lasts no longer than 1 ms, and is brought to an abrupt stop ('sodium gates shut').
2. The outward movement of K^+ ions starts after about 1 ms or less from the time of the stimulus, and the start of K^+ ion movement may overlap with the end of the Na^+ ion movement.
3. The size (in μA) of the two currents can be measured; and since the voltage is also known (being pre-set by the observer), a calculation is possible by Ohm's Law of the resistance of the membrane to the two ionic currents. (In fact physiologists

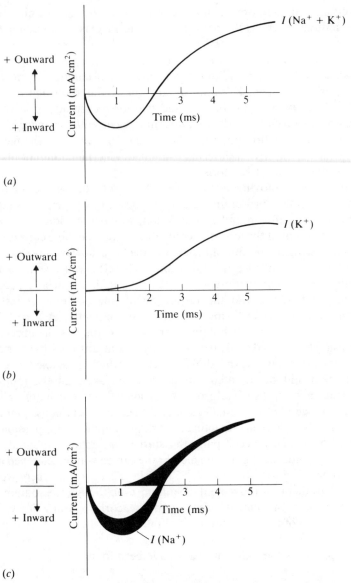

Figure 9.3 Ionic currents (I) during voltage clamping of an unmyelinated axon. Voltage is set at threshold for this axon, about 20 mV more positive than resting membrane potential. (*a*) In normal sea water. Current flows (positive inwards) for about 1 ms, then reverses direction and flows (positive outwards) for as long as the voltage clamping is maintained. (*b*) In sodium-free water (NaCl replaced by choline chloride). Initial inward-positive phase of current flow disappears, and the outward-positive flow starts after about 1 ms. This shows that the initial ionic current is associated with a cation (Na^+) moving inwards, not an anion moving outwards. Use of a specific blocker of K^+ ion channels (tetraethyl ammonium) has given evidence of the association of the positive-outward current with K^+ movement, though there may be inward Cl' movement also. There is an overlap in the period from 1 to 2 ms from the application of the clamp when the two cations are moving in opposite directions; K^+ flux starts before Na^+ flux has finished. (*c*) Na^+ current calculated by subtraction of the K^+ current as observed in (*b*) during this period from the total current observed in (*a*).

often calculate the *reciprocal* of the resistances, i.e. the conductances, abbreviated g_{Na} and g_K.)

4. By measuring ionic sodium current (about 500 $\mu A/m^2$) and the time for which it flows (2 ms or so) it is possible to calculate how many coulombs of electric charge have entered the membrane during the brief surge of increased sodium permeability. The charge on 1 mole of monovalent ion, F, is 96 500 coulombs, so it is possible to calculate the number of moles of Na^+ entering at one nerve impulse. Corresponding calculations can be made for the number of moles of K^+ leaving the axon. There is an entry of 3 to 4×10^{-12} moles Na^+ per cm^2 of surface per impulse, and a loss of the same amount of K^+. These minute gains and losses to and from the axoplasm would be quickly restored by a small amount of extra work done by the $Na \rightleftharpoons K$ exchange pump.

Once again it must be emphasized that these ionic currents, the direction of which is only into and out of the membrane along its entire length (in unmyelinated nerves), are totally different from the local circuits by which impulses travel. In the local circuits there are no streams of ions simultaneously moving in one direction. In the voltage-clamp experiments there is of course no nerve impulse, and no local circuits. The whole purpose of the voltage clamp is to eliminate these events so that the ionic currents which normally accompany an action potential are the only events observed.

Myelinated nerves and saltatory conduction

As mentioned earlier, most nerve axons of vertebrates have a thick myelin sheath consisting of tightly wrapped layers of Schwann-cell membrane, with nodes of Ranvier between the cells. At the nodes the axon comes into close contact with extracellular fluid, separated from it only by the thin neurilemma. In myelinated nerves, as in unmyelinated ones, conduction of the impulse occurs by local circuits. Ingenious experiments were carried out to determine whether the 'external' part of such local circuits is set up in the very narrow space outside the axon membrane but inside the myelin (Schwann-cell) sheath, or whether the currents flow right outside the myelin sheath. It was found that the local circuit goes outside the myelin sheath, and in fact it goes in at one node of Ranvier and out at the next; then this node excites the next adjacent one, creating another local circuit, and so on (Huxley & Stämpfli, 1949). Since the impulse jumps from node to node, this type of transmission is called saltatory conduction (L. *saltare*: to jump). It is likely that the depolarizing, the reverse polarity, and sodium and potassium fluxes, occur only at the nodes, not along the whole internodal length. There must be part of the local circuit flowing within the axoplasm along the internode, but this does not disrupt the potential of this segment of the membrane (Fig. 9.4).

It has been suggested that restricting the ionic fluxes and the changes of membrane potential to these very short regions of axon, just at the nodes, is an energy-saving device: very few additional Na^+ ions would enter through this restricted area, so little work would have to be done in expelling the extra sodium. It has not yet been shown,

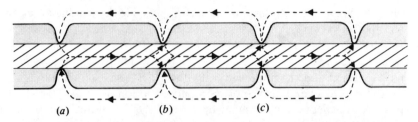

Figure 9.4 Saltatory conduction in myelinated nerve. An action potential at node (a) generates a local circuit through the axoplasm and interstitial fluid, and this depolarizes node (b) to its threshold. This in turn generates a local circuit in the (b)–(c) internode, and so on. Axoplasm, shaded; myelin, stippled.

however, that myelinated nerves really do have a lower energy requirement for conduction than unmyelinated ones.

If saltatory conduction is to work efficiently, there must be an optimum internodal length. If the second node is too far away from the first, the resistance of the axoplasm along the internodal stretch of the axon would be so great that the effect of depolarization and excitation at the first node would be attenuated before the second node is reached, so the second node cannot be brought to its threshold. If the second node is too close to the first, effort will be wasted: local circuits which would be permitted by axoplasmic resistance to make jumps of, say, 1 mm between nodes are forced to make an unnecessary number of jumps if the nodes are only 0.7 mm apart, and conduction will be slower than it need be. It turns out that the optimum internodal length, which is found in many species of adult vertebrates, is about 1.1 mm.

In a young animal the myelin is not fully developed and the nodes are closer. In fact as an animal grows and its nerves lengthen the number of Schwann cells and nodes does not increase; the growth is a matter of elongating the internodal length. But conduction velocity does not increase with age. So it seems likely that in the young animal, the nodes may be so close that not every node is depolarized during saltatory conduction. The local circuits might skip over one or two nodes, and depolarize, say, every fourth node along the axon.

Velocity of conduction, myelination and diameter

For myelinated nerves every local circuit must pass along a certain (internodal) length of axoplasm, and out through a node, and through a length of extracellular fluid. It is easy to understand that for myelinated nerves the velocity of impulse conduction is proportional to the length of each internodal jump. The main delay in setting up each local circuit is due to the electrical resistance at the node, a resistance which is greater than either the axoplasmic or the external resistance. The fewer the nodes in a given length of nerve (i.e. the greater the length of each internode), the longer the jumps, and the faster the impulse will be conducted. It happens that for myelinated nerves internodal length is proportional to total external diameter, inclusive of myelin sheath;

so for such nerves velocity of conduction is proportional to external diameter: the thicker the nerve, the faster it conducts. For most such nerves, also, the ratio of axon diameter to total diameter is fairly uniform (close to 0.6), so velocity must be linearly related to axon diameter.

For non-myelinated nerves the velocity is proportional, not to diameter, but to the square root of the diameter. The consequence of this difference in the relationship of speed of impulses to diameter of fibre in the two types of axons is that very thin nerves conduct with greater velocity if non-myelinated. Figure 9.5, a plot of velocity against diameter, illustrates this point. In the figure, line *a*, showing the square-root relationship, is seen to rise quickly at the origin but the slope of the line soon decreases compared with that of line *b*, showing the linear relationship. It is observed that, in the mammalian body, nerves of diameter less than 1 μm are indeed non-myelinated. These fine nerves are mainly (sensory) slow-pain fibres and (efferent) postganglionic autonomic fibres. A note on conduction velocity in unmyelinated nerves is given in Appendix 8.

The most rapidly conducting mammalian fibres are about 20 μm in diameter and conduct at 120 m/s; the slowest are about 0.5 μm and conduct at about 0.5 m/s. So there is considerable variation in speed, within one type of animal. One may ask how this wide range of velocity comes about. It might have been expected that speedy reaction to external stimuli would be of so great a selective advantage that all peripheral nerves would conduct at uniform high speed; the wide range of speed seems surprising. But it may simply be a matter of available space in the CNS. A mixed nerve containing hundreds of sensory and motor axons would have to be so thick and bulky if all the axons had a diameter appropriate to maximum conduction velocity that sheer limitation of space might dictate the need for some thinner (and therefore slower) axons.

Much of the activity of the nervous system involves sensory–motor arcs. Information about the external world or about the body's own internal condition

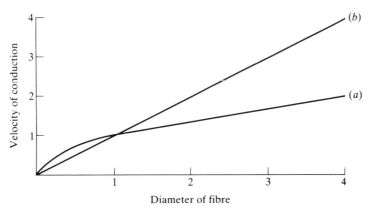

Figure 9.5 Conduction velocity. (*a*) Unmyelinated nerve axons. (*b*) Myelinated nerve axons. For (*a*), velocity = k$\sqrt{D}$, and for (*b*), velocity = kD, where D = axon diameter and k is a constant. (Arbitrary units.)

enters the system via a sensory nerve, usually through a sense organ. The information is conveyed by nerve impulses to the CNS, that is, to some part of the brain or spinal cord. From the CNS, impulses are sent down motor nerves to muscles (or glands), which then respond by contraction (or secretion).

The main part of the time between stimulus and response is spent in the CNS, among the dozens of interneurones and synapses where one cell impinges on another and transmitters are released. It is the CNS that has to sort out all the information coming in continuously from hundreds of sensory axons before the appropriate response can be made; and the time required for this ('central delay time') is much greater than the time of transmission of the impulse along a peripheral sensory or motor nerve, and therefore conduction time in axons is not so important.

A myelinated nerve of diameter, say, 9 μm would carry impulses three times as fast as a myelinated nerve of diameter 3 μm. But in the space occupied by the cross-sectional area of the 9 μm axon, nine axons of 3 μm diameter could be packed (Fig. 9.6). If these are sensory nerves, the number of possible patterns of activity received by the CNS, according to whether one or another of these nine axons is firing or not firing, would be more than 500. So from these axons the CNS could receive a large amount of information. Thus at a small sacrifice of speed the extra informational

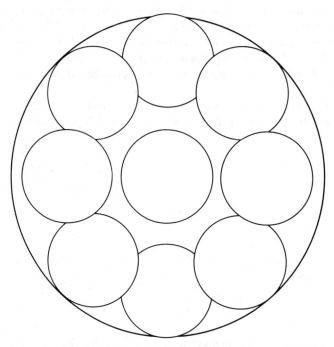

Figure 9.6 Packing of nerve fibres in cross-sectional area of limited diameter. Nine fibres of 3 μm diameter could occupy approximately the same space as one fibre of 9 μm diameter; the group of nine fibres could convey more information than the single fibre, though at a slower speed.

content achieved by having nine axons in the place of one is enormous; and since the central delay time is so long anyway, the reduced velocity of the sensory input is of little importance. This point was well expressed by Rushton:

> The consideration then simply of economy would suggest that large fibres should supply monosynaptic reflexes and other responses involving rapid reaction with little analysis of input. On the other hand, where the response depends upon a more exact appreciation of the sensory pattern, great speed is in any case impossible owing to the central delay, so it would be more economical to increase the detail of the sensory picture by multiplying the number of fibres at the expense of a small increase in conduction time.
>
> (Rushton, 1951)

A 'nerve' seen in the body by the naked eye is (as indicated in Chapter 2) a mixed bundle of fibres, large and small, myelinated and non-myelinated, afferent and efferent, conveying impulses, at velocities determined by their structure, in one direction or the other. Such a nerve may be artificially stimulated near its root at the spinal cord, by a stimulus large enough to be above threshold for all the fibres within it; and the consequent action potentials can be recorded in leads placed close to the endings of the fibres, at a distance from the spinal cord. (Some of these action potentials, those in the afferent nerves, would of course be conducted antidromically in this experiment—that is, in the direction opposite to that in normal life.) Action potentials recorded in this way are splayed out, arriving in bunches or groups with gaps between the groups. This suggests that there is not a uniform or random variation of possible velocities of conduction. There is a limited number of possible velocities, and all fibres belong to one or other of these velocity groups. This point is further discussed in Chapter 13.

Capacitance and gating currents

Two other electrical phenomena of axon membranes, capacitance currents and gating currents, should be mentioned. They are detectable at the moment when an action potential is initiated, but only with difficulty, because they tend to be masked by the much larger ionic currents that immediately follow them. The capacitance current (positive inward) is a simple physical effect. The membrane can be regarded as a small capacitor—two surfaces carrying positive and negative charges separated by a dielectric—which releases its stored charge at the moment when the surfaces are connected, that is, at the start of the action potential; and this capacitance current is detected as predicted. In fact a major cause of the refractory period after each action potential is the time required for recharging the membrane capacitance.

Of more physiological interest are the gating currents (also called asymmetric displacement currents). A gating current is a very small positive-*outward* current just before the moment of take-off of the action potential. It is thought to be associated with the rearrangement of surface charges on protein molecules which allows sodium 'gates' to open, with consequent influx of Na^+ ions. At the end of the action potential there is a small positive-*inward* current, interpreted as a closing of the sodium 'gates'. Gating currents are now subject to intense study in the hope of gaining understanding of the process by which Na^+ ions cross the membrane. It is possible, for instance, to block Na^+ ion channels by a specific poison, tetrodotoxin, without blocking the gating current; but another substance, gluteraldehyde, which is known to form cross-bridges in protein molecules, does block gating currents. The nerve axon, and also the muscle fibre—another excitable cell with variable sodium permeability—are contributing in this way to the study of a fundamental aspect of the properties of biological membranes.

Movement of material along axons

It is only in the cell body that the constituents of the cell can be synthesized, though certain substances can be recycled at the nerve endings. Portions of cell membrane and transmitter molecules used at the axon terminal in the stimulation of the receptor surface can be taken back into the nerve ending and used again. Some axons are very long; the length from the cell body in the spinal cord of a large mammal to the far end of its limbs would be a metre or more. A mechanism of transport from cell body to axon ending is clearly a necessity.

There is certainly a steady constant flow of axoplasm along the axon from the cell body. This can be shown by cutting an axon: at the cut the central end (the end nearer the cell body) oozes axoplasm, perhaps for hours; the peripheral end does not. Incidentally, when such a cut is made, the nearby Schwann cells change shape and start to multiply. The peripheral end of the axon degenerates. If the central and peripheral Schwann-cell sheaths are kept in alignment, the central end of the nerve will sprout and eventually regrow down its original route and may even remake its connection with the muscle or receptor surface.

However, the movement of material along axons does not depend simply on the bulk flow of the whole axoplasm. If this were the case, all substances would move along axons at the same rate, and in the same direction: cell body towards axon terminal. Ligatures can be tied around axons to reduce movement of chemicals without destroying axoplasmic continuity; and observations with such ligatures have shown that some substances move towards the cell body, not away from it. Furthermore mitochrondria seem to move in both directions, up and down the axon. Proteins, as shown by radioactive labelling, move along an axon at 400 mm per day, whereas the axoplasmic stream and probably the newly formed mitochondria move at only a few millimetres per day.

The mechanism of such movements is at present unknown. Microtubules and microfilaments as shown by electron microscopy in axons are probably concerned; the problem of axon transport awaits solution.

Summary and problems

Nerve fibres make use of the charge on the membrane to convey information from sensory endings to the CNS, from the CNS to effectors, and within the CNS itself. The information is encoded in the form of a series of electrical events: rapid depolarizing, reversal of charge and repolarizing of the membrane surface, the whole sequence comprising an action potential. The mechanism involves transient sequential ionic currents across the membrane, the surface being first depolarized, and then the membrane potential is restored. Each depolarized portion of membrane excites the next portion along the axon, so the action potential is conducted as a series of local circuits. The speed of conduction depends on the length of these local circuits along the axon. The thick sheath of myelinated nerves, interrupted at nodes of Ranvier, speeds conduction by limiting the transmembrane parts of local circuits to the position of the nodes. The information is sent to and from the CNS, which recognizes the origin and number of individual axons involved and the frequency of impulse transmission in each axon.

The precise nature of the changes in membrane structure which allow the transient sequential alterations in permeability and consequent ionic fluxes is a topic currently under investigation. Another problem awaiting solution is the mechanism underlying the movement of specific chemical substances and organelles in both directions along the length of the axon.

10 Autonomic nervous system

Introduction

The concept of an autonomic nervous system regulating and coordinating the functions of the internal organs was first introduced early in this century by Langley (1929), who was also responsible for the classification of the system into sympathetic and parasympathetic branches. The autonomic system controls the visceral efferents for circulation, respiration, metabolism, excretion, and heat and energy balance, as well as for reproduction. It supplies smooth and cardiac muscle and secreting glands. The autonomic nervous system as originally described was purely a motor system. Many still keep to this definition, but it is convenient to consider visceral afferents under this general heading and many descriptions of the autonomic nervous system include sensory as well as motor elements.

The pathway for the efferent outflow comprises two neurones (Fig. 10.1). The first

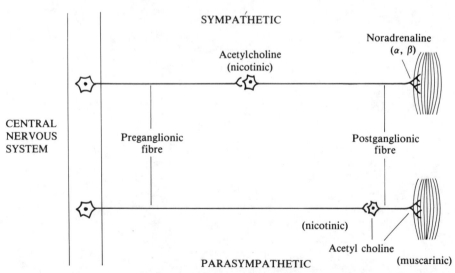

Figure 10.1 Arrangement of the preganglionic and postganglionic fibres of the autonomic nervous system and the neurotransmitters involved.

neurone runs from the central nervous system (CNS), from either the brain stem or the spinal cord, to an autonomic ganglion where it synapses with a second neurone which passes to the target organ. Because of its relationship to the synapse the first neurone is called the preganglionic fibre and the second the postganglionic fibre. Despite this basic similarity, the sympathetic and parasympathetic branches show many differences, namely in the origin of the preganglionic fibres, the position of the autonomic ganglia, the transmitter substances in the target organs and the effects they produce. Each visceral organ may receive either sympathetic or parasympathetic innervation, or both. In the latter case one is inhibitory, the other excitatory.

Peripheral autonomic system: anatomy

In mammals the cell bodies of the preganglionic *sympathetic* neurones are located in the thoracic and upper-lumbar spinal cord. The myelinated axons of these neurones leave the spinal cord in the ventral roots and pass via the white rami communicantes to the autonomic ganglia lying outside the CNS (Fig. 10.2). The sympathetic ganglia are segmentally arranged on both sides of the vertebral column and linked together in the form of a chain called the sympathetic trunk. Those fibres supplying the organs of the head and chest regions synapse in two or three cervical ganglia and in the upper-thoracic sympathetic-trunk ganglia. (In many species the inferior cervical and the first thoracic are fused to form a single large ganglion called the stellate ganglion.) In contrast, the fibres to the organs of the abdomen and pelvis pass through the ganglia of the sympathetic trunk and synapse in non-paired sympathetic plexuses.

The cell bodies of the preganglionic neurones of the peripheral *parasympathetic* nervous system are located in the sacral spinal cord, and in the brain stem (cranial outflow) (Fig. 10.3). The preganglionic parasympathetic fibres are for the most part unmyelinated and very long, because the parasympathetic ganglia are located in the vicinity of the effector organs. The postganglionic fibres are therefore very short in comparison with those of the sympathetic system. The parasympathetic axons to the thorax and abdomen run in the vagus nerve (cranial X), while fibres in the

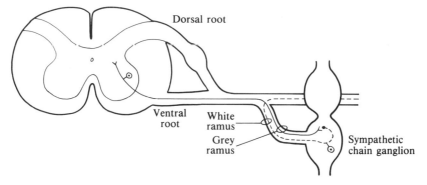

Figure 10.2   Motor pathways of the sympathetic nervous system, showing the location of the ganglia.

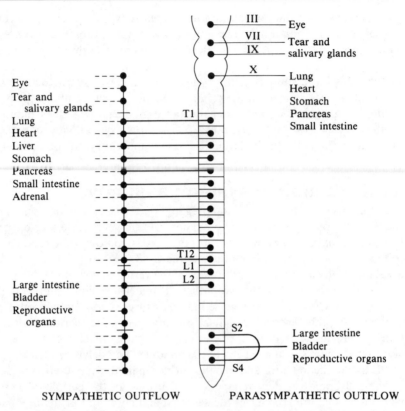

SYMPATHETIC OUTFLOW   PARASYMPATHETIC OUTFLOW

Figure 10.3 Automatic nervous system, showing on the left the sympathetic outflow and on the right the parasympathetic outflow.

oculomotor, trigeminal, facial and glossopharyngeal nerves (cranial III, V, VII and IX) run to the head. All the parsympathetically innervated organs such as the heart, lungs, gastrointestinal tract and bladder are also innervated by sympathetic fibres. The converse is not true; for example blood vessels, with a few possible exceptions, have only a sympathetic supply.

The gross anatomy of the autonomic nervous system is similar throughout the vertebrates. The parasympathetic widened its control during phylogenetic development through cranial expansion and sacral outflow in the land vertebrates. Addition to the cranial output accompanied the evolution of the digestive and respiratory systems. The sacral component seems to be related to the appearance of the cloacal bladder in amphibia and became expanded with the differentiation of the cloacal region into separate urinogenital and rectal passages as seen in land vertebrates.

In addition to these efferent pathways, some afferent pathways as already mentioned are considered to form part of the autonomic nervous system. These afferent fibres are structurally no different from the somatic afferents and may be grouped within the autonomic system simply because they carry impulses from the organs of the thorax and abdomen where most autonomic efferents end. These afferent pathways can arise from receptors in the viscera of the thorax, abdomen and pelvis, as well as in blood-vessel walls. These receptors respond to mechanical stimuli, indicating intramural pressure, as for example in arterial blood vessels, or degree of filling of the veins, intestine or bladder. They may also respond to chemical stimuli such as the partial pressure of oxygen (Po_2), pH and electrolyte content of the blood and also of the stomach. Finally, they detect noxious stimuli in the visceral organs. The visceral afferents like the somatic afferents enter the spinal cord in the dorsal root. A large number of afferents from the abdomen and thorax run in the vagus nerve (cranial X) directly to the brain stem.

Peripheral autonomic system: neurotransmitters and receptors

As indicated in Chapter 13, the transmission of impulses between two neurones or between a neurone and an effector usually involves a chemical mediator termed a 'transmitter'. This exerts its effect by binding with different kinds of receptors on the cell surface. As described in Chapter 14, receptor molecules are proteins or lipoproteins. Binding of the transmitter with the receptor alters the cell permeability or activates an enzyme.

Excitation is transmitted from the preganglionic to the postganglionic fibre in the ganglion via acetylcholine (Fig. 10.4). There are two well-characterized types of acetylcholine receptors, called muscarinic and nicotinic receptors. They are so named because the action of acetylcholine upon them may be mimicked by one of two potent alkaloids, either muscarine, which is obtained from toadstools, or nicotine, obtained from the tobacco plant. The receptors in all ganglia are nicotinic, whereas those in smooth muscle or glands are muscarinic.

Acetylcholine

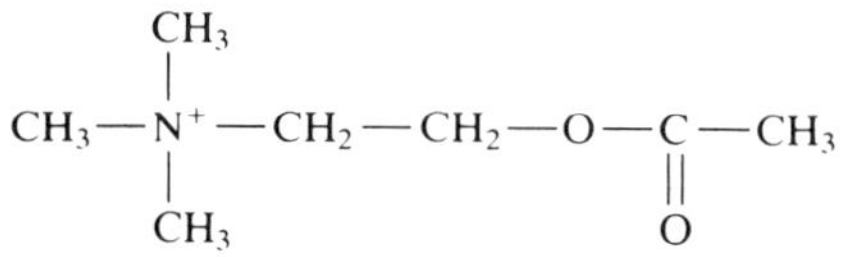

$$CH_3-\overset{\overset{\displaystyle CH_3}{|}}{\underset{\underset{\displaystyle CH_3}{|}}{N^+}}-CH_2-CH_2-O-\overset{\displaystyle C}{\underset{\displaystyle O}{\|}}-CH_3$$

Noradrenaline

$$HO-\langle\text{benzene ring}\rangle-CHOH\cdot CH_2NH_2$$

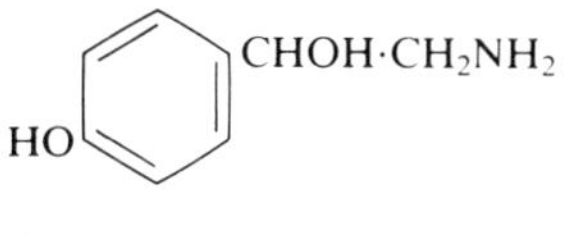

Figure 10.4 Structure of neurotransmitters in the autonomic nervous system.

The structure of the nicotinic receptor has been identified in fetal striated muscle. It is a protein with a molecular weight slightly in excess of 250 000 and composed of five subunits which extend through the cell membrane. They are arranged in an almost symmetrical manner to produce a channel which is wider at the outer face and narrows as it passes through the membrane. It is believed that when two acetylcholine molecules bind to the receptor there is a configurational change so that the channel is opened through the membrane and there is an increased influx of Na^+ ions. The muscarinic receptor is quite different; the receptor protein appears to pass through the cell membrane seven times, snaking back and forth. No acetylcholine circulates in the blood and the effects of cholinergic discharge are generally discrete and of short duration, because of the high concentration of acetylcholinesterase at the nerve endings. Blockade of the nicotinic receptor is possible with high doses of nicotine and with some quaternary ammonium compounds designated 'ganglion-blockers'.

Acetylcholine is also the transmitter at the postganglionic terminals of the parasympathetic system. In general terms this arm of the autonomic nervous system is concerned with the vegetative functions of the body. Thus cholinergic activity favours digestion and absorption of food, with increased activity of intestinal smooth muscle, increased gastric secretion and relaxation of the pyloric sphincter. Arrival of an impulse at the cholinergic terminal results in increased calcium influx and release of acetylcholine. This then diffuses across the synaptic cleft and reacts with the muscarinic receptors in the effector organ. The result may be depolarization, as seen in the gastrointestinal tract, or hyperpolarization, as seen in the heart. The acetylcholine then undergoes hydrolytic cleavage and is inactivated.

The effector response can be influenced by substances which affect the release of acetylcholine, its action with the receptor or its destruction by acetylcholinesterase. The nerve impulse may be blocked by local anaesthetics and tetrodotoxin and the subsequent entry of calcium into the presynaptic terminals by a number of agents including propranolol. Release of acetylcholine may be blocked by substances such as tetanus toxin, produced by the bacterium *Clostridium tetani*, and botulinus toxin, produced by *C. botulinum*, which is responsible for one type of food poisoning. There are some substances which can substitute for the natural transmitter. These are the direct parasympathomimetics and include carbachol and pilocarpine. The action of acetylcholine may be intensified through the inactivation of acetylcholinesterase by substances such as neostigmine and some organophosphates which are the chief ingredients of certain pesticides and nerve gases. Finally, there are a group of substances, including the alkaloids atropine and scopolamine, which possess a high affinity for the muscarinic receptors and displace acetylcholine without influencing the membrane potential. This form of antagonistic action is called competitive inhibition.

The sympathetic nerves discharge in concert in emergency situations, a phenomenon of considerable value. Heart rate is increased, there is vasoconstriction of skin vessels, raised blood glucose and dilation of the pupils. This is not, however, the sole function of the sympathetic fibres; for example the tonic discharge to the blood vessels maintains them partly constricted, thus maintaining blood pressure.

Transmission in the effector organ depends on the release of noradrenaline (Fig.

10.4) from the postganglionic fibre. Noradrenaline is synthesized in the sympathetic nerve endings from tyrosine. The first step is the hydroxylation of the tyrosine to form dopa and then decarboxylation follows with the formation of dopamine. This is taken up into the synaptic vesicles where a further hydroxylation occurs, with the formation of noradrenaline. Additional methylation of the hormone occurs in the chromaffin cell of the adrenal medulla through the action of N-methyltransferase, with the formation of adrenaline. This does not occur in the nerve terminals. On excitation of the postganglionic fibre, entry of Ca^{++} ions into the nerve ending triggers release of

Table 10.1 Autonomic effects on organs in mammals

Effector organ	Effect of sympathetic stimulation	Adrenergic receptor type	Effect of parasympathetic stimulation
Eye (pupil)	Dilated (dilator pupillae)	α	Contracted
Glands			
– Lacrimal			Secretion
– Salivary	Thick viscous secretion	α	Profuse watery secretion
	Amylase secretion	β_2	
– Nasopharyngeal			Secretion
– Bronchial			Stimulation
Skin			
– Blood vessels	Vasoconstriction	α	
	Vasodilatation	(cholinergic)	
– Sweat glands	Secretion	(cholinergic)	
– Piloerector muscles	Contraction	α	
Heart			
– Muscle	Increased rate	β_1	Decreased rate
	Increased force	β_1	Decreased contractility (atria only)
– Coronary vessels	Vasodilatation	β_2	Vasoconstriction
Lungs			
– Bronchi and bronchioles	Dilation	β_2	Constriction
– Blood vessels	Vasoconstriction	α	Vasodilatation
Systemic blood vessels			
– Visceral	Vasoconstriction	α	
– Muscle	Vasoconstriction	α	
	Vasodilatation	β_2	
	Vasodilatation	(cholinergic)	
Gastro-intestinal tract			
– Longitudinal and circular muscle	Decreased motility	α_1, β	Increased motility
– Sphincters	Contraction	α	Relaxation
Urinary bladder			
– Detrusor muscle	Relaxation	β	Contraction
– Internal sphincter	Contraction	α	Relaxation
– Ureter	Increased motility	α	
Genital organs			
– Male	Ejaculation	α	Erection
– Female uterus	Variable	α_1, β	Variable

noradrenaline from the vesicle by exocytosis. The noradrenaline then acts on receptors in the postsynaptic tissue, which results in depolarization or hyperpolarization, leading to activation or inhibition of the target organ. The action of noradrenaline is terminated by its reuptake into the nerve endings.

There are at least two kinds of adrenergic receptors, α and β, which may be distinguished through pharmacological reactions. Two further subtypes have been described: α_1 and α_2, β_1 and β_2. Noradrenaline is most effective at α-receptors, with only a weak effect on β-receptors. Adrenaline excites both types of receptor. Examples of the contribution of the different receptor subtypes are given in Table 10.1. Of the drugs which imitate the effects of sympathetic stimulation, the sympathomimetics, some act with receptors, and others promote the release of transmitters or inhibit their uptake. Specific antagonists have also been produced which are directed against the various subtypes. Many of these are used in the treatment of hypertension. In general, activation of α-receptors in smooth muscle leads to contraction, whereas activation of β-receptors results in relaxation. In the heart the positive inotropic and chronotropic effects are elicited by β_1-receptors. It is only in the higher vertebrates that noradrenaline is the postganglionic transmitter. In animals phylogenetically below the reptiles the sympathetic nerves to visceral muscles of organs, including the stomach and lungs, are cholinergic. The gradual evolutionary change from cholinergic to adrenergic sympathetic control of the digestive tract may account for certain anomalies seen in mammals.

The adrenal medulla is also part of the sympathetic nervous system. It is a transformed sympathetic ganglion and consists of modified postganglionic neurones. When the preganglionic neurones supplying the adrenal medulla are activated, the postganglionic neurones release into the bloodstream a mixture of 80 per cent adrenaline and 20 per cent noradrenaline. These substances reinforce the effects of sympathetic stimulation on organs, but their primary function is metabolic. Their release results in mobilization of substrates such as glucose and free fatty acids from glycogen and fat deposits. The secretions of the adrenal medulla therefore ensure that fuel is quickly made available when the sympathetic system is activated, which is particularly important when severe demands are made on the body.

Some effects of autonomic activity

Most organs innervated by the autonomic nervous system function even in the denervated state. Most of these are hollow organs such as the gastrointestinal tract, the bladder and the blood vessels. Their function is regulated by the degree of filling or the internal pressure. Increased internal pressure leads to stretching of the smooth muscle in their walls and this in turn results in depolarization of their membranes. As a result the smooth muscle generates an increased force, which causes displacement of the contents of these hollow organs.

The activity of the efferent autonomic nervous fibres is superimposed on the inherent activity of the organs. The sympathetic and parasympathetic activities are mostly antagonistic in their effects on the organs. Thus cholinergic impulses produce an increase in the motility and tone of the stomach and intestine and relaxation of the sphincters, as well as contraction of the gall bladder, whereas noradrenergic impulses usually produce a decrease in the motility and tone of the stomach and intestine, contraction of the sphincters and relaxation of the gall bladder. Similarly, parasympathetic stimulation leads to a decrease in heart rate and in atrial contractility, whereas sympathetic stimulation leads to an increase in heart rate and an increase in conduction velocity and contractility in the atria and ventricles. These responses together with the control of the diameter of the blood vessels (largely under the control of the sympathetic system) contribute to the maintenance of blood pressure (Fig. 10.5). Both sympathetic and parasympathetic outflows respond to visceral sensory input from cardiac receptors, blood vessels and receptors in the CNS. As described in Chapter 5, these reflexes can selectively alter blood flow to individual organs. Generalized disorders of peripheral visceral nerve fibres cause a loss of adjustment in blood pressure with changes in posture, and orthostatic hypotension results: when patients stand their arterial blood pressure falls and they become faint.

The skin receives extensive sympathetic innervation, a supply running to the sweat glands, the piloerector muscles and the blood vessels. Increased sympathetic activity results in constriction of blood vessels, sweating and erection of the hair. It is this response that produces the cold clammy skin associated with fear or anxiety. The changes that occur in the skin resistance with sweating and vasoconstriction in response to emotional stimuli play an important role in the recordings made in lie-detector tests. There is no parasympathetic innervation to the skin, so loss of sympathetic innervation will lead to a warm dry skin.

Micturition (urination) is also primarily under the control of the autonomic nervous system. The neural supply to the bladder and urethra is mainly parasym-

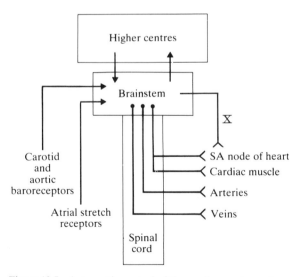

Figure 10.5 Autonomic control of the cardiovascular system.

pathetic and some somatic (Fig. 10.6), though there is a small sympathetic supply also, and sympathetic nerves participate in the urination reflexes in some species. The reflex centre of micturition lies in the sacral portion of the spinal cord. Most bladder and urethral activity is mediated through this centre, via the pelvic (parasympathetic) and pudendal (somatic) nerves from roots S_2 to S_4, and is initiated by sensory input from bladder stretch receptors. Bladder activity is modulated through descending pathways from the cerebral cortex, which inhibit the parasympathetics and stimulate the pudendal nerves to the external urethral sphincter. This sphincter lies at the base of the bladder and is composed of skeletal muscle, which holds the urethra closed. Thus the input from the stretch receptors of the bladder wall is opposed and urination can be delayed at will.

The genital organs of the male have a parasympathetic supply through the pelvic nerves from the third and fourth sacral segments. Stimulation of these nerves produces increased secretion of prostatic fluid and penile erection produced by vasodilatation in the corpora cavernosa. The sympathetic innervation of the genital organs is via the sympathetic trunk and the pelvic plexus. Stimulation of the nerves produces contraction of the musculature of the seminal vesicles and ejaculation, in addition to constriction of the internal urethral sphincter. Sensory nerves from the genitalia are found in both sympathetic and parasympathetic pathways.

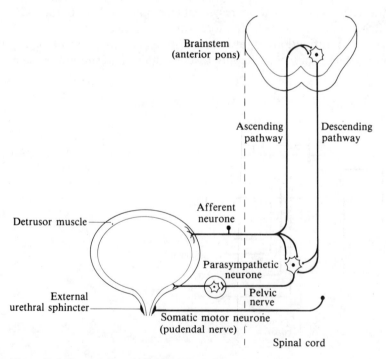

Figure 10.6   Innervation of bladder and urethra.

The pupil of the eye changes in size automatically under the control of the autonomic nervous system in response to changes in environmental illumination and other afferent or emotional stimuli. Pupil size is controlled by two sets of muscles. There are the constrictors, a circular band of muscles supplied by parasympathetic fibres, and the dilators, a radial band supplied by sympathetic nerve fibres. The size of the pupils is a matter of the relative activity of these two systems. A large pupil results from overactivity of the sympathetic fibres or underactivity of the parasympathetic fibres.

A summary of autonomic effects is given in Table 10.1.

Central autonomic control

Autonomic and somatic reflexes

As already described, autonomically innervated organs can show independent activity which can be modified by the sympathetic and parasympathetic outflow. For descriptive purposes the regions of the brain stem and spinal cord in which the regulatory signals arise are called 'centres', as for example the vasomotor and cardiac inhibitory centres. A centre is a localized group of neurones with a specific effect on certain organs or organ systems. The various autonomic centres are intimately linked. To date they have been identified in studies employing stimulation, recording and ablation techniques, but not morphologically. For this reason the term 'autonomic centres' is used only in a functional sense.

The autonomic ganglia are relay stations without independent activity, but the connector cells within the spinal cord show tonic activity even when the cord is severed from the brain. Autonomic reflexes demonstrable in such spinal animals (including man) are those concerned with blood pressure, which remains low but stable; sweating; and reflex emptying of the bladder, rectum and seminal vesicles. As with the somatic reflexes the simplest connection between afferents and autonomic efferents is situated at the segmental level, the neuronal circuit being called the autonomic reflex arc. The afferent fibres of the autonomic reflex arc are both visceral and somatic, and enter the spinal cord in the dorsal root. In contrast to the monosynpatic reflex arc of the somatic nervous system, at least two neurones are interposed between the afferent neurone and the postganglionic neurone: an interneurone and the preganglionic neurone. The fact that visceral and somatic afferents are connected with autonomic and somatic efferents at the segmental level of the spinal cord can be deduced from observations made when pathological processes occur in the viscera. Thus in gastritis and cholecystitis it is noted that the muscles over the site of the disorder are taut and the skin area innervated by fibres of the same spinal-cord segment as the effector organ is reddened. The abdominal pains caused by contraction of the intestines can be eased by changes in the skin temperature of the dermatome (skin area) innervated by the same spinal-cord segment as the affected intestine.

Above the spinal cord there are many levels at which autonomic nerve activity is controlled; again there is considerable overlap between the autonomic and somatic centres of integration. There are centres concerned with the reflex control of blood pressure and respiration in the medulla and pons. These centres obtain information from various parts of the body, and P_{CO_2} and pH are also monitored in the brain stem. Higher centres of integrative control include the hypothalamus, the limbic system, the thalamus and corpus striatum, and the cerebral cortex.

Control by the hypothalamus

The hypothalamus, in addition to being important in the control of hormone secretions, is the main site of integration of the whole of the autonomic nervous system. It is located below the thalamus in the ventral part of the diencephalon (interbrain), where it forms the floor and inferior and lateral walls of the third ventricle (Fig. 10.7). Most of the work on the hypothalamus has been performed on the rat, which has fairly well-defined hypothalamic nuclei and peptide and neurocrine pathways. In the human there is a much less clear differentiation into nuclear clusters, and the cells in a given location may not be homologous with similarly located cells in the rat. In addition to the ascending somatic and visceral afferents, the hypothalamus receives inputs from the thalamus and limbic system. Nervous efferent outflow is via the midbrain and autonomic tracts and the limbic system. The major secretory output is via the hypothalamic releasing and inhibiting hormones, which enter small nearby capillaries and control anterior pituitary function; and also via the neurohypophysial hormones oxytocin and vasopressin released into the general circulation. In addition to receiving afferents from many areas, the hypothalamus has receptors within it. There are receptors which detect changes in body temperature and in plasma osmolarity, and possibly also glucose receptors. There are also some cells which are sensitive to the circulating concentrations of hormones released from the target organs, including gonadal steroids.

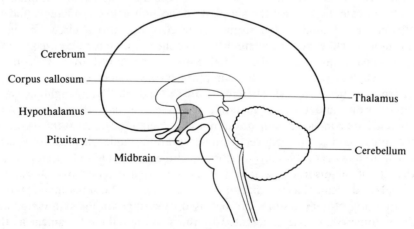

Figure 10.7 Location of the hypothalamus (shaded area).

The hypothalamus is the integrating centre for three functions in particular:

1. energy balance, including feeding behaviour and satiety;
2. water balance, including thirst and control of plasma volume and osmolarity;
3. heat balance or control of deep body temperature.

It was mentioned in Chapter 4 that the hypothalamus contains centres of hunger and satiety; in rats experimental lesions placed in certain specific regions cause hyperphagia (overeating); a lesion in another specific region causes anorexia, so the animal dies unless force-fed. Maintenance of fluid balance depends on thirst and on renal water conservation under the influence of vasopressin as explained in Chapters 7 and 14; and secretion of vasopressin in turn is under the influence of the hypothalamus.

Stability of body temperature is a matter of heat gain or retention, and heat loss—processes of the utmost importance in mammals, and birds. The signal initiating thermoregulatory responses is the flow of slightly warmer or cooler blood over the hypothalamus: a 0.01 °C change is sufficient. In some conditions information from the skin thermoreceptors contributes to the input. The responses to hypothalamic warming are reactions enhancing heat loss: dilatation of skin blood vessels, stimulation of sweat glands in some species, panting or gular flutter (flutter of the floor of the mouth and throat). Body heat, whether from a hot environment or produced by exertion, is thereby dissipated by radiation and evaporation from the surfaces of the skin and respiratory tract. The responses to hypothalamic cooling are intense vasoconstriction of skin blood vessels, a process providing the core of the body with a protective shell of cooler tissue; and piloerection, which in many species has the effect of thickening the shell of still air around the skin. An increase in metabolic rate, increased muscle tone and shivering all have the effect of producing more heat (thermogenesis). Deposits of brown fat scattered about the body close to major blood vessels are highly thermogenic and their metabolic breakdown is stimulated by sympathetic nerves and by circulating adrenaline. In such ways body core temperature is maintained in a cool environment, or suddenly raised when a hibernating animal is roused. The topic of heat balance is considered also in Chapter 17.

Though the hypothalamus is the controlling and integrating centre for these feeding and thermoregulating responses, the responses themselves obviously involve somatic as well as autonomic nerves. Sweat glands, piloerector muscles, blood vessels and brown fat are indeed autonomically innervated, but skeletal muscles participating in shivering and of course the muscles of jaws and lips involved in food intake have a somatic nerve supply. These regulatory processes in fact involve an entire behaviour pattern. The seeking for and consuming of food and drink dominates the active life of many mammals. Thermoregulatory behaviour is shown by animals which seek shade and stretch out in a warm environment, and seek shelter and lie curled up in a cold one. The resting camel places its legs in such a way as to minimize contact with the hot ground, and seats itself with its long axis parallel with the sun's rays. The making of shelter and clothing, and the use of fire, are a part of man's behavioural response to the problem of thermoregulation.

In experiments using electrical stimulation a number of patterns of behaviour have been shown to be controlled by the hypothalamus. Among the most striking are the 'flight or fight' reaction, and defence behaviour. The behavioural responses are associated with emotional effects, and the emotional responses have also a physical side, consisting of changes in visceral and skeletal muscular activity. Fear is accompanied by increased heart and respiration rates, vasoconstriction of skin blood vessels, sweating ('cold sweat'), piloerection, pupillary dilatation and dryness of the mouth. Muscular tremors also occur. Thus both sympathetic and somatic systems are affected. In man, grief is accompanied by tears, excess nasal secretion and skin pallor. Muscle tone is reduced and movements are slow and feeble. These complex patterns associated with emotion are achieved by the prefrontal–hypothalamic–thalamic complex. In the defence reaction an animal will arch its back, snarl, growl or hiss. The accompanying autonomic effects include salivary secretion, erection of hair, and decrease of motility and blood flow in the intestines. Further changes seen in the defence response are the activation of the adrenal medulla and cortex, the latter resulting from activation of the hypothalamo–pituitary axis.

Limbic system

The hypothalamus is, in a sense, subordinate to the limbic system, where experiences are evaluated affectively (in terms of feelings) and stored. On the basis of this information the body can modify the elementary hypothalamic behavioural patterns and adapt them to the prevailing environmental situation. The limbic system comprises a ring of cortical tissue on each side of the midline encircling a number of structures which have a complex series of interactions (Fig. 10.8). These structures include the amygdala, hippocampus and the septal nuclei.

In addition in animals the limbic system is the brain structure which controls drive and instinctive actions. In humans this area has special significance with respect to emotional reactions. It is also involved in the analysis of olfactory signals, a fact which may account for the powerful emotional responses produced by various odours. The close connection of the limbic system with the hypothalamus explains why emotions

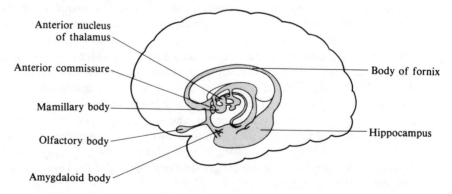

Figure 10.8   General arrangement of the principal structures of the limbic system.

are accompanied by a series of autonomic reactions: the rise in the heart rate, blood pressure and production of sweat, as well as a rise in circulating concentrations of catecholamines and glucocorticoids. Autonomic effects such as changes in blood pressure and respiration may be elicited from excitation of many limbic structures, and it is difficult to locate any particular part of the limbic system responsible for these responses.

Some localization of activities is possible, however. Stimulation of the amygdaloid nuclei causes movements such as chewing, licking and other activities related to feeding. Lesions in the amygdala produce moderate hyperphagia (overeating). However, in contrast to the responses seen in animals with lesions in the ventromedial regions of the hypothalamus, animals with amygdaloid lesions eat indiscriminately, taking tainted food and all variety of objects. This suggests that different mechanisms underlie the responses. Amygdaloid lesions also affect sexual behaviour in the male animal, producing hypersexuality, although such lesions produce no effect in the female.

Summary

While somatic sensory and motor systems establish contact with the external world, the autonomic nervous system deals with the inner world by responding to stimuli from the internal environment by altering the activity of the visceral organs and glands. The autonomic nervous system is similarly organized to the somatic system in that it has long afferent (sensory) and efferent (motor) components which act at different levels in maintaining a suitable environment. The reflexes involve smooth muscles, including those of the blood vessels and gastrointestinal tract, secreting glands and the heart. The autonomic nervous system differs from the somatic system in that many of the effector organs function without external control, visceral reflexes can occur solely in the periphery without involving the CNS and much of the control is not exerted directly but via hormones.

11 Muscle

Introduction

Muscles move one part of the body in relation to another, and also move the body as a whole, in space. In all types of muscle the cells form bundles of long thin fibres. In the case of *skeletal muscle*, also termed *striated muscle*, the fibres are gathered up at each end into tendons of connective tissue, which are firmly attached to particular points on the rigid bony skeleton. If the muscle spans a joint, contraction of the muscle brings the two ends closer together and two bones move at the joint, which takes the form of a hinge. *Cardiac muscle* forms the walls of the chambers of the heart, and its action is to propel the blood through the circulatory system, starting with the aorta and pulmonary trunk. *Smooth muscle* of the visceral and vascular systems forms sheets, ribbons and cords which make up the walls of hollow organs such as the alimentary canal, bladder and blood vessels; the sheets of smooth muscle are arranged in such a way that contraction of the fibres squeezes the contents along. There are also a few small smooth muscles near the surface of the body: for instance iris muscles changing pupil size of the eye, and piloerector and ptiloerector muscles pulling hair and feathers out at a steep angle to the skin surface.

Skeletal muscle has been studied in more detail than the other two types. It will be described first in this chapter. Cardiac muscle will be described briefly, with emphasis on its differences from skeletal muscle, and how these differences relate to its difference in function. (The main account of the function of the heart is in Chapter 5.) Next comes a brief account of the properties and activities of smooth muscle. The chapter concludes with a description of some of the ways in which muscle function has been studied.

Skeletal (striated) muscle

The action of skeletal muscle is completely dependent on its extrinsic nerve supply. Unlike cardiac muscle it has no inherent rhythmic activity; unlike visceral smooth muscle it has no intrinsic nerve plexuses which, in intestinal muscle for instance, can maintain peristaltic movement in the absence of extrinsic nerves. If the main motor nerve to a muscle is cut, the muscle not only loses its function but it also quickly degenerates. It is appropriate then to start this account of the contraction of a skeletal muscle fibre by describing events at the nerve–muscle junction.

Events at the neuromuscular junction

Close to its junction with the muscle the (myelinated) motor nerve axon breaks up into numerous unmyelinated branches, each one of which ends in a slight swelling. This tip reaches the muscle fibre at a point called the motor endplate. In embryological origin motor endplates are themselves modified muscle fibres. The perineurium surrounding the nerve axon fuses with the sarcolemma (sheath) of the muscle fibre at the motor endplate. The endplate lies in a shallow depression in the muscle fibre, and its surface forms a series of folds (Fig. 11.1a). In electron microscopy (EM) photographs numerous mitochondria are visible both in the nerve terminal and in the motor endplate below the folds. There is always a space of 20–50 nm between the plasma membrane of the nerve and that of the motor endplate. This is called the synaptic cleft.

The electron microscope also reveals in the nerve endings a number of small vesicles called synaptic vesicles. They are assumed to contain acetylcholine (ACh) (Fig. 11.1b).

When muscular activity is initiated, a burst of nerve impulses passes along the axon invading the nerve terminals. The electrical effect of these action potentials at the terminal is to start a sudden influx of Ca^{++} ions from the extracellular fluid into the terminal. This causes a large number (perhaps 200–300) of the synpatic vesicles to fuse with the nerve cell membrane and empty their contents by exocytosis into the synaptic cleft (Fig. 11.1c). The ACh attaches to receptor molecules of the motor endplate membrane, and this attachment has the effect of altering the ionic permeability properties of the membrane. It becomes more permeable to Na^+ and K^+ ions *simultaneously*, and both ionic species quickly diffuse down their chemical gradients. The potential of the endplate membrane thus changes from its resting value of about -70 mV to about -15 to -10 mV. (The endplate potential, unlike the action potential of a nerve axon or muscle fibre, never reaches zero or becomes electropositive.) The ACh is quickly inactivated by an enzyme, acetylcholinesterase, which hydrolyses it. Some of the choline may be taken back into the nerve terminal, reacetylated by the enzyme choline acetylase found there, and quickly re-used. The walls of the emptied synaptic vesicles are also pinched off, back into the cytoplasm of the nerve ending, and refilled and re-used.

The reduction of the endplate potential, to about -15 mV, acts as the stimulus which initiates an action potential conducted rapidly in both directions along the length of the muscle fibre in just the same way as that in a nerve axon, transiently reversing the polarity of the fibre's membrane, from about -90 mV to about $+30$ mV. It is the muscle's action potential which causes excitation of the muscular elements.

This picture of the sequence of events at the motor endplate has been built up gradually, by electrical recordings, by chemical and pharmacological observations, and by EM photographs. The production of ACh from the nerve can be shown by perfusing the motor endplate with a fluid containing the drug eserine, which inhibits acetylcholinesterase. During stimulation of the nerve, ACh appears in the perfusion fluid, and can be collected and assayed. Without eserine the hydrolysis of ACh is so rapid that it becomes almost undetectable. Direct stimulation of the muscle or motor

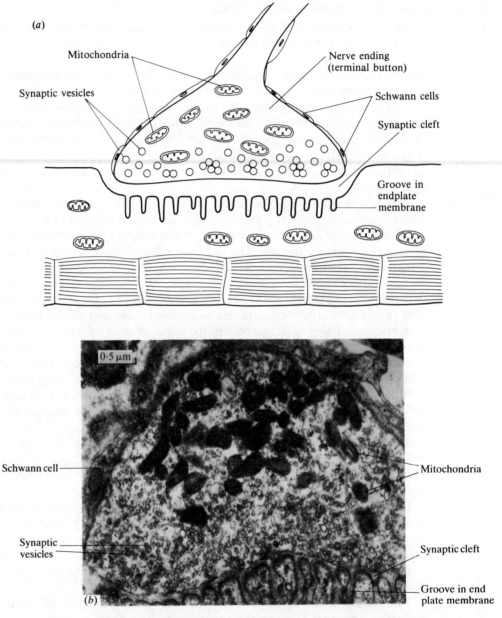

Figure 11.1 Neuromuscular junction. (*a*) Nerve ending and motor endplate. (*b*) Nerve terminal, showing numerous mitochondria and synaptic vesicles. Grooves in endplate membrane and collection of vesicles opposite the grooves are visible. Phrenic nerve (rat). EM. (Reproduced by permission from Jones, S. F. and S. Kawanbunbumpen, *Journal of Physiology*, **207**, 31–50, 1970.) (*c*) Nerve terminal, showing fusion of synaptic vesicles (arrows) with presynaptic membrane (P). The postsynaptic membrane is shown at S. Note that magnification is higher than for (*b*). (Reproduced by permission from Hubbard, J. I. and S. Kawanbunbumpen, *Journal of Physiology*, **194**, 407–420, 1968.)

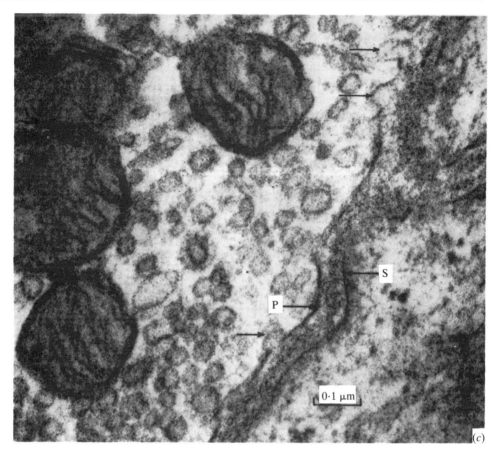

(c)

Figure 11.1 (*continued*)

endplate does not produce ACh, an observation showing that it is the presynaptic neuronal cell which is the source of ACh. The drug curare (tubocurarine) attaches itself to the receptor sites on the motor endplate; it does not stimulate them, but prevents access of ACh to the receptor. The nerve continues to produce ACh but the muscle is paralysed.

Direct electrical recordings made from the motor endplate region (with the help of voltage clamping in muscle fibres in which action potentials and movement have been blocked by curare) have revealed the size and sign of the endplate potential in many muscles to be -15 to -10 mV. Furthermore even in an inactive neuromuscular junction it is possible to record extremely small randomly occurring potentials, called miniature endplate potentials (mepps). These are normally about 0.5 mV, and occasionally there appears in a train of such recordings a single mepp of twice or three times this voltage, but never of any intermediate voltage, always a simple multiple of

0.5. This finding gives support to the idea that ACh is liberated in quanta or 'packets' (such as might be contained in the vesicles seen in nerve endings); and that the mepps are due to chance fusion of vesicles with the presynaptic membrane in the course of random kinetic movement through the cytoplasm of the nerve ending, and the discharge of their contents into the synaptic cleft. The larger mepps would occur when two or three such events happened simultaneously. The nerve impulse would cause the simultaneous fusion of many vesicles with the membrane, and the discharge of a large amount of ACh. Vesicles of the same size and appearance as those of the presynaptic nerve terminal have been extracted by differential centrifugation from grey matter of the brain, and shown by direct assay to contain ACh. Poisoning a nerve–muscle preparation by the venom of the black-widow spider is known to cause a large outpouring of all the ACh from the nerve terminal, and EM photographs of such poisoned terminals show no vesicles.

Excitation–contraction coupling

As already indicated (Chapter 3 under Cells as components of tissue), each striated muscle fibre is a syncytium composed of a number of cells, the nuclei of which lie along the outside of the fibre just below the covering sheath, the sarcolemma. Each fibre is composed of numerous parallel myofibrils; the mitochondria lie among and between the myofibrils. A set of narrow tubes, the T-system, which are in fact invaginations of the cell membrane, run down into the sarcoplasm (cytoplasm), encircling each myofibril. The transverse striations, staining as light and dark bands, which give striated muscle its name, are in register across all the myofibrils in the muscle fibre. In many mammalian species the T-system runs through the fibre at a point between the dark and light bands (called A- and I-bands, respectively). In other species including the frog it runs through at the point of the Z-line, which bisects the light band.

The muscle action potential spreads along the surface of each muscle fibre as a self-propagating series of potential changes similar to that in nerve axons. The action potential passes down the system of T-tubules, thus penetrating the thickness of each muscle fibre and affecting all the myofibrils, even the innermost ones. Close to the tubules of the T-system are large cavities, called terminal cisternae, of the muscle fibre's sarcoplasmic (endoplasmic) reticulum (SR). The SR has a regular structure, more so than the rather randomly arranged endoplasmic veticulum of most cells. Within each myofibril each terminal cisterna of SR is connected to the next or adjacent cisterna by narrow, longitudinally running tubes of SR; half way along these tubes is an area, the fenestrated area, where the tubes appear to have holes or pores connecting their lumen directly with the sarcoplasm. Within the SR, calcium is found, partially stored in non-ionic form bound to a protein called calsequestrin. In the walls of the SR is a very active Ca^{++} ion pump which can transfer Ca^{++} rapidly out of the sarcoplasm into the SR. Figure 11.2a and b show the relation of the T-system and SR to the A- and I-bands.

The consequence of the electrical change running through the T-system during the muscle action potential is that the cisternae which are closely adjacent to the T-system

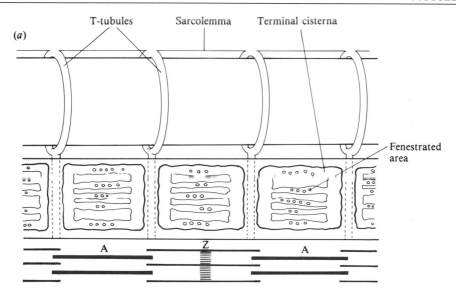

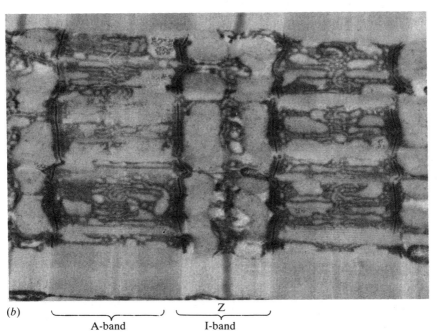

Figure 11.2 T-tubules and SR. (*a*) Upper myofibril is shown as a cylindrical structure to indicate the continuity of T-tubule with sarcolemma. Lower myofibril is shown in longitudinal section to show proximity of T-tubules to the terminal cisternae of the SR. A–Z–A at the base of the diagram indicates the relation of T-tubules to A-band and Z-line of mammalian skeletal muscle. (*b*) Muscle, showing T-tubules and SR in longitudinal section. Myofibril at the base of the photograph, cut in a slightly different plane, clearly shows Z-line, A- and I-bands, and thick and thin filaments, thus indicating relation of T-tubules and SR to these structures. Tibialis (mouse). EM. $\times 25\,500$. (Courtesy of M. S. Forbes.)

are affected and Ca^{++} ions are released from the entire SR into the sarcoplasm. It is this sudden flood of Ca^{++} ions around and between the protein filaments of the myofibrils which initiates the muscular activity: either contraction or isometric action. The Ca^{++} ions are immediately removed, being pumped back into the cavities of the SR, so the 'pulse' of Ca^{++} in the sarcoplasm has only a transient effect and relaxation is also rapid. In the sarcoplasm of relaxed muscle the free Ca^{++} ion level is very low: $0.1\ \mu\text{M}$ or less. During activity the level reaches $15\ \mu\text{M}$, but within the cavities of the SR it is concentrated a thousand-fold, present in *milli*molar amounts. Therefore the pump has to work against a steep concentration gradient.

Contractile proteins of muscle

To understand how release of Ca^{++} ions initiates muscular contraction, it is necessary to study the structural arrangement of the contractile proteins. It has been shown by EM that the A- and I-bands are composed of thick and thin filaments lying parallel with the long axis of the myofibril (Fig. 11.3a). The two main proteins extractable from muscle tissue are myosin and actin. These proteins have different solubility properties (myosin is soluble in buffered KCl, actin in KI); extraction by dissolving each protein in turn from a fibre viewed by phase-contrast light microscopy (LM) has shown that myosin is associated mainly with the A-band and actin with the I-band. (The Z-line bisecting the I-band does not disappear after treatment with either solvent. It consists of a different and highly specialized protein.) Figure 11.3b shows phase-contrast LM photographs illustrating these points. Electron microscopy photographs of transverse sections through myofibrils at various points along the bands have revealed that the thick and thin filaments interdigitate at the outer ends of the A-bands, forming a highly ordered pattern, in which the thick (myosin) filaments lie at the corners of equilateral triangles and each one is surrounded by a hexagonal pattern of thin filaments (Fig. 11.3c). More detailed study has shown that the thick filaments carry on their surface a set of evenly spaced projections or cross-bridges, which are in fact the ends or 'heads' of myosin molecules; and that within each thin filament is a pair of spirally wound threads of actin protein molecules, together with smaller amounts of two other proteins, tropomyosin and troponin, which lie in the groove between the spirally wound actin threads (Fig. 11.4a and b). These threads are each fixed firmly at one end by a pair of 'feet', to the Z-line, the structure of which is not known in detail but which seems to represent a grating rather than a solid disc. The length between one Z-line and the next is called a sarcomere. The free ends of the actin filaments project towards the middle of the sarcomere but they do not meet; there is a space in the centre of the sarcomere which contains no thin filaments but only thick myosin filaments. When the muscle contracts, the I-bands become narrower and the Z-lines draw closer together, so each sarcomere shortens longitudinally. If this occurs simultaneously in all the myofibrils of all the fibres of a muscle, there is a pull on the tendon at each end of the muscle, with consequent movement of the bone, or increase of tension in the tendons and connective tissue.

The shortening of the sarcomere is brought about because the cross-bridges of the

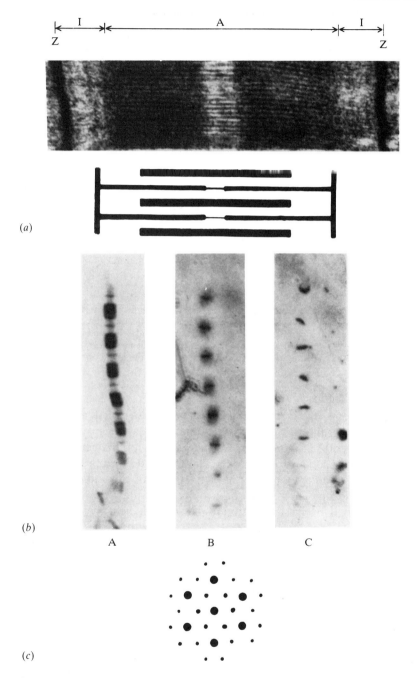

Figure 11.3 Thick and thin filaments, and muscle proteins. (*a*) A- and I-bands and Z-lines of skeletal muscle; at the outer edges of the A-bands, thin filaments of the I-bands interdigitate with thick filaments. EM. (*b*) A: Skeletal muscle fibre, slightly stretched. B: Same fibre after removal of myosin. C: Fibre after removal of actin. In (C) only the Z-lines of the fibre are clearly visible. Phase-contrast LM. (*c*) Diagrammatic cross-section of interdigitating region of a myofibril to show hexagonal arrangement of thin filaments around each thick filament, and thick filaments at corners of equilateral triangle. (Reproduced by permission from Huxley, H. E., *British Medical Bulletin*, **12**, 171–173, 1956, Churchill-Livingstone.)

F-actin   Troponin   Tropomyosin

Z-line

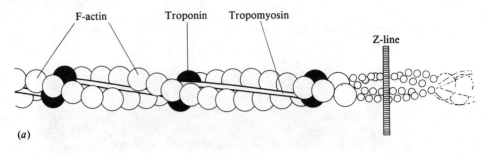

(a)

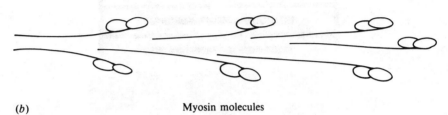

(b)   Myosin molecules

Figure 11.4   Proteins of muscle. (a) Arrangement of the three proteins forming the thin filament. Actin, arranged as two spirally wound threads of 'beads', is fixed at Z-line, each thread having two attachment feet. Fibre of tropomyosin lies in the groove between the actin threads; troponin is placed at intervals along the tropomyosin. (b) Myosin molecules, showing paired 'heads'. The heads form the cross-bridges attaching at points on thin filaments, and appear to be hinged to the tail, the hinge providing a small movement.

myosin filaments make contact with certain points called 'active sites' on the actin filaments lying among them. This contact causes the myosin 'head' to flip over towards the centre of the sarcomere, pulling the actin filaments with it. Immediately, the cross-bridge connection is broken and the head flips upright again. It then makes contact with another point on the actin filament, flips across, and pulls the actin further; and so on. The repetition of the make-contact/move/break-contact cycle of the myosin cross-bridges in relation to the actin filaments has the effect of moving the actin filaments from each end of the sarcomere towards the centre, consequently shortening the distance between the Z-lines. The process could continue until the actin filaments from each end overlap in the middle, and the myosin filament comes up against the Z-line.

When the muscle is relaxed the active sites on the actin threads are in some way protected from contact with the myosin cross-bridges by the presence of the tropomyosin and troponin lying along the spiral groove between the pair of actin threads in each filament. Troponin has a strong affinity for Ca^{++} ions, the concentration of which is extremely low in the sarcoplasm of relaxed muscle. But as soon as Ca^{++} ions come flooding out from the SR, the troponin molecules take them up and this binding alters the configuration of the tropomyosin so that it no longer protects the active sites on the actin threads. So the adjacent myosin heads, which have a strong affinity for these active sites, make contact and start the process of flipping back and forth, creeping along the actin filaments and so dragging the Z-lines towards the centre of the sarcomere.

There is much evidence in support of this idea of the interdigitating (sliding) of the actin and myosin filaments during contraction of a muscle. It gives an explanation of the reduction of the width of the I-band when the muscle shortens. It also provides an interpretation of the fact that maximum tension in an isolated myofibril is generated at the Z-line spacing (sarcomere length) at which there is maximum overlap between thick and thin filaments, and thus maximum opportunity for the formation of cross-bridges. In experiments in which sarcomeres of a myofibril are pulled out to give less overlap of actin and myosin, or shortened to the point at which actin filaments from opposite ends of the sarcomere overlap in the centre, the tension developed on stimulation of the myofibril is much less than maximal: in both the too-long and the too-short condition, there would necessarily have been less than maximal formation of cross-bridges (Fig. 11.5).

The whole process of shortening clearly depends on a series of minute movements as the cross-bridges (myosin heads) flip to and fro. The source of energy for this process is the strongly exothermic splitting of ATP molecules, of which there are an abundance in the sarcoplasm. Furthermore the head of the myosin molecule is itself an ATP-splitting enzyme, so the energy is released precisely where it is required. It is thought that, for each cycle of movement of the cross-bridges, two ATP molecules are split: one at (or before) the binding to the actin, and one at the breaking from the active site. The energy is used not only in the movement or tension development but

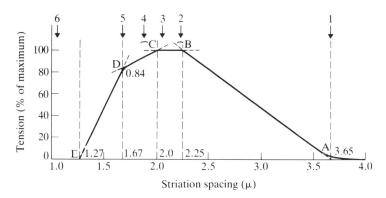

Figure 11.5 Sarcomere length and maximal isometric tension. The arrows along the top are placed opposite the striation spacings at which the critical stages of overlap of filaments occur. At point *A*, where the sarcomere has been stretched to the point where there is no overlap between thick and thin filaments. no tension can be developed. As sarcomere length decreases, the increasing overlap of the filaments permits increasing tension and between points *B* and *C*, where overlap is maximal, tension is also maximal. Further shortening of the myofibril causes thin filaments from the two ends of the sarcomere to lie alongside each other. allowing fewer cross-bridges (*C–D*); and still further decrease in tension development occurs at short sarcomere lengths where the ends of the thick filaments abut against Z-lines (*D–E*). (Reproduced by permission from Gordon, A. M., A. F. Huxley and F. J. Julian, *Journal of Physiology*, **184**, 170–192, 1966.)

also in the active transport of Ca^{++} from the sarcoplasm back into the SR, the enzyme involved here being a Ca^{++}-activated ATPase. The ATP is immediately rephosphorylated by creatine phosphate. The more remote source of energy is muscle glycogen, from which energy is released by glycolysis.

It is clear from this description that the trigger for contraction is the sudden release, caused by an electric signal in the T-tubule system, of Ca^{++} ions from the SR into the sarcoplasm. The T-tubule system, the ordered arrangement of the SR, and the Ca^{++} pump of SR membranes which makes possible this quick Ca^{++} release and reuptake, are very well developed in striated muscle; and it is this which makes striated muscle so rapid in contraction and relaxation.

This chapter so far has been concerned with events at myofibrillar or molecular level in single muscle fibres. We will now consider properties of muscular activity as a whole.

Properties of muscular activity

Motor units, muscle tone and gradation of response

Each striated muscle is innervated by a large number of nerve axons and each axon terminates at its branched end on several muscle fibres. An axon plus its muscle fibres is called a motor unit. The number of muscle fibres served by one axon varies between 8, in eye muscles, and 200, in the large gastrocnemius of the leg. The smaller number of muscle fibres is found in small muscles and relates to fine movements.

Even when the muscle is relaxed there is a continuous slight asynchronous activity in the nerve, just a few impulses per second, and correspondingly slight asynchronous activity at the motor endplates and muscle fibres. This activity, being asynchronous— a few fibres randomly affected from moment to moment—is too slight to cause even a visible twitching of the muscle. It is called muscle tone. In its absence, produced by cutting or paralysing a nerve for instance, the muscle rapidly degenerates. The existence of muscle tone means that the individual fibres are kept 'alert', ready to respond when a high-frequency burst of action potentials arrives synchronously along many motor axons and the entire muscle is made to contract. It means also that postural muscles exert a small but constant degree of tension, maintaining the body's position in space.

Since the nerve–muscle system consists of a large number of motor units, there exists the possibility of gradation of muscular activity: the greater the number of motor units involved, the larger will be the amount of movement, or tension development. Clearly a gradation of activity for the muscle as a whole has the advantage of providing flexibility, and the matching of effort precisely to the task which it is currently performing.

The gradation of muscular action can be readily shown experimentally in an isolated nerve–muscle preparation, where increasing strength of the stimulus to the nerve increases the muscle's response, which reaches a maximum at the point where all axons, even those of the highest threshold, have been stimulated. In the body such a situation does not occur: if all the fibres of a muscle exerted their maximum tension simultaneously, they would probably break the tendon.

Latent and refractory periods, summation and tetanus

In the description of the interdigitating of the filaments of actin and myosin, it was implied that the shortening of the muscle fibre was immediately followed by its relaxation—in other words, that the muscle gives a twitch. In reality, of course, muscles do not work in this way. Movement does not work in a series of jerky twitches, but in smooth sustained contractions. Careful analysis of time-intervals during single and multiple applications of stimuli to an isolated muscle, and recording of the muscle's shortening, can reveal how a twitch can turn into a sustained contraction.

An application of an electrical stimulus directly to an isolated muscle, the tendon of which is fixed to a recording apparatus, results in the record of a twitch (Fig. 11.6a) starting after a very short latent period (about 3 ms) after the stimulus. It is supposed that the latent period is the time-interval required for the spread of electrical excitation through the T-tubule system and the release of Ca^{++} ions from the SR. If a second stimulus is applied very shortly after the first, a further contraction is superimposed on the first and the whole contraction is greater: that is, there is further shortening. This effect is called summation (Fig. 11.6b). It could be seen as the effect of an additional quantity of Ca^{++} released into the sarcoplasm before all that released previously had been taken up. If, now, a whole series of stimuli are applied at short

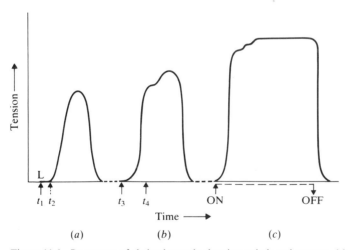

Figure 11.6 Responses of skeletal muscle showing twitch and tetanus. (a) Response (twitch) to a single stimulus applied at time t_1; muscle after a short latent period, L, gives a twitch; a second stimulus applied at t_2 very soon after the first is ineffective as it falls in the refractory period of the muscle. (b) Response (summation) of muscle to two stimuli, when the second is applied after the end of the refractory period; the effect is to cause further tension development; t_3 and t_4 show times of application of stimuli. (c) Response (tetanus) to application of stimulus throughout the period shown by dotted line along abscissa.

intervals, the muscle does not get a chance to relax; the effect of each stimulus summates with the one before it, and the result is a sustained smooth muscular contraction, called a tetanus (Fig. 11.6c). This is how a muscle normally works, since in the body a quick succession of stimuli are provided by a high frequency of nerve action potentials in numerous axons.

Relaxation at the end of a tetanus depends on rapid reuptake of Ca^{++} ions into the SR, and this in turn depends on rapid restoration of the resting membrane potential at the surface of the fibre and throughout the T-tubule system. The restoration of the membrane potential takes place by a process similar to that of the falling phase and after-potential of the nerve action potential (Chapter 9); there is a transient increase in K^+ conductance, and also, in the case of muscle, of Cl' conductance. The muscle membrane is highly permeable to Cl' ions, which helps in the rectification process. The resting membrane potential (E_m) is close to the equilibrium potential for the Cl' ions (ε_{Cl}); the Cl' permeability ensures rapid restoration of resting E_m and thus of relaxation.

In a rare genetic disease of humans and goats (myotonia genetica), muscle membrane permeability of Cl' is reduced. So after a strong muscular effect such as a jump, muscle contraction does *not* cease as soon as the burst of motor nerve impulses ceases. The muscles go into a spasm and take several seconds to relax, since the lowered Cl' permeability has slowed down the rate of restoration of the resting muscle, E_m.

If in an isolated muscle a second electrical stimulus is applied very shortly after the first (well before the muscle has reached the maximum of the twitch), the muscle is unresponsive to the second stimulus. This unresponsive period is called the absolute refractory period. (It could be that muscle action potentials resulting from the first stimulus are still travelling along the muscle fibres.) The absolute refractory period is followed by a relative refractory period in which the muscle can respond to a second stimulus, but only if the stimulus is large—well above that of the muscle's normal threshold; the excitability of the muscle in fact is temporarily reduced. The duration of the absolute and relative refractory periods is very short in all striated muscle, but varies slightly from one muscle to another.

Isotonic and isometric activity

Broadly speaking, striated muscle fibres have two kinds of activity: *isotonic contraction*, in which the whole muscle shortens, the ends come closer together and there is visible movement at a joint, as shown for instance in the joints illustrated in Fig. 2.14b and c; and *isometric action*,* in which there is little or no visible shortening of the muscle, but there is an increase in tension along its length. Any muscle, for instance, resists the effect of a passive pull which without this resistance would lengthen it; and an extensor muscle at a joint by its isometric activity resists the effect of a push which would otherwise bend the joint. In so doing, the muscles increase the

---

* Isometric action is often called isometric *contraction*. This is a misnomer because 'contraction' means 'shortening' and 'isometric' means 'same length'.

tension in the so-called 'series-elastic components': the tendons, sarcolemma, connective-tissue fibres, and probably also the 'hinges' at the myosin heads.

To illustrate these two kinds of activity, one may consider the bending of the arm at the elbow. This is obviously an isotonic contraction. Several upper-arm muscles (the biceps is one of them) shorten in length, and bulge outward in diameter. The action performs external work, the raising of the weight of the forearm and hand. This work would be quite small (but could be increased if a heavy object were to be held in the hand during the bending). Now suppose a man is standing, his arm hanging loosely by his side, his fingers flexed. A heavy bucket is now hung onto his fingers, and he supports its weight. There is no visible muscular movement, but his fingers and arm muscles are now doing work against gravity, and there is increase in tension along their length—isometric action of the muscles. Normal forms of physical exercise using muscles of all the limbs involve both isotonic and isometric activity, whereas in weight-lifting or a tug-of-war the action is almost entirely isometric.

Types of muscles and types of fibres

Certain muscles called *fast* muscles have short latent and refractory periods. They contract rapidly on stimulation and relax equally rapidly. Other muscles, the *slow* muscles, reach their maximum contraction or tension more slowly on stimulation, and relax more slowly; and there are intermediate speeds between the extremes. Individual muscle fibres are also of several types, which are biochemically distinct. Red muscle fibres contain abundant myoglobin, the pigment giving the red colour and acting as a short-term oxygen store. They also contain numerous mitochondria, and a rather low level of ATPase. Red muscle fibres use oxidation as their energy source. White muscle fibres contain few mitochondria, no myoglobin, a limited amount of glycogen, and an abundance of glycolytic enzymes and of myofibril ATPase. (These two types can be further subdivided by biochemical properties.)

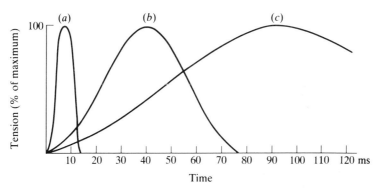

Figure 11.7 Fast and slow muscles. Muscles having various proportions of fast (white) and slow (red) fibres take different times to develop their maximal tension on stimulation. (*a*) Internal rectus (an eye muscle). (*b*) Gastrocnemius (leg). (*c*) Soleus (leg). (Adapted from West, J. B. (ed.) *Best & Taylor's Physiological Basis of Medical Practice*, 11th edn, Williams & Wilkins, Baltimore, 1985.)

Muscles contain red and white fibres in various proportions; in general, slow muscles contain a preponderance of red fibres and quick muscles a preponderance of white fibres. White fibres are quick-acting but fatiguable, presumably because of their limited glycogen supply, and limited availability of oxidative metabolism. Red muscles are more fatigue-resistant, and many such muscles are involved in maintaining sustained isometric tension for long periods; muscle tone is a prominent feature of these muscles. The human soleus muscle in the leg consists mainly of red fibres; the gastrocnemius, another leg muscle, contains red and white fibres in about equal numbers. Corresponding muscles of different species may differ: the leg muscles of the rabbit are mainly red, those of the hare mainly white. The velocity of shortening of three muscles is shown in Fig. 11.7.

Length–tension relationship

In the body a muscle is normally under slight tension even when apparently relaxed. This is obvious because the muscle shortens when one or other tendon is cut. Its (relaxed) length in the body is known as 'optimal length', and its length after cutting the tendon is called 'initial length'. If a muscle at 'initial length' is passively pulled out, and its tension simultaneously measured, it will be found that no tension develops until it reaches its 'optimal length', and thereafter the tension rises quite steeply, presumably by the stretching of the series-elastic components of the fibres. (One may think, by analogy, of a coiled-wire spring, first compressed to an 'initial length', then drawn out to its natural equilibrium length, then pulled out beyond this length, when the spring would start resisting the pull.) The relation of length and tension is shown in Fig. 11.8 by the graph labelled 'passive stretch'.

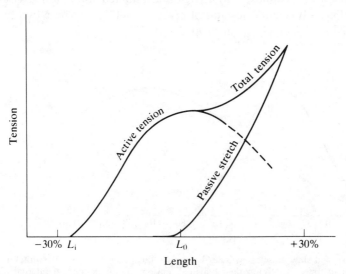

Figure 11.8 Length–tension relation during activity and during passive stretch. L_0: 'optimal length'; L_1: 'initial length'.

The experiment can be repeated using a muscle being stimulated (by a pair of electrodes either directly on the muscle or through its nerve), again starting from various known lengths and measuring isometric tension. The results are shown in Fig. 11.8 by the graph labelled 'active tension'. This has its maximum at about 'optimal length'; we can surmise by comparison with Fig. 11.5 that at 'optimal length' most of the sarcomeres in most of the fibres are at the length which gives maximum overlap between the actin and myosin filaments.

Since the action is isometric (that is, the muscle is not being permitted to shorten under these experimental conditions), the filaments cannot be sliding, and the tension must be developed by the rapid and repeated make-and-break of each myosin cross-bridge at the same active site on the actin filament. If the muscle is pulled out beyond this 'optimal length', there will be less overlap of the filaments, so fewer cross-bridges, and so less tension. But on still further stretching and stimulating, we reach the point where the passive stretch of the series-elastic elements generates the tension and contributes more and more to the total tension of the system: 'total tension' in Fig. 11.8. A similar though not identical length–tension relationship exists for cardiac muscle.

Force–velocity relationship

Common experience shows that isotonic movements can be made more quickly if the force involved is small: a small weight can be lifted for a given distance faster than a large one. So velocity of movement is inversely related to force, but the relation is not linear. Experiments with isolated muscle, and also with human subjects bending the forearm at the elbow against various weights attached to the hand, have shown that the relationship of force to final velocity (i.e. velocity at the end of the movement) is curvilinear, as shown in Fig. 11.9. At the final stage of zero velocity, the weight is so heavy that it cannot be moved, and the effort made by the arm muscles represents their maximal *isometric* tension.

Work, heat and sources of energy

Muscular activity is invariably accompanied by output of heat—again a matter of common experience. The external work output—say moving a weight through a distance—and simultaneous heat output of a muscle working at different velocities can be measured experimentally. The results of such an experiment are shown in Fig. 11.10, in which rate of total energy output (work + heat) is plotted against velocity (as a fraction of maximum velocity: that is, when no external work is being done). It can be seen that:

1. Work (W) production rate is at a minimum at very high velocity (no load) and also at very low velocity (load too large to be moveable), and at a maximum at intermediate velocities.
2. Heat (H) production rate increases linearly with velocity.
3. At the higher velocities, rate of heat production forms an increasingly large proportion of total energy output.

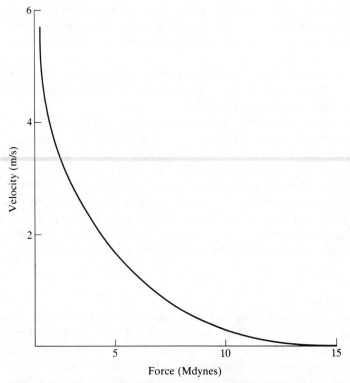

Figure 11.9   Force–velocity relationship in a group of skeletal muscles during flexion of elbow joint. The final velocity attained during the movement is maximal when the action is performed against zero load; against a very heavy load, movement is prevented (zero velocity) and the action is entirely isometric. Note that 1 Mdyne = 10^5 N. (Adapted from Wilkie, D. R., *Journal of Physiology*, **110**, 249–280, 1950.)

4. Efficiency, measured as $[W/(W + H)] \times 100$, is highest at about 50 per cent of maximum velocity.

Heat output at various points during contraction and relaxation of single muscles and single fibres has been measured by means of a cleverly contrived and quickly responding piece of apparatus. It has been found that there is an *initial heat* accompanying activation and shortening, presumably related to the chemical events involved: ATP splitting, formation of cross-bridges and so on; and a *delayed heat* associated with relaxation: the release of energy stored in the series-elastic components, as the stretched tendons relax.

The splitting of ATP as the immediate source of energy in muscular activity, and its rapid rephosphorylation from creatine phosphate, was mentioned earlier. Creatine is later rephosphorylated in resting muscle from ATP:

$$\text{Creatine} + \text{ATP} = \text{Creatine phosphate} + \text{ADP}$$

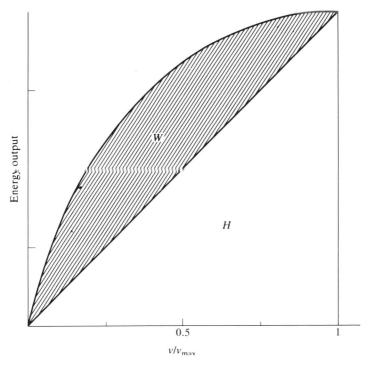

Figure 11.10 Energy output during muscular activity at different velocities. Total energy output is divided between external work (W; shaded area) and heat (H; unshaded area). Velocity (v) is expressed as a fraction of maximum velocity (v_{max}). Maximum work is achieved when muscles are working at or slightly below half their maximum velocity. (Adapted from Davson, H. and M. B. Segal, *Introduction to Physiology*, vol. 2, Academic Press, London, 1975.)

This ADP is then rephosphorylated by a process which involves glucose and inorganic phosphate:

$$\text{Glucose} + 2\text{ADP} + 2\text{P}_i = 2 \text{ Pyruvic acid} + 2\text{ATP}$$

Glucose may be derived from glycogen by glycogenolysis, a process in which no oxygen is used. In actively working white muscle fibres, pyruvic acid and its reduction product, lactic acid, accumulate and leak out from the muscles into the blood (a fact apparent from the observation that the pH of plasma during vigorous exercise falls slightly). These acids can be taken up from the blood by liver cells and resynthesized into glycogen, or they may be used directly by cardiac muscle fibres.

The oxidative reactions in muscle are associated with recovery. The energy required for synthesis of the high-energy phosphates (ATP and creatine phosphate) is derived in the long run from oxidation of a compound called acetyl coenzyme A (acetyl Co-A), derived from pyruvic acid, a reaction process associated with oxidative phosphorylation and the citric-acid cycle, a process perhaps familiar to some readers. Although glucose (either taken up directly from the blood or derived from its stored form, glycogen) is the main source of acetyl Co-A of muscle, free fatty acids and amino acids also produce acetyl Co-A in their metabolism. So fat and protein are available as energy sources for working muscles, and indeed are used increasingly during long-continued muscular exercise such as marathon-running.

Cardiac muscle

Structure

Anyone familiar with EM photographs of striated muscle would at once recognize Fig. 11.11 (EM photograph of cardiac muscle tissue) as being muscular tissue. The A and I striations, the thick filaments lying longitudinally, the Z-lines across the I-bands, are all easily identifiable. There are a number of differences, however, at microscopic and submicroscopic level, and these are related to the characteristic mode of function of heart muscle.

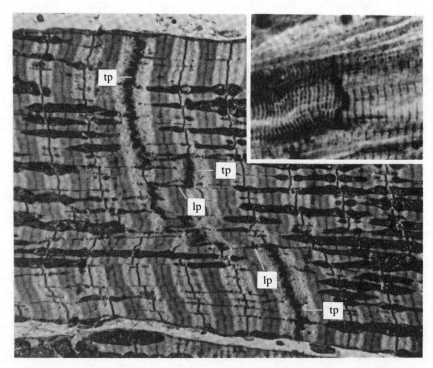

Figure 11.11   Cardiac muscle and intercalated disc. Inset shows that the intercalated disc is made up of transverse and longitudinal parts (tp and lp on main photograph). Transverse parts coincide with Z-lines of myofibrils and give cohesion to the myocardium; intercellular transfer of material and charge probably occurs through the longitudinal parts. EM. × 3400 for main photograph, × 670 for inset. (Reproduced by permission from Ham, A. W. and D. H. Cormack, *Histology*, 8th edn, Lippincott, Philadelphia, 1979.)

As with skeletal muscle the cardiac muscle fibres are made up of myofibrils; but these do not all lie parallel from end to end of the fibre in a neat array of cylinders. They branch and join and divide, and numerous mitochondria lie in among them (Fig. 11.11). Each cardiac muscle fibre has its own nucleus lying centrally. The fibres are joined to each other by structures called intercalated discs (Fig. 11.12). The term 'disc' is a misnomer; these are not rigid transverse structures as the word would imply. They show (in longitudinal section) a zig-zag appearance, running in places transversely and in other places longitudinally between the myofibrils.

The transverse portions show under EM many desmosomes, presumably making firm cell-to-cell contacts. They are normally seen in the region of a Z-line, and actin filaments are inserted here (Fig. 11.12). The longitudinal sections of the intercalated disc show many gap junctions (also called nexuses), which are areas of low electrical resistance. So it is probably through these nexuses that the wave of electrical excitation is spread from fibre to fibre throughout the heart.

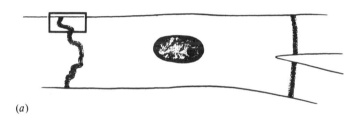

(a)

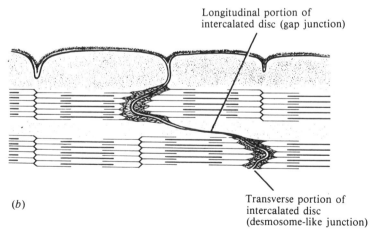

Longitudinal portion of intercalated disc (gap junction)

(b)

Transverse portion of intercalated disc (desmosome-like junction)

Figure 11.12 Intercalated disc. (a) shows portion of disc enlarged in (b). Disc is composed of two types of junction; the transverse parts are approximately in line with Z-lines of underlying myofibril. (Reproduced by permission from Ham, A. W. and D. H. Cormack, *Histology*, 8th edn, Lippincott, Philadelphia, 1979.)

There are T-tubules open to extracellular fluid, as in striated muscle, but cardiac muscle T-tubules have somewhat wider openings. Neither the T-tubule system nor the SR shows the clearly defined and ordered pattern present in the corresponding structures of striated muscle; the general arrangement seems more random.

Inherent rhythm and spread of excitation

Certain portions of cardiac muscle tissue show spontaneous activity, beating by rhythmic contraction and relaxation; and this activity is associated with spontaneous depolarization and repolarization of the membrane of the cardiac muscle fibres of such areas. It is remarkable that this rhythmic activity is totally independent of nervous input. It appears during embryonic development before any nerves have reached the heart; and a single cardiac muscle fibre grown in tissue culture will continue to beat. It appears that the membrane potential of these cardiac muscle fibres is inherently unstable. It slowly drifts away from its resting potential (known here as the diastolic level) of about $-80\,\mathrm{mV}$, to become slightly more positive, say up to $-60\,\mathrm{mV}$. This is the threshold at which an action potential starts. The potential suddenly shoots up to about $+10\,\mathrm{mV}$, then repolarizes, at first quickly, then more slowly to its former value of $-80\,\mathrm{mV}$. The whole cycle is then repeated (Fig. 11.13).

The portions of cardiac muscle to show this inherent instability of membrane potential are:

1. the sinoatrial node, lying at the point where the main veins enter the right atrium;
2. the atrioventricular node, lying between the atria and the ventricles;
3. the Purkinje fibres of the ventricles.

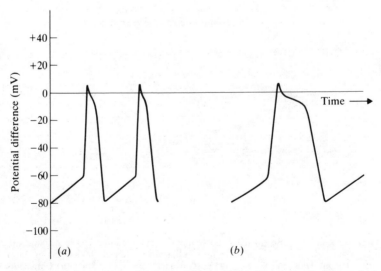

Figure 11.13 Action potentials in cardiac muscle. (*a*) At atrial node (pacemaker). (*b*) In Purkinje fibre.

Of these, the fibres at the sinoatrial node have the fastest inherent rhythm. The sinoatrial node therefore acts as a pacemaker; its inherent rhythm is imposed on the whole heart to give the normal rhythmic beat. The action potentials are generated at this point and spread rapidly via the nexuses throughout the whole of the rest of the heart muscle. Action potentials cause contraction of each portion of the cardiac muscle in turn, followed by relaxation as the potential falls to the diastolic level, -80 mV. The inherent instability and rhythmicity of other cardiac muscle fibres can be detected by experimental methods, and the slightly slower rhythm of atrioventricular node fibres is sometimes apparent in pathological conditions.

Shape of action potential and ionic fluxes

The shape of the action potential of cardiac muscle is characteristic (Fig. 11.13), and somewhat different from that of either nerve or striated muscle fibres. There is the rapid depolarization from -80 mv to about $+10$ mV. Then follows a rapid repolarization to about $+5$ mV, or 0 mV, or -10 mV, according to the region of the heart; this is followed by a 'plateau' or period of no change in electrical potential; the plateau is especially distinct in Purkinje fibres of the ventricles. It is in turn followed by the rapid repolarization to the diastolic level, -80 mV. The initial depolarization is accompanied by an influx of both Na^+ and Ca^{++} ions. The first stage of rapid repolarization is accompanied by inactivation of the Na^+ current and by inward flux of Cl' ions. The plateau might be due to continued simultaneous inward flux of both Ca^{++} and Cl'—ions of opposite sign. The final rapid phase of repolarization is due to increased permeability to K^+—the outward K^+ ion current as in other excitable tissues during repolarization.

The influx of Ca^{++} ions during the initial depolarization means that cardiac fibres, unlike striated muscle fibres, cannot function in the complete absence of external Ca^{++}: they depend on entry of Ca^{++} from the external medium. Indeed the tension developed during a contraction is proportional to the amount of Ca^{++} free in the sarcoplasm. Nevertheless cardiac muscle, like striated muscle, does have SR, which takes up Ca^{++} ions during relaxation and can release them during a subsequent contraction. This can be illustrated by observations on isolated cardiac muscle fibres. If a bundle of such fibres is held at a depolarized potential for a few seconds by voltage clamping, and then allowed to contract at its normal rhythm, these subsequent contractions for the next few seconds generate much more tension (up to eight times more) than a normal contraction. The suggested interpretation of this increased contractility is that Ca^{++} ions, which have entered the fibre during the depolarization (when its membrane is very Ca^{++} permeable), have been taken up in some part of the SR from which the ions can be made readily available and their high concentration in the sarcoplasm gives the more forcible beats.

Even though the heart will continue to beat when the extrinsic nerves (vagus, cranial X, parasympathetic; and nerve accelerantes from T_1, sympathetic) have been removed, action potentials in these nerves are able to modify both the rate (*chronotropic effect*) and contractility (*inotropic effect*) of the cardiac muscle. As might

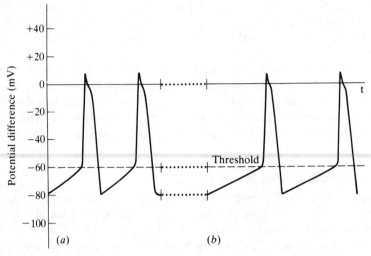

Figure 11.14 Effect of vagus stimulation on electrical change at cardiac pacemaker.(*a*) Potentials before stimulation. (*b*) Potentials during vagal stimulation, which prolongs the time required for the attainment of threshold.

be expected, the nerves have most of their terminals close to the pacemaker fibres. An example of the effect of an extrinsic nerve is given by vagus-nerve stimulation at the pacemaker (or by application of acetylcholine, the normal neuromuscular transmitter). This has the effect of increasing permeability to K^+ ions. This causes the membrane potential to approach ε_K which is slightly more electronegative than the diastolic level of $-80\,mV$; in fact the membrane tends to hyperpolarize, towards, say, $-90\,mV$. This delays or prolongs the normal spontaneous depolarization up to the threshold $-60\,mV$ (Fig. 11.14). The action potentials, and thus the contractions, come further apart in time—the heart beat is slowed. Vagal (parasympathetic) stimulation thus has a *negative* chronotropic effect on the heart beat.

General properties of cardiac muscle

The time-course of events in cardiac muscle is very different from that in striated muscle. The action potential accompanies the contraction of the cardiac muscle and lasts almost as long as the cycle of contraction and relaxation. In striated muscle the action potential is finished well before the muscle has developed its full tension. Furthermore the refractory period for cardiac muscle is much longer than for striated. The consequence is that cardiac muscle cannot be tetanized by a series of stimuli applied at high frequency: the later stimuli would arrive during the refractory period consequent on the first, and would be ineffective. (It is sometimes possible to demonstrate summation of two stimuli, if the second is applied during the *relative* refractory period resulting from the first.) The fact that cardiac muscle cannot be

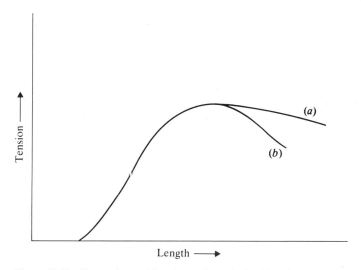

Figure 11.15 Comparison of length–tension relationship of (*a*) cardiac and (*b*) skeletal muscle fibres. Graph (*b*) is similar to the line shown for 'active tension' in Fig. 11.8.

tetanized is clearly important for its normal functioning. A tetanus, or prolonged contraction, would prevent pumping and thus would not permit the entry of blood into the chambers of the heart, the process which normally takes place as the fibres are relaxing.

Like striated muscle, cardiac muscle fibres can carry out isometric action as well as isotonic shortening, and both processes occur during every heart beat. As with striated muscle the tension developed on contraction is related to the initial length of the fibre (length–tension relationships already described.) In contrast, if cardiac muscle fibres are passively pulled out beyond the sarcomere length representing maximum overlap between actin and myosin fibrils, the force of the subsequent contraction does not fall off at increasing initial length as abruptly as is the case with striated muscle (Fig. 11.15). This may be because of the structural properties and mechanical arrangement of the connective-tissue fibres around and among the cardiac muscle. It has the effect of preventing rupture of the fibres, if the heart becomes overfilled.

The spread of the wave of contraction and relaxation over the myocardium, and the events of the cardiac cycle, are considered in Chapter 5.

Smooth muscle

Smooth muscle, present in a number of different organs, is itself functionally diverse, and shows different degrees of dependence on its innervation. *Visceral smooth muscle*, for instance, forming the main part of the intestinal wall, has two networks of nerve fibres (Auerbach's and Meissner's plexuses) outside and between its layers. The muscle fibres themselves show spontaneous slight and irregular depolarizations and there are numerous gap junctions through which excitation of one fibre could affect another. An isolated portion of an animal's intestinal wall hung in a dish of warm oxygenated Ringer solution will continue to show peristaltic movements (becoming long and narrow, or short and wide) for many hours. However, the muscle is also innervated by extrinsic nerve fibres, which affect the rate of such movement, and have a particular effect at the sphincters—the specialized rings or collars at certain points of the alimentary canal, where a strong contraction can close the lumen altogether.

For *vascular smooth muscle*, particularly the circular smooth muscle in the walls of arteries and arterioles, there is a rich innervation of (sympathetic) fibres which are tonically active. There is a continuous impulse traffic of moderate frequency, the effect of which is to keep the muscle partially contracted: in most organs a greater frequency increases, a lesser frequency decreases, the amount of contraction; thus the lumen of the arteriole can be narrowed or widened. The innervation of muscles in the walls of veins is much less abundant, and some vein muscles can show spontaneous depolarizations. *Multi-unit smooth muscle* does not contract spontaneously; it is normally activated in several regions by many motor nerves. It is entirely dependent on innervation, and functions more like striated muscle, and much more rapidly than other smooth muscle. The iris muscles of the eye and piloerectors of the skin are examples. These three sorts of smooth muscle are not as distinct as this description suggests, and there is some overlap.

The autonomic nerves supplying smooth muscles do not end on a definite motor endplate. The nerve endings show a series of swellings lying 'like a string of beads' along and between the muscle fibres; each bead contains vesicles, presumably full of the chemical transmitter. For visceral smooth muscle there is often a time-lag, even up to 2 s, between nerve stimulation and muscular response. There is a delay, too, if smooth muscle is stimulated directly, between muscle action potential and development of maximum tension. A general property of all types of smooth muscle is their great sensitivity to blood-borne chemicals, including hormones.

Thick and thin filaments are visible in EM photographs of smooth muscle, and actin and myosin have been identified by chemical means in smooth-muscle extracts (Fig. 11.16). Though there is some evidence of the existence of SR, it is likely that Ca^{++} ions have to diffuse in from the extracellular fluid, when contraction is initiated.

The typical mode of activity of smooth muscle is isotonic: the muscle fibres shorten, but do not (for the most part) develop tension along their length. The shortening brings the ends closer, and of course decreases the lumen or capacity if the muscles are arranged circularly in the walls of a tube or hollow organ.

Smooth muscle responds to a passive pull in a characteristic way. A pull has the immediate effect of increasing the tension, but this tension gradually drops away so that soon the fibres are under no greater tension than they were at the original shorter length. A further pull on this lengthened muscle causes the same response: a sudden transient rise of tension, then a slow accommodation to the increased length. So smooth muscle cannot be said to have any particular 'resting' length. This property of

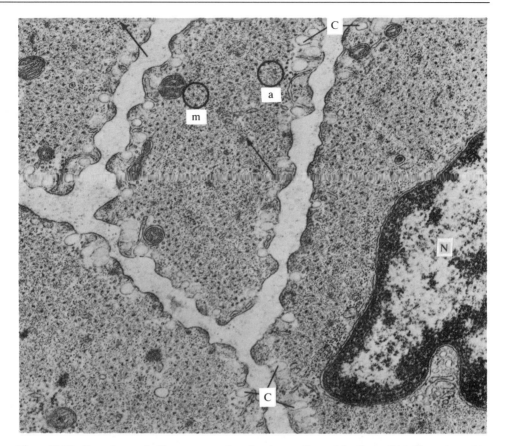

Figure 11.16 Smooth muscle. Transverse section showing portions of 4 cells. m: thick filaments; a: thin filaments; arrows: filaments of intermediate size; C: caveolae lying beneath cell membrane; N: nucleus of one of the fibres. EM. × 32 300. (Reproduced by permission from Smolyo, A. P., C. E. Devine, A. V. Smolyo and R. V. Rice, *Philosophical Transactions of the Royal Society of London*, **265B**, 223–229, 1973.)

smooth muscle is called plasticity. It is a noticeable and useful feature of the walls of hollow organs such as stomach and urinary bladder, which by this property can increase their capacity as they fill up, without any undue tension on the walls, until a limit is reached at which further filling causes wall tension which makes the signal for evacuation of the organ. The mode of contraction of smooth muscle is shown in Fig. 11.17*a–d*.

Some methods of studying muscle

When one considers how the information is obtained, it is not surprising that striated muscle is much better understood than either cardiac or smooth muscle. Simple experiments on isolated nerve–muscle preparations using striated muscles have

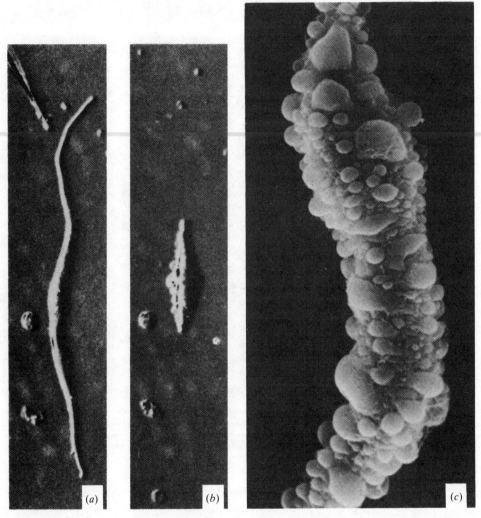

Figure 11.17 Contraction of smooth-muscle fibre. (*a*) and (*b*) Frames from cine-film showing contraction of a single smooth-muscle fibre from the stomach of the toad *Bufo marinus*. (*a*) Before contraction. (*b*) Fully contracted, 12 s after application of stimulus. × 270. (*c*) Scanning EM photograph of smooth-muscle fibre contracted to one-third of its initial length. Notice that in (*b*) and (*c*) the caveolae of the surface membrane have ballooned out. (*a–c*: Reproduced by permission from Fay, F. S. and C. M. Delise, *Proceedings of the National Academy of Sciences of the USA*, **70**, 641–645, 1973.) (*d*) Suggested mechanism of smooth-muscle contraction. A: Relaxed. B: Contracted. (*d*: Adapted from Ham, A. W. and D. H. Cormack, *Histology*, 8th edn, Lippincott, Philadelphia, 1979.)

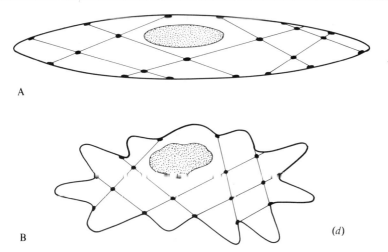

A

B

(d)

Figure 11.17   (*continued*)

elucidated such properties as refractory period, gradation of response, and length–tension relationship. Striated muscle forms 40 per cent by weight of the soft tissue of the body, so there has been an abundance of material on which to study the biochemistry of muscle, both in respect of the energy sources (glycogenolysis, ATP-splitting and citric-acid cycle) and in relation to the chemistry of the contractile proteins (structure of myosin heads and so on). Furthermore the large fibres of striated muscle make possible the use of internal electrodes for the study of muscle action potentials.

Visceral smooth muscle, particularly its sensitivity to hormones and neurotransmitters, has been studied for many years, especially by pharmacologists. A short length of intestine, excised and mounted in a water-bath, continues its spontaneous peristaltic movements, which can be recorded and modified by application of chemicals.

Much of our knowledge of events at the motor endplate has been derived from the refined microelectrode methods which have made possible voltage clamping of motor endplates; from EM, which has allowed study of synaptic vesicles; and from pharmacological methods permitting the stopping of the sequence of events at particular stages. Knowledge of the sliding or interdigitation of actin and myosin filaments during muscle contraction is based on EM study together with biochemical study of the contractile proteins. The continuity of the T-system with extracellular space was also proved by EM: by observation of the entry of ferratin particles into T-tubules.

Vesicles of SR can be prepared and studied *in vitro*. They have been shown to be able to concentrate calcium, and to release Ca^{++} ions (as revealed by radioactively labelled Ca^{++}) under electrical stimulation. Microinjection of Ca^{++} (and only Ca^{++}, among several ions tested) leads to contraction of fibres. Ingenious experiments connecting the presence of a transient 'pulse' of free Ca^{++} in the sarcoplasm with the initiation of muscle action have been carried out by the use of the bioluminescent substance aequorin, derived from the light-emitting organs of the jellyfish *Aequorea*. This substance emits a flash of light, *only* when in the presence of free Ca^{++}. Simultaneous recordings of light emission and tension development in an aequorin-loaded muscle show that the calcium transient precedes the tension development. Responses of the muscle to stimuli of various strengths and durations suggest that the rate of development of tension is proportional to $[Ca^{++}]$ in sarcoplasm, as shown by the light emission (Fig. 11.18).

For cardiac and smooth muscle the small size of the fibres has made the use of intracellular electrodes extremely difficult. The only exception is the Purkinje fibres of the ventricles of the heart, which are longer, wider and straighter than most cardiac fibres, and so permit intracellular recording. Action potentials of Purkinje fibres are transmitted rapidly, a feature connected with the large nexuses between their cells. In fact their conduction is more noticeable than their contraction, and they seem to

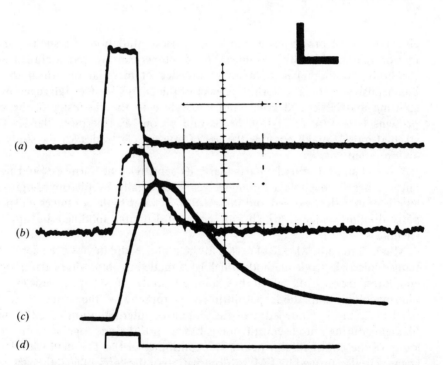

Figure 11.18 Calcium transient in contracting muscle. Recording of the effects of stimulating a muscle fibre from the barnacle *Balanus nubilis*. (*a*) Action potential of muscle. (*b*) Calcium-mediated light emission from aequorin pigment previously injected into muscle. (*c*) Isometric tension. (*d*) Stimulus marker. Notice that light emission indicating free Ca^{++} starts after the beginning of the action potential, but its start precedes the rise of tension. Maximum tension is not reached until light emission is declining. Calibration bars, top right: ordinate (*a*) 10 mV, (*b*) 5×10^{-11} lm, (*c*) 120 mg; abscissa 100 ms. (Reproduced by permission from Ashley, C. G. and E. B. Ridgway, *Journal of Physiology*, **200**, 74P–76P, 1969.)

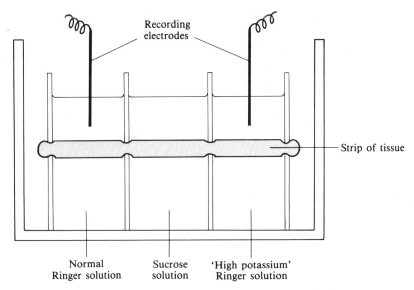

Figure 11.19 Sucrose-gap apparatus, for recording action potentials of narrow strips of cardiac or smooth muscle.

behave more like nerves than muscles. For recording electrical activity in other cardiac tissue and in smooth muscle, researchers have used a more indirect procedure called the sucrose gap. In this, a strip of cardiac or smooth muscle tissue is set up in a three-compartment chamber with minute holes in the barriers separating the compartments, in such a way that the strip straddles all three. The muscle is arranged so that its two ends and its central region can be perfused with different solutions. One end is placed in Ringer solution, the other end in 'high-potassium Ringer', a solution similar to sarcoplasm in electrolyte composition; so the membranes of this region would be depolarized. The central portion of the chamber is filled with a solution of sucrose, a non-electrolyte. The sucrose solution thus takes on the role of the cell membrane, and the potential difference between the two outer compartments is the membrane potential; it can be recorded and its alteration by various experimental manipulations can be studied (Fig. 11.19).

Summary and problems

The main part of this chapter is an account of the activity of striated muscle. Chemical and electrical events at the motor endplate are first described. Then follows a section on excitation–contraction coupling and then contraction itself: how the action potential of the muscle fibre brings about the reaction between the protein filaments by way of the T-tubules, SR and Ca^{++} ions; and how these ions allow contact and relative movement of the filaments. The isotonic and isometric activities of muscles as a whole are then described.

In the account of cardiac muscle we see how the spontaneous depolarization of a certain part can initiate an action potential, which spreads through nexuses over the entire myocardium. The long-lasting refractory period which makes tetanus impossible, and great stiffness at elongated fibre length, make cardiac muscle suitable for its function.

Smooth muscles in various parts of the body show different degrees of dependence on nerves for their normal function, but are all very sensitive to chemical stimuli. As with other types of muscle their activity depends on reversible linking of actin and myosin filaments. Their action is nearly always shortening rather than tension development. In organs where smooth muscle forms the wall of a tube or hollow organ this shortening of the muscle fibres results in squeezing or movement of the contents, or, in the case of vascular smooth muscle, a change of blood flow. The plasticity of visceral smooth muscle permits the filling of hollow organs without accompanying increase in wall tension, until a limit is reached and the organ is emptied.

In this brief account many problems concerning the function of muscles have not been considered. The role of Ca^{++} ions is clearly of central importance. How exactly do Ca^{++} ions make possible the simultaneous binding and opening of large numbers of vesicles at the presynaptic membrane of a motor nerve ending? Would any divalent cation, if it were able to enter the nerve terminal, be equally effective? Again, how exactly does the electrical change running through the T-tubule system release Ca^{++} from the cisternae of SR? And what is the significance of Ca^{++} in making the characteristic shape and long duration of the action potential of cardiac muscle? Research on all these questions is currently in progress.

The adaptive power of muscle is one of its striking properties. Physiological hypertrophy, the thickening of fibres of particular muscles as a result of much use, has been mentioned (Chapter 3 under Cell division). Furthermore under experimental conditions of prolonged low-frequency stimulation a typical 'white' muscle can become a 'red' muscle: there is an increase in the capillary density, a change from mainly glycolytic to mainly oxidative enzymes, a change in chemical structure of the myosin heads, much greater resistance to fatigue, and a slower speed of contraction. Such observations raise interesting speculations about the ability of capillaries to branch, and muscle fibres to produce different proteins and enzymes according to the type of activity being demanded of them. Adaptation of this kind, especially the alterations of capillary beds, must underlie the ability of cardiac muscle fibres to recover from mild 'heart attacks' which result from interruption of blood supply. One must admire the flexibility and versatility with which muscles can adapt to the demands made on them. One may also admire the ingenuity with which muscle physiologists have invented methods of observing submicroscopic events, and very rapid events. There is still plenty of scope for ingenuity in solving further problems in the physiology of muscle.

12 Sense organs and sensation

Introduction

General properties of sensation

Sense organs and sensory endings provide the first part of the route through which information about the environment or about the internal state of the body is conveyed to the central nervous system (CNS). Some sense organs are close to the surface of the body: skin sensory organs, the eye, the olfactory surface of the nose, and the cochlea of the ear are obvious examples. Other sensory endings are deep within the body: these include stretch-receptor fibres of the arterial walls, or muscle spindles lying among the fibres of striated muscle. These examples also illustrate the widely differing degree of specialization and complexity among sense organs. At one end of the scale is the highly specialized eye, adapted for focusing light onto a light-sensitive surface and initiating a photochemical reaction. At the other end are the various skin sensory organs, which may be no more than a much-branched naked ending of a sensory nerve fibre, unrelated to any obvious permanent structure. Muscle spindles, themselves small modified muscle fibres, are of intermediate complexity. One useful way of classifying sense organs is by reference to the type of stimulus to which they are most sensitive—light, sound, mechanical pressure, chemicals and so on. But before the listing and classification of the sense organs on this basis, consideration will be given to some general properties of sense organs and sensation.

In all cases energy in some form impinges on the sensory ending or organ, directly or indirectly affecting the membrane potential of a sensory nerve, in which action potentials are initiated and conveyed to some part of the CNS. Sense organs are therefore transducers—devices which convert one form of energy to another. In the case of the eye, for instance, light produces in the pigment of the retinal rods and cones a photochemical reaction which initiates the action potentials in optic nerve fibres. Again, the kinetic energy (pressure) of an object brought onto a touch receptor via the skin starts an action potential in the sensory nerve. There are several intermediate steps between energy input and sensory-impulse production. For some sense organs (the eye for instance) these intermediate steps are well known; for others (say, the taste buds) the steps must exist but are still quite obscure.

Müller's Law

Certain general facts about sensation and sense organs are generally recognized. One, summarized as Müller's Law of Specific Nerve Energies, is that a sense organ, however stimulated, gives rise to a certain modality or type of sensation dependent on the sense organ and its connections within the CNS, but not on the nature of the stimulus. (It seems that Müller himself considered the specificity of the various types of sensation to reside in the sensory nerve fibres; we now know that it is a matter of the sensory fibres' central pathways and connections.) An illustration of Müller's Law is the fact that a blow or pressure on the eyeball large enough to give the retina a mechanical stimulus produces the sensation of seeing a flash of light. Again, a needle inserted into a touch receptor of the skin, which might be expected to produce a sensation of pain, gives nothing but the sensation of touch at that point.

Weber–Fecher Law

The sensory organ not only gives an indication of the nature of the stimulus but also its intensity: the greater the stimulus, the greater is the number of sensory cells stimulated, and the rate of firing of the sensory nerves. Thus we can perceive differences in brightness between two lights or differences in loudness between two sounds; and the just-perceptible difference in intensity is called the difference threshold. A generalization about sensation (or about the *perception* of sensation) is summarized as Weber's Law: the difference threshold (ΔI) is a constant proportion of the mean intensity level (I) at which it is being measured (i.e. $\Delta I/I$ is constant). This means, for instance, that two rather bright lights must differ considerably in brightness if any difference between them is to be perceptible, whereas for two rather dim lights a very small difference in brightness is perceptible. Weber's Law holds fairly well for any sense organ over a large range of moderate intensities; for human vision, for instance, for moderate intensities the ratio is about 1/100; for hearing, about 1/5; for touch, about 1/10. But there are considerable departures from Weber's Law at very low and very high intensities. Weber's Law was later used by Fechner to find a relationship between intensity of stimulus and intensity of sensation. Fechner derived the formulation:

$$\text{Sensation intensity} = \text{Constant} \times \text{Logarithm of stimulus intensity}$$

This relationship has been modified as a result of later experiments, but is still useful, especially in relation to the sense of hearing, where our measurement of loudness (decibels) is in fact made on a logarithmic scale.

Generator potential

It is probable that the sequence of events occurring in all sense organs is as follows:

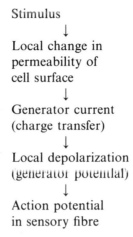

Stimulus
↓
Local change in
permeability of
cell surface
↓
Generator current
(charge transfer)
↓
Local depolarization
(generator potential)
↓
Action potential
in sensory fibre

It is difficult to study these separate steps, particularly in mammalian specialized sense organs, where the end of the sensory nerve is small, inaccessible and deeply embedded in the sense organ. Invertebrate sense organs are somewhat more accessible, and have been much used in the study of sensation. Also, the Pacinian corpuscle, a touch and deformation receptor present in mammalian connective tissue and in skin, can be dissected out and studied *in vitro*, providing a useful model for other sense organs. The Pacinian corpuscle is a hard ovoid structure consisting of a number of concentric layers of connective tissue, in the centre of which lies the free unmyelinated nerve ending of a myelinated sensory nerve (Fig. 12.1).

When the whole structure with sensory fibre is dissected from the mesentery and placed in a dish of Ringer solution (artificial extracellular fluid), a stimulus in the form of a measurable small movement can be applied, and a response recorded from the corpuscle itself and from the nerve fibre. In this way it is possible to record from the corpuscle a *generator potential*, the size of which increases with increasing strength of stimulus. An *action potential* is observed in the nerve fibre when the generator potential has reached a certain threshold voltage. The generator potential is thus *not* an all-or-none phenomenon, but a graded response. It has the same properties as those of the endplate potential, or the local excitatory state of a single nerve axon; it quickly dies away and decreases at a distance from its source. The action potential in the sensory nerve axon appears to start when the first node of Ranvier is depolarized, so it seems that the sensory threshold means a stimulus strong enough to allow adequate generator potential to reach and depolarize this first node. The Pacinian corpuscle functions just as well *in vitro* after all the layers of connective tissue have been removed. Clearly the connective tissue is not essential and the sense 'organ' is the nerve ending itself.

Generator potentials (also called receptor potentials) have been identified (with some difficulty) in other sensory structures and it is assumed that these potentials occur in all such structures and are the immediate stimulus to the sensory fibre. It is suggested that the generator potential is itself started (like the action potential) by an

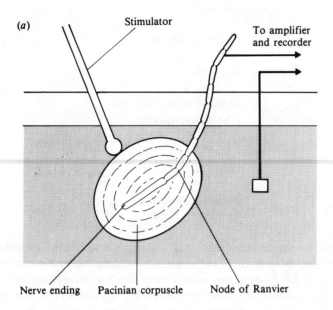

(a)

Stimulator

To amplifier
and recorder

Nerve ending   Pacinian corpuscle   Node of Ranvier

(b)

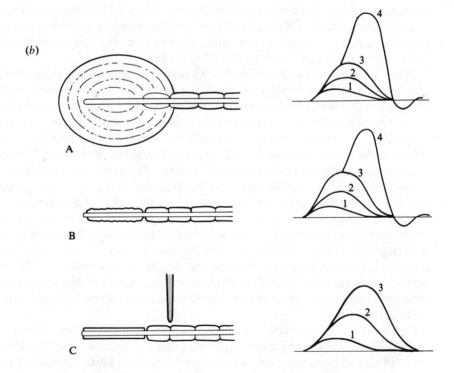

A

B

C

alteration in membrane permeability and influx of Na^+ ions, but direct evidence is hard to obtain.

Classification of sensory receptors

Table 12.1 gives a list, classified according to the type of initiating stimulus, of the main types of sensory receptors. It is clear from this table that mechanoreceptors—the organs sensitive to touch, pressure, deformation, movement of solid bodies or of air—

Table 12.1 Sensory receptors

Stimulus	Intermediate process	Examples of receptor types and sensation
Mechanical force (including sound waves)	Unknown ?Change in permeability of nerve ending. ?Release of specific chemical	1. Pressure and touch receptors in skin and subcutaneous tissue
		2. Muscle spindles and Golgi tendon organs, responding to alteration in length and tension of muscle, and giving position sense
		3. Stretch receptors (baroreceptors) in walls of heart and blood vessels
		4. Vestibular apparatus of inner ear, sensitive to head movement
		5. Cochlea of ear, serving hearing
Light	Photochemical reaction in visual pigments, giving stimulus to optic nerve	Photoreceptors (rods and cones) in eye, serving vision
Heat	Unknown	Thermoreceptors: two types, for (a) warm and (b) cold
Substances in solution	Unknown. ?Direct excitation receptor cell surface. ?Smell-substances attach to receptor surface	Chemoreceptors for (a) taste, and (b) smell. Osmoreceptors. Carotid and aortic-body receptors
Extremes of mechanical deformation or heat or cold, certain chemicals	Destruction of tissue cells. ?Release of chemical substance from them	Pain sensation

◀ **Figure 12.1** Pacinian corpuscle, a simple sense organ. (a) Apparatus used for applying very small stimuli to a single Pacinian corpuscle and recording the potentials in the nerve. (b) A: A series of generator potentials of increasing amplitude (1–3) result from application of stimuli of increasing strength to the intact Pacinian corpuscle shown beside the trace; only when a still greater stimulus is applied is an action potential (4) produced. B: The same result is obtained when the layers of connective tissue are stripped from the nerve ending within the corpuscle. C: When the first node of Ranvier is compressed, no action potential can be elicited, however large the stimulus. (Reproduced by permission from Mountcastle, V. B. 'Sensory receptors and neural encoding: introduction to sensory processes', in Mountcastle, V. B. (ed.), *Medical Physiology*, 14th edn, Mosby, St Louis, 1980; modified from Lowenstein, W. R., 'Biological transducer', *Sci. Am.*, **203**, 98, 1960.)

are themselves a heterogeneous collection, of differing degrees of complexity. The stretch receptors (baroreceptors) lying among smooth muscle fibres in the circumference of the walls of blood vessels have been mentioned in Chapter 5. Muscle spindles and tendon-organs, signalling length and tension of striated muscle, will be considered in detail in Chapter 13. The vestibular apparatus and the cochlea, both quite complex structures and of great importance to most vertebrate species, including man, are the subjects of later sections of this chapter.

The order in which sensory receptors are considered in this chapter is more or less arbitrary, but it follows a sequence of increasing complexity of structure, starting with skin sensory endings, both mechano- and thermoreceptors; and finishing with the eye. Perception of pain is considered in a separate section.

Skin sensory endings

Nerve endings in the skin are capable of responding to four modalities of sensation: warmth, cold, touch and pain. But there are no anatomically distinctive receptors corresponding with these modalities. A dense interlocking network of small sensory

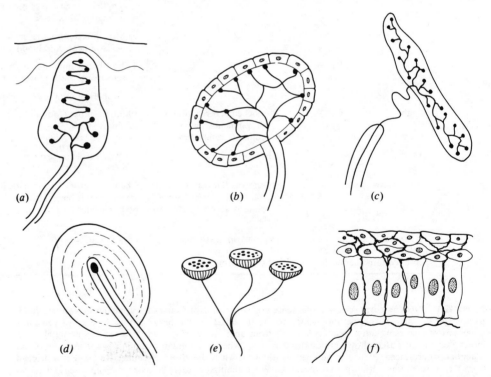

Figure 12.2 Cutaneous receptors. (*a*) Meissner's corpuscle. (*b*) Krause's end-bulb. (*c*) Ruffini ending. (*d*) Pacinian corpuscle. (*e*) Merkel's disc, expanded ends of sensory fibre. (*f*) Naked nerve endings among cells. (Reproduced with permission from Ganong, W. F., *Review of Medical Physiology*, 13th edn, copyright Appleton & Lange, San Mateo, 1987.)

nerve endings is found below the epidermis. Among this network there are found some nerve endings which are encapsulated in layers of connective tissue forming various shapes; other nerve endings lie free among the epithelial cells of the skin, and may themselves be of several shapes. Histologists have given names to the encapsulated endings on the basis of their shape and position: Meissner's corpuscles, Krause's end-bulbs and Pacinian corpuscles. Types of free nerve endings are named Ruffini endings and Merkel's discs (see Fig. 12.2). It is not possible to relate any particular modality of sensation on the skin surface to any particular morphological structure in the sensory ending lying below that portion of skin. If an area of skin is carefully mapped by locating and marking spots sensitive to warmth, cold or touch, and then the skin is excised and examined histologically, no anatomically specific sensory ending below the spots is found. Indeed sensitive spots on the skin may shift around: the 'map' itself changes, even from day to day, as sensory endings are dying or being destroyed and then re-forming as regenerating nerve fibres approach the skin surface.

Touch

Pacinian corpuscles and Meissner's corpuscles are mechanoreceptors, and the rich network of sensory endings around the base of hair follicles is sensitive to movement of the tip of the hair. Touch-sensitive spots are common on hairy skin, and also on the glabrous (hair-free) skin of the fingertips and lips, but the number of Meissner's corpuscles in the fingers decreases with age, and also with heavy use of the hands. The ability to identify simultaneous touch of two separate points on the skin as two (not one) depends on the part of the body touched. In humans, on the skin of the back the two points have to be about 70 mm apart to be recognized as two (the 'two-point threshold'). On the fingertip the two-point threshold is 2 mm; on the back of the finger it is about 6 mm. Again, the threshold of pressure or deformation of the skin surface which is just perceptible as a touch depends on the area of skin stimulated, the most sensitive areas in this respect being the skin of the fingertips, lips, nose and forehead, and the least sensitive the thick skin on the soles of the feet. Blind readers of Braille, and carpenters who test smoothness of wood surfaces by the fingers, are well aware of the value of the touch receptors of the fingertips.

Adaptation is a striking feature of the sensation of touch. It means the cessation of the sensation even though the stimulus is still present. Many sensory modalities show adaptation to some extent (though pain sensation shows very little adaptation). Adaptation may be a peripheral phenomenon in some cases—the sensory nerve fibres reduce or cease their action-potential traffic; in other instances it may be a matter of a central process—the perception or awareness of the sensation ceases, even though sensory nerve impulses continue. It seems that touch-sensory fibres are of two kinds. One kind shows a sudden burst of impulses as soon as a stimulus is applied and then adapts quickly, but may show another burst when the stimulus is removed. The other kind shows an initial burst at high frequency and then a steady long-continued train of action potentials at lower frequency as long as the stimulus is present. So this type of fibre would respond both to movement or deformation of the skin *and* to steady pressure. But there must also be a central component in adaptation to touch: by an effort of attention one can become aware of the touch of clothing on one's skin surface, although this sensory input is normally ignored.

Temperature

In humans temperature-sensitive areas of the skin surface can be found and carefully plotted and recorded, by means of stimuli consisting of small test-tubes containing water of various known temperatures. In animals action potentials in temperature-sensitive nerve fibres can be recorded during the application of such stimuli. In this way it has been found that one group of sensory endings are stimulated in the temperature range 35–40 °C; these are called 'warm receptors', though there is no receptor which can be identified anatomically and 'warm *endings*' would be better a term. Another group of fibres is stimulated in the temperature range 10–30 °C, and *also* above 45 °C. These are called 'cold receptors'.

Figure 12.3 records the frequency of impulses in temperature-sensitive fibres in the tongue of a cat at various temperatures. It is apparent that at about 16 °C, and also at about 37 °C, the 'cold receptor' is discharging at about 3 impulses/s; but at 37 °C, there is *also* some warm-ending impulse traffic, whereas at 16 °C, there is none. It is the combined message of both sets of sensory endings that gives the CNS information about the temperature of the skin. When 'warm' and 'cold' endings in the skin of a man's back are stimulated simultaneously by a flow of warm and cold water through two separately coiled tubes placed against his skin, he has the sensation of being scalded. The precise range of temperature sensitivity of the sensory endings varies in

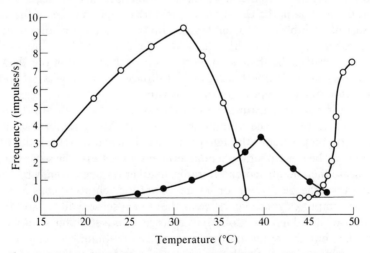

Figure 12.3 Impulses from temperature-sensitive endings in tongue of cat, at various temperatures. (O—O) Cold receptor; (●—●) warm receptor. (Reproduced by permission from Dodt, E. and Y. Zotterman, *Acta Physiologica Scandanavica*, **26**, 345–357, 1952.)

different parts of the body. For the receptors of the tongue of a cat, where the ambient temperature is about 37 °C, the cold receptors discharge maximally at about 32 °C. The human skin is normally at a lower temperature, and human-skin cold endings show a maximum frequency at about 30 °C.

Observations on several mammalian species including humans have revealed a significant difference in response of thermal receptor endings according to whether the temperature is rising or falling. During a rise in temperature a warm-sensory nerve shows a burst of impulses of high frequency and then settles down to a steady frequency level somewhat higher than its rate of discharge before the temperature rise; conversely, as temperature falls the firing rate first falls steeply, then settles to a steady but slightly lower firing rate. Thermal sensory endings are thus able to convey information about direction of change in temperature of the skin, as well as its absolute temperature.

As in the case of the sensation of touch there is adaptation in the sensation of cutaneous warmth and cold. The sensory ending continues to discharge and the adaptation is entirely a central effect. The size of the just-detectable change in skin temperature of an area of skin depends both on the general background of skin temperature and on the rate of application of the change in temperature. For a test temperature change suddenly applied, humans can detect a change in skin temperature (up or down) of as little as 1 or 2 °C. But at a gradual rate of change, the change has to be made much larger before it can be detected.

Temperature sense, particularly skin temperature, is of considerable biological importance to mammals and birds, in which deep body temperature is normally maintained at a steady level, fluctuating only in a small range. The skin sensory input is one of the factors providing information to the CNS, in consequence of which various temperature-controlling responses come into action: in a cold environment, for instance, shivering and piloerection or ptiloerection (the fluffing out of hair or feathers) would be initiated (see Chapter 10).

Chemoreceptors

Chemoreceptors are stimulated by the presence of certain substances in solution touching the chemosensitive cell. It is supposed that the chemical substance combines with a specific receptor group on the cell surface, and it is this chemical reaction which triggers the action potential along the sensory nerve; however, the intermediate steps are not clear. Many animals, including many invertebrate species, have far more acute chemosensation than humans have. It is astonishing that pheromones—substances secreted by female moths and other insects—can cause a response in receptor cells on the antennae of male moths some miles away, a distance over which the pheromone molecules must have become greatly diluted. Again, elasmobranch fish such as sharks can detect prey by water-borne chemicals at a great distance through the ocean. These two examples also illustrate two of the functions of chemoreception: the finding of a mate and the finding of food. A third important function for some mammalian species is avoidance of danger: the timely detection of the scent of a predator or rival may facilitate the escape of the prey or prevent a damaging fight.

To act as a stimulus, a chemical substance must be water-soluble or fat-soluble (or both). Marine and freshwater animals are surrounded by water-borne chemicals; but for terrestrial species the stimulating substance must either be taken into the mouth and dissolved in saliva; or be volatile: that is, it must have sufficient vapour pressure to give abundant airborne molecules which reach a chemoreceptor surface and dissolve in a layer of moisture there. The sniffing shown by dogs and many creatures when close to an object of chemical interest brings a stream of airborne molecules into the nose and over the olfactory surface. Metals—iron, for instance—have so little vapour pressure that they cannot be smelt (at least by man); but ferrous salts taken by mouth do have a distinctive taste.

This section describes the receptors which serve the senses of taste and smell in mammals. These are called chemical *exteroceptors*, because they are on or near the surface of the body. The reader is reminded that chemical *interoceptors* deep within the body have already been mentioned. Examples are the cells of the carotid and aortic bodies, sensitive to the level of blood oxygen and responsible for initiating potentials to the respiratory and circulatory centres (Chapter 6); and the osmo-receptor cells of the hypothalamus of the brain, sensitive to the total osmolar concentration of the plasma and responsible for sending information to the neurohypophysis (Chapter 7).

Taste

The receptors serving the sense of taste (gustation) are the taste buds, which occur in groups on the tongue on small structures called papillae, which are of various shapes and sizes. Taste buds are also present on the surface of the epiglottis and on the insides of the cheeks. There are more in children than adults, and there are said to be about 9000 taste buds in adult man. The greatest concentration occurs on the top and sides of the front two-thirds of the tongue.

Each taste bud is a barrel-shaped structure made up of a group of about 50 elongated cells (modified epithelial cells), lying just below the epithelial surface of the tongue. The upper ends of the cells bear microvilli which project into a small pore (taste pore) on the epithelial surface; and it is, presumably, by the microvilli that the taste bud makes contact with the substances dissolved in the saliva. The innervation arises from the base of the taste bud; each afferent nerve fibre is much branched, and its branches go to several taste buds and several receptor cells within each taste bud. Around and below each taste bud are basal cells, forming a stock available for replacement of receptors. It is thought that each individual taste-bud cell (in mammals) lasts only about a week; there is continuous turnover as the basal cells differentiate and then degenerate. This means that there must be continuous remodelling of the synaptic connection between taste-sensory fibres and receptor cells.

Humans can distinguish four types of taste, which are called sweet, sour, salty and bitter. It is likely that other species can distinguish other and more numerous tastes:

taste-sensory fibres in the chorda tympani branch of the dog's facial nerve (cranial VII) respond with a train of action potentials when distilled water is made to flow over the tongue. The sensation of 'sweet' is produced not only by sugars but also by numerous organic compounds, including glycerol and amino acids, and even by lead acetate. 'Sour' is produced by acids; 'salty' by many salts, especially those of sodium and potassium; and 'bitter' by various organic substances, including quinine. It is likely that the taste buds or receptor cells within them are not specific for one kind of taste: they may have a lower threshold to one than another, though several may provide some degree of stimulation. Taste buds on all areas of the tongue are sensitive to all tastes, but it is thought that the tip of the tongue is the most sensitive area to 'sweet', the sides to 'salt' and 'sour', and the back to 'bitter'.*

The 'taste' of food is compounded of a mixture of sensations including smell and touch as well as taste. The 'tastelessness' of food while a person suffers from a cold in which mucous secretion blocks the olfactory surface of the nose is a familiar experience. The biological value of taste is obviously a matter of seeking nutritious foods and rejecting poisonous ones. Some animals, particularly herbivores on salt-poor pastures, show a craving for salt, and will travel long distances to salt-licks. Humans, too, if suffering from a salt-losing disease, show a 'salt-appetitite'; and in parts of Africa edible earths containing salts having nutritional value are used as condiments.

Smell

The sense of smell (olfaction) is served by the olfactory surface, lying in a cavity in the inside roof and side-wall of each nostril. The end-organs are themselves nerve cells, so a distinction between 'generator potential' and 'action potential' would be meaningless here. The cell bodies are rather elongated, and are supported between tall sustenicular cells (see Fig. 12.4a–c). Small hair-like projections are present on the outer surface of each receptor cell. The inner end tapers to a typical unmyelinated nerve axon which passes through a small bony plate (cribriform plate) into the cranial cavity, where it immediately makes synaptic connections with neurones of the olfactory bulb. From the mitral and tufted cells of the olfactory bulb two main tracts of nerve axons arise: the medial olfactory tract, which passes to the opposite side of the brain; and the lateral olfactory tract, which lies on the same side as the original olfactory surface. Both tracts terminate in a region called the prepyriform cortex, which was one of the earliest portions of the brain to develop in evolutionary history, and which is more prominent in other mammals than in primates. Indeed behaviour patterns suggest that the sense of smell is far more significant in the lives of other mammals than in human life.

An impressive feature of the sense of smell is the enormous diversity and variety of smells which can be distinguished and identified. The sense can be trained, too, as

---

*In man the ability to taste certain substances is genetically controlled. Most humans can taste the (unpleasant-tasting) substance phenylthiourea. Inability to taste this substance is inherited as a Mendelian recessive.

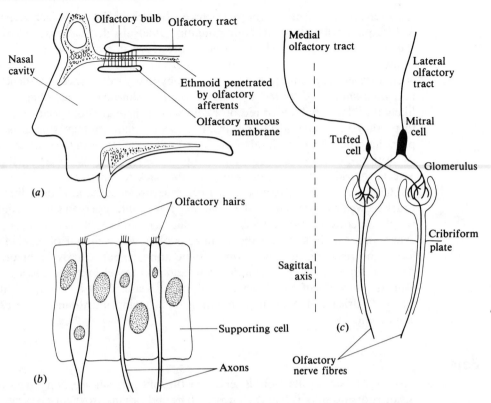

Figure 12.4 (*a*) Position of olfactory surface in man. (*b*) Structure of olfactory cell. (*c*) Olfactory pathways to sensory cortex of brain. (Reproduced by permission from Horrobin, D. F., *Medical Physiology and Biochemistry*, Arnold, London, 1968.)

gourmets and dog-handlers are well aware. But to find any anatomical explanation for this diversity of sensation is a baffling problem. Unlike tastes, smells cannot be sorted or classified into a few primary types, though several attempts have been made to group odiferous substances on the basis of chemical structure or molecular shape. Because of its inaccessibility and small size, one cannot record from a single axon of the olfactory surface. Within the olfactory bulb thousands of axons contribute to each single bunched network of fibres—called a glomerulus—and each glomerulus receives dendrites from dozens of different mitral and tufted neurones, and thereafter sends impulses up different olfactory tracts. There are thus enormous possibilities of divergence and convergence in the patterns of action potentials received in the prepyriform cortex, and it must be these complicated patterns of activity which become recognized by the brain and identified with the odiferous substances.

For many species olfaction is essential. The seeking of food, mating behaviour and avoidance of danger are dependent on the sense of smell. For man the sense is useful but perhaps not essential. It adds much to the pleasure of eating and drinking. It contributes to the avoidance of substances harmful to eat. It is also an emotive sense, and has a remarkable power to evoke memories. Many people have experienced, on smelling a rare or unusual odour, an instant recall of the last occasion of smelling it, perhaps many years previously.

Adaptation, at least in man, is a noticeable feature of the sense of smell. This property may in fact be dangerous. A person may notice the smell of a poisonous gas for the time of one or two breaths, then quickly adapt to it, and so fail to move out of danger. It is not known whether the adaptation is a cessation of the initial sensory impulses or of the central processes.

Vestibular apparatus

In the vestibular apparatus of the inner ear, we may study at last a structure worthy of the name of sense *organ*. The skin receptors and chemoreceptors are indeterminate; as we have seen, warm and cold spots move in position and alter in number as sensory endings degenerate and regrow; the cells of taste buds are impermanent and have a rapid turnover; and from the appearance of receptors giving the senses of touch, thermal sense, taste and smell, one could make no intelligent guess as to what was their normal type of stimulus or what sensory information they conveyed. For such tenuous transient structures the general terms 'receptors' and 'sensory endings' are appropriate. For the eye, cochlea and vestibular apparatus the position is quite different. Here are large, conspicuous and permanent organs. The eye is so like a camera and the tympanum so like a drum surface that one may readily surmise not only their sensitivity to light and sound but also something about their mode of action. From the structure of the three semicircular canals of the vestibular apparatus, set at right angles to each other in the three planes of space, one could deduce a sense organ somehow connected with orientation or the movement of the body in space. The vestibular apparatus is an ancient structure in terms of vertebrate evolution. The three semicircular canals are present in fish and birds as well as terrestrial animals. Indeed the essential component of the vestibular sense organs—the hair cells embedded at their tips in a semisolid structure, and of which the bending by a shear force can stimulate action potentials—is present in the otolith organ of invertebrates also. Lateral-line organs of fish and the organ of Corti in the cochlea are modifications or elaborations of this general pattern.

The inner ear of mammals contains two separate sense organs; the cochlea, serving the sense of hearing; and the vestibular apparatus, supplying information about orientation and movement in space (Fig. 12.5). This consists of the three semicircular canals, the utriculus and the sacculus. The vestibular apparatus and the cochlea together are called the *labyrinth*.* They fit into a hollow portion of the temporal bone of the skull, called the *bony labyrinth*, to distinguish it from the thin-walled membranous labyrinth within. Inside the cavities of the membranous labyrinth,

_____

* The terms 'labyrinth' and 'vestibular apparatus' are used interchangeably in some textbooks. In much of the medical literature the term 'vestibular apparatus' is replaced by 'labyrinth'.

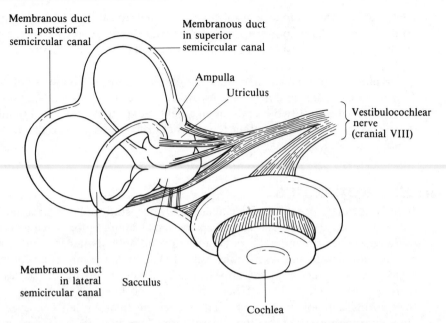

Figure 12.5 Vestibular apparatus, showing its relation to the cochlea. (Reproduced by permission from Vander, A. J., J. H. Sherman and D. S. Luciano, *Human Physiology: The Mechanisms of Body Function*, 4th edn, McGraw-Hill, New York, 1986.)

including the central canal of the cochlea, is a fluid called endolymph, which like intracellular fluid has a high potassium concentration. Between the bony and the membranous labyrinth, percolating a meshwork of connective tissue, is a fluid called perilymph, which like extracellular fluids elsewhere is high in sodium. (Perilymph is also present in two of the three canals of the cochlea.)

The three semicircular canals, which lie in the three perpendicular planes of space, are joined at their ends to the utriculus, and close to one end of each canal is a swelling, the ampulla. The sense organs consist of three *cristae*, one present in each ampulla, and two *maculae*, one found in the utriculus and one in the sacculus; these five structures in each inner ear are the vestibular proprioceptors. Each sense organ consists of a bunch of elongated sensory epithelial cells, with supporting cells among them, and a long extension or sensory hair projecting from the tip, and embedded in a gelatinous mass (the cupula) over the top of the crista or macula. In the case of the macula the gelatinous cupula has small crystals or particles of calcite embedded in it.

The sensory innervation of all five vestibular organs is provided by the vestibular branch of the vestibulocochlear nerve (cranial VIII). The cell bodies lie close to the middle ear in the vestibular ganglion, and the sensory fibres run mainly to the vestibular nuclei and midbrain; a few run directly to the cerebellum.

The stimulation to the sensory nerve is initiated by distortion of the hair cells embedded in the cupula when the cupula moves relative to the crista or macula. In the

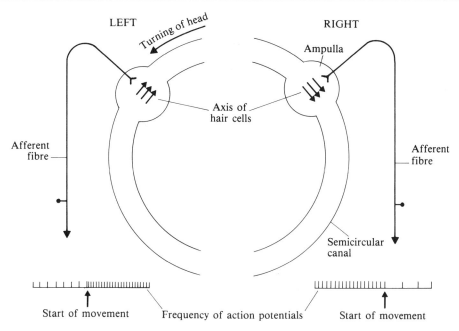

Figure 12.6 Movement of fluid in horizontal semicircular canals, man. When the head is turned to the left (as shown by long arrow) the endolymph within the *left* semicircular canal is 'left behind' by its own inertia and the effect is to force the hair cells of its ampulla to bend in the direction shown by the short arrows; in the right semicircular canal, the inertia of the endolymph forces the bending of the hair cells in the opposite direction. (Adapted from Vander, A. J., J. H. Sherman and D. S. Luciano, *Human Physiology: The Mechanisms of Body Function*, 4th edn, McGraw-Hill, New York, 1986.)

case of the semicircular canals this distortion is caused by inertial movement of endolymph fluid, during rotation of the head.

When the head is suddenly turned to the left, the endolymph lags behind, and presses against the cupula, distorting the hair cells. When the rotation of the head suddenly stops, the fluid continues to move, and the hairs are pulled in the opposite direction. In this way the nerve is stimulated at the beginning and at the end of the rotatory movement. If a smooth rotating movement of the head were continued, say on a turntable moving at a constant velocity, the cupula would return to its resting position by its own elasticity, the hair cells would not be bent, and the person might be unaware of the movement until it stopped, thereby causing another inertial movement of the endolymph (Fig. 12.6).

In the case of the utriculus and sacculus the hair cells of the sensory surface (macula) have their tips embedded in a structure called the otolith membrane, consisting of fibrils embedded in a gelatinuous mass which includes a layer of calcite crystals, the otoconia.

Figure 12.7 shows the effect of gravity on the utriculus. With head erect the otolith membrane lies uniformly on the hair cells of the macula. When the head tips forward,

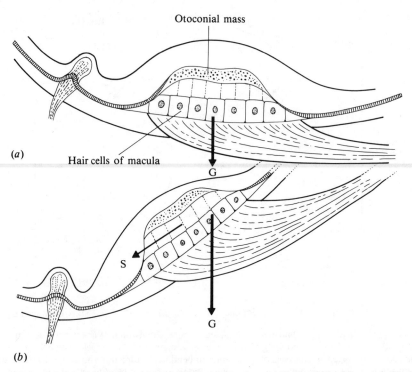

Figure 12.7 Action of the utriculus (man). (*a*) Head erect. (*b*) Head tilted forward. The hair cells of the macula are sensitive both to movement, as the head is tilted forward; and also to position, as this tilt is held. G: direction of gravity; S: direction of shearing force as otoconial mass moves on hair cells. (Adapted from Davson, H. and M. B. Segal, *Introduction to Physiology*, vol. 4, Academic Press, London, 1978.)

the otolith membrane slides downwards and the resulting shearing force on the hair cells causes discharge of the sensory neurones.

In man when the head is upright the plane of the macula in the utriculus is approximately horizontal, and that in the sacculus is approximately vertical, parallel with the sagittal axis of the body. The cristae of the semicircular canals, by movement of the endolymph against the cupula, give information about *change* in position of the head; the maculae of the utriculus and sacculus signal both the *change*, as for instance when the head nods forward, and the *sustained position* of the head in this position, where the effect of gravity on the otolith membrane is different from that in the upright position. In fact these receptors do not adapt.

Hearing

Hearing and vision are the chief means by which man and many other vertebrate species extract information from the environment at a distance from the body surface; and in many animals the search for food and for a mate, and the avoidance of danger, are carried out through these senses. The fact that humans and other animals can produce sounds as well as hearing them means that information can be communicated between individuals of the same or other species. The alarm call of a blackbird warns other birds of danger; the cry of an infant brings its mother. But this communication is made possible only by the past history and learning of each individual. Human speech, a highly complex set of sounds, can communicate the most subtle ideas and emotions, but only if the language used is known to the hearer.

Properties of sound

Sound waves are a series of waves of condensation and rarefaction in air (or water). The distance from the centre of one condensation to the next is called a cycle, and the pitch of a sound is determined by the number of cycles per second reaching the ear. The sound waves cause vibration of the eardrum (tympanum) at the inner end of the auditory meatus; these vibrations, transferred and amplified via a series of small bones (ossicles) and another membrane (fenestra ovalis), initiate movement of fluid in the spiral tube (cochlea) where the auditory nerves originate. It is these fluid movements, causing movement of the hair cells of the organ of Corti within the cochlea, that initiate action potentials in the auditory nerve. Normal human hearing covers a range from 20 cycles per second (cps, or hertz, abbreviated to Hz) up to 20 000 Hz, or 20 kHz. The sounds of human speech are normally in the range 200–4500 Hz. Many species of animals can hear (and produce) sounds of frequencies above the range of human hearing. Dogs can hear whistles inaudible to man. Humans tend to lose hearing in old age, particularly of high frequencies ('high-tone deafness'); many children but few adults can hear the squeak of a bat.

Structure of ear and route of sound waves

The main parts of the ear are shown in Fig. 12.8.

The pinna is of use in many species (rabbit and elephant, for instance) in locating the source of sounds in the environment. It is moved by small muscles at its base to face in the general direction of a source of sound; this is a reflex action stimulated by the sound itself, and its result is to increase the precision with which the sound is located. In man the pinna and its muscles are vestigial; in many aquatic mammals it is non-existent. Sound waves enter the auditory meatus. In adult man the size and shape of this tube is such that it has a natural resonance frequency of about 3000 Hz, which is in the middle of the range of frequencies to which the ear is most sensitive. It acts as an amplifier at these frequencies; and the effect is to increase the energy at the inner end, the tympanum, as compared with that at the outer end.

Beyond the tympanum is another air-filled space, the middle ear, across the top of which are suspended the three ossicles: the malleus (hammer), incus (anvil) and stapes (stirrup). The 'handle' of the malleus lies against the tympanum, and the 'footplate' of the stapes lies against another much smaller membrane, the fenestra ovalis (oval

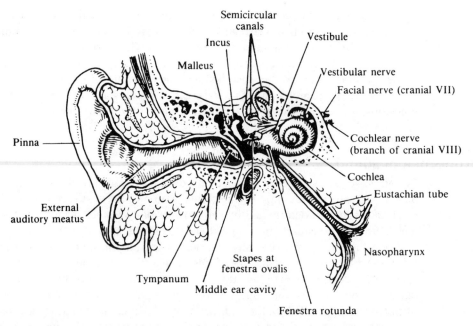

Figure 12.8 The main structures of the ear (man). (Reproduced by permission from Young, J. Z., *The Life of Mammals: Their Anatomy and Physiology*, 2nd edn, Oxford University Press, London, 1975.)

window) stretched across a perilymph-filled space, the vestibule, at the base of one channel of the cochlea itself.

The three small ossicles are hinged against each other and move in series; the hinging arrangement reduces the *amplitude* of movement, from handle of malleus to footplate of stapes, by a factor of two-thirds, and this increases the *pressure* at the fenestra ovalis by a factor of one and a half, as compared with the pressure at the tympanum. Furthermore the fact that the fenestra ovalis is a much smaller membrane than the tympanum increases the pressure differential, and it is calculated that the pressure at the fenestra ovalis is 22 times that at the tympanum (Fig. 12.9).

The structure of the tympanum, including both circular and radial fibres, and having the handle of the malleus lying along one radius, means that it has no natural resonance frequency: it is completely damped, and stops vibrating as soon as the sound waves cease in the auditory meatus. The tympanum is not quite flat, but slightly conical, the tip of the cone lying inwards towards the middle-ear space. A small muscle, the tensor tympani, is attached to the handle of the malleus; its contraction pulls the malleus and thus the tympanum slightly inwards. Another small muscle, the stapedius, is attached to the stapes, as shown in Fig. 12.9. Contraction of these muscles has the effect of stiffening the tympanum, slightly decreasing the movement of the ossicles and thus reducing the audibility of sounds. The muscles are reflexly stimulated by sound: the louder the sound, the greater the contraction of the muscles. It is

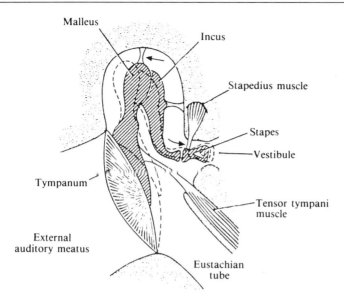

Figure 12.9 Ossicles of the ear, showing their movement during displacement of the tympanum. (Reproduced by permission from Young, J. Z., *The Life of Mammals: Their Anatomy and Physiology*, 2nd edn, Oxford University Press, London, 1975.)

thought that this device is protective, saving the delicate structures of the cochlea from damage by excessively loud noises. Some species of bat have an additional function for the middle-ear muscles. Bats use echo-location during flight, emitting squeaks the sound of which, reflected from solid surfaces and returning to the ear, enables the bat to perceive the position and distance of objects in its flight path. The middle-ear muscles move rhythmically in relation to the squeak-producing larynx: they contract about 5 ms before the squeak is emitted and relax again over the next 10 ms; thus the audibility of the sound during its emission is reduced, but the ear is fully sensitive in time to receive the returning echo.

Another important feature of the middle ear is the Eustachian tube, which connects the air-filled space beyond the tympanum with the pharynx at the back of the mouth, thus allowing equalization of pressure on the two sides of the tympanum. A sudden change in atmospheric pressure such as occurs during an aeroplane's descent may strain the tympanum causing pain, but this can be relieved if the subject makes swallowing movements, thereby opening up the pharyngeal end of the Eustachian tube.

Cochlea

The actual organ of hearing lies in the cochlea, a membrane-lined tubular space inserted into the temporal bone. The tube is coiled into a spiral; the number of turns of

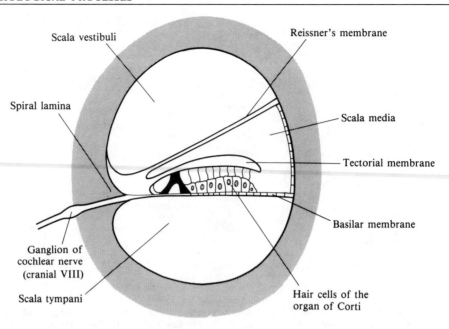

Figure 12.10   Cross-section through one turn of the cochlea, to show three segments divided by two membranes, and position of organ of Corti.

the spiral varies in different species: there are three and three-quarter turns in man, for instance, and four and a half turns in the guinea-pig. The lumen of the cochlea is divided by two membranes into three segments; the membranes are attached along one edge to a projection (spiral lamina) from the central bony core of the spiral (the modiolus), and along the other edge to the outer side of the bony tube (see Fig. 12.10).

Two of these three segments, the scala vestibuli and the scala tympani, are filled with perilymph; the third, the scala media, is filled with endolymph. In fact one may think of the scala media as being formed by a finger-like outgrowth of the wall of the sacculus, which pushes its way out into a pocket of perilymph, the vestibule, gradually separating two portions of this perilymph, one above it and one below (Fig. 12.11). The two portions are never quite separated: a tiny hole (helicotrema) connects them, at the apex of the cochlea.

Pressure waves impinging on the fenestra ovalis (Fig. 12.11) at the base of the scala vestibuli are transmitted to the perilymph within and this causes corresponding vibration of Reissner's membrane, which is under tension. This in turn causes vibration of the endolymph of the scala media, and of the basilar membrane, the (upper) surface of which is modifed to form hair cells and supporting cells. These cells constitute the organ of Corti, the organ of hearing, and they are responsive to pressure changes of the endolymph. Pressure changes of the endolymph are gradually dissipated as movements of the basilar membrane, transferred to the perilymph of the

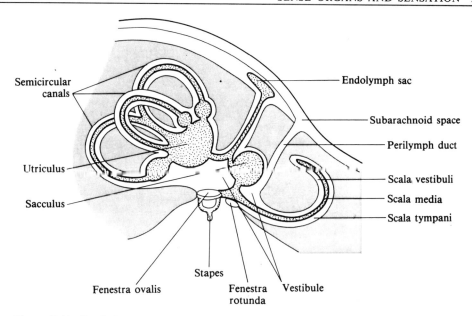

Figure 12.11 Vestibular apparatus and cochlea, to show relation of perilymph and endolymph. Bone, shaded; perilymph, white; endolymph, stippled. The endolymph within the semicircular canals is connected via the sacculus with that in the scala media of the cochlea. (Reproduced with permission from Ganong, W. F., *Review of Medical Physiology*, 13th edn, copyright Appleton & Lange, Los Altos, 1987.)

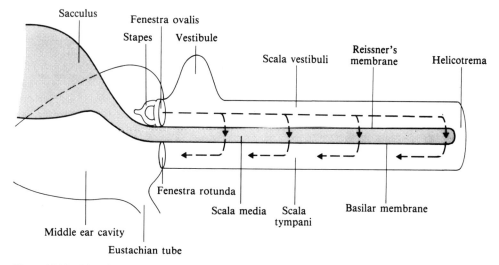

Figure 12.12 Direction of movement of pressure wave through vestibule and scalae of cochlea as stapes vibrates during reception of sound.

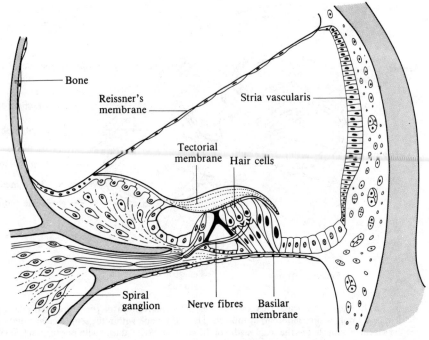

Figure 12.13 Organ of Corti. (Reproduced by permission from Young, J. Z. *The Life of Mammals: Their Anatomy and Physiology*, 2nd edn, Oxford University Press, London, 1975.)

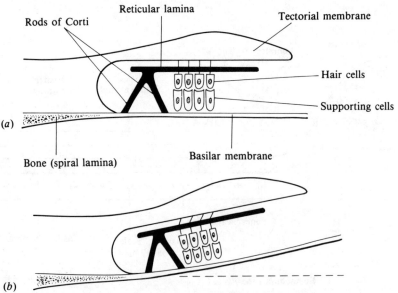

Figure 12.14 Basilar membrane. (*a*) At rest. (*b*) During an upward deflection, showing how the rigid rods of Corti and reticular lamina cause a shear on the hair cells.

scala tympani, cause bulging in and out of the fenestra rotunda (round window) into the air space of the middle ear: inward movements of the oval window cause outward movements of the round window (Fig. 12.12) and vice versa. The helicotrema at the apex is too small to permit flow of fluid or transmission of pressure.

Figure 12.13 shows the organ of Corti diagrammatically. Figure 12.14 indicates the changes as the basilar membrane moves. The 'hairs' at the tips of the hair cells project through the reticular lamina, a thin tough sheet, and their ends are embedded in a viscous elastic structure, the tectorial membrane, the inner edge of which is attached to the bony shelf projecting from the modiolus. The reticular lamina is supported at its inner end by a rigid triangular arrangement, the rods of Corti, standing on the basilar membrane. So when the basilar membrane moves, the reticular lamina moves correspondingly. A shearing action between the stiff structures (tectorial membrane and reticular lamina) bends the hairs on the hair cells. This bending stimulates the sensory nerve endings in among the supporting cells below the hair cells. The cell bodies of these sensory endings form the spiral ganglion which lies in a cavity in the modiolus, whence axons run to collections of nerve cell bodies in the wall of the brain stem at the point where the vestibulocochlear nerve (cranial VIII) emerges.

Perception of pitch, loudness and timbre

The frequency or pitch of a sound determines the precise point along the length of the basilar membrane which is maximally displaced by the vibratory movements, and thus which particular hair cells are maximally stimulated. Loudness or intensity of sound is detected by the amount or amplitude of the basilar membrane's displacement, and thus, presumably, by the number of hair cells and sensory fibres activated, and the frequency of the impulse traffic along the sensory fibres. The interpretation of quality or timbre of a sound is thought to depend on the precise form of the wave in the basilar membrane. It is the timbre of sounds—a matter of overtones, resonance and various ill-defined properties—which permits the human ear to distinguish a note of a given fundamental frequency sounded on, say, a violin from the note of the same frequency on a piano or a bell. Timbre also allows recognition of individual voices. Such recognition has to be learnt, and in childhood it is learnt very quickly: the 3-week-old human infant can apparently distinguish its mother's voice from other female voices. The ear can also be trained: Mozart is said to have been able to distinguish notes differing by a quarter of a semitone. It is remarkable, too, that many humans can pick out the individual notes of a chord sounded simultaneously on the piano, in spite of the effect of the masking of high notes by those of lower pitch.

The nature of the wave in the basilar membrane set up by sounds has been elucidated mainly by brilliant work on the guinea-pig's cochlea, which is about 35 mm in length. Sound sets up in the membrane a travelling wave moving from the stapes at the basal turn towards the apex of the cochlea; and the rate of travel is extremely rapid. Even if, under experimental conditions, vibration is initiated at the apical end of the cochlea, the wave still travels from stapes to apex. This implies that the direction of travel of the wave is a matter of the structure of the basilar membrane itself, not of the

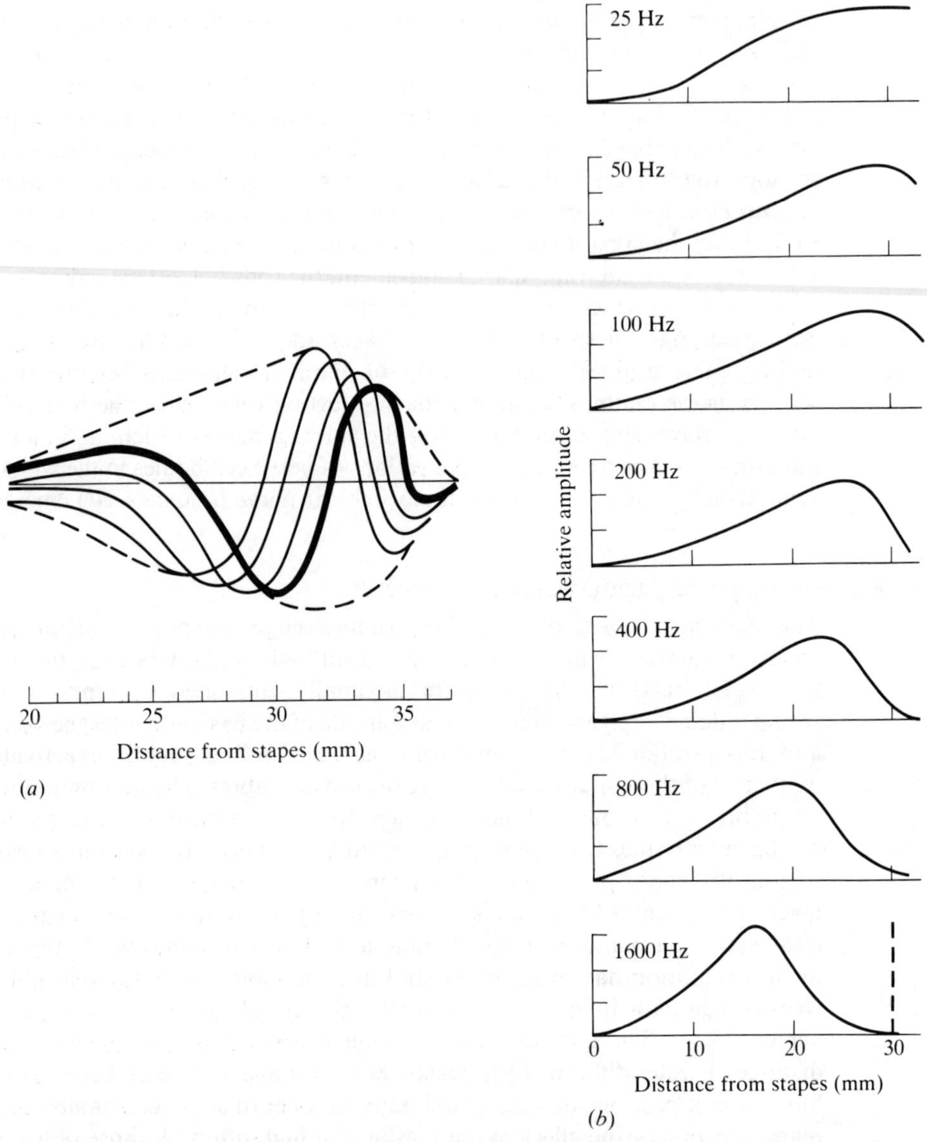

Figure 12.15 (*a*) Travelling wave along basilar membrane, 200 Hz sound. Displacement of membrane at four sequential instants, the dark curve occurring last. Dotted lines show envelope of displacement waves. (*b*) Sound waves of different pitch (frequency) are seen to cause maximum movement of the basilar membrane at points different distances from the stapes; the lower the frequency, the further is the point of maximum displacement. (*a* and *b*: Adapted from Békésy, G. von, *Experiments in Hearing*, McGraw-Hill Book Co. Inc., New York, 1960.)

place where vibration has started. The membrane is narrower (60 μm in the guinea-pig), thicker and stiffer at the base of the spiral (stapes end); wider (500 μm), thinner and more compliant at the apical end; there is a graded increase in compliance of more than 100-fold, from stapes to apex. A similar variation in width and compliance is found in the human basilar membrane. The shape of the wave is shown in Fig. 12.15. Figure 12.15a indicates the 'envelope' of displacement of the basilar membrane, for a sound of 200 Hz. Figure 12.15b shows that the maximum displacement of the membrane takes place at different points of the membrane, according to the pitch of the sound: further from the stapes for low notes, closer to the stapes for high notes.

Some problems in the physiology of hearing

It was implied earlier that the pitch of a pure tone is detected by the precise position along the basilar membrane at which maximum vibrating displacement occurs—the so-called 'place theory' of pitch discrimination. But this theory is not altogether satisfactory: there is not a sharp peak at the summit of the basilar membrane's displacement curve, and at every frequency a large number of hair cells are activated, not a few specific ones. In a cat, for example, it has been estimated that 3000 hair cells are activated by a tone of 1000 Hz at a given loudness, and 2940 of these same hair cells are activated by an adjacent tone (distinguishable by the cat's ear) of the same loudness. The physical basis of pitch discrimination is not yet fully explained.

Another mystery is exactly how the hair cells initiate the generator potential which starts the action potential in the auditory nerve fibres. One idea is that the bending of the hairs of the hair cells may alter the cells' membrane potential (60 mV, inside negative). There exists also a potential difference across Reissner's membrane, between the perilymph of the scala vestibuli, and the endolymph of the scala media (80 mV, endolymph positive). The vascular lining (stria vascularis) against the bony wall of the scala media actively maintains this potential difference. Shifts in these membrane potentials have been detected during auditory stimulation, and are called cochlear microphonics. They might cause a current flow which releases some chemical transmitter which might stimulate the auditory nerve endings. The current flow might cause the generator potential, and in fact intracellular recordings from hair cells during a sound stimulus have detected 20-mV generator potentials.

A number of other problems in the physiology of hearing remain to be elucidated. The basilar membrane and hair cells seem too blunt an instrument to be the only source of the very precise and subtle analysis and discrimination of sounds. Such analysis at least in respect of pitch and intensity may start here at the periphery in the organ of Corti. But several orders of neurones are interposed between the hair cells and the auditory cortex of the brain, with much branching and overlap between their axons; the interpretation of sounds could lie in the learning of the precise path of the nerve impulses along this complex network, and the precise region of the auditory cortex thus activated. Moreover there are efferent (descending) fibres originating in a particular region of the brain (superior olive) and terminating on the hair cells of the organ of Corti or on nearby afferent neurones. The effect of impulse traffic along these descending tracts is to *inhibit* the response of the hair cells or afferent nerves. These impulses are thought to assist in providing 'fine-tuning' or 'discrimination', enabling a hearer to pick out a particular sound from simultaneous masking noises. Certainly, cutting the olivary–cochlear tract in experimental animals impairs their ability to make discriminations. But it is not clear yet exactly how the system works.

Another problem is the ability to locate sources of sound in the vertical plane. Location of sound sources from one or other side of the body (horizontal plane) is done by assessment of the different times at which the sound waves reach the two ears, and by the partial blocking or 'shadowing' effect of the head. But it is hard to explain one's ability to locate a sound source directly in front of the body as being either high above the head, or down close to the ground, or in front of the face; presumably the sound waves from such sources would reach the two ears at exactly the same moment. In fact location in the vertical plane is not very efficient; high-pitched sounds tend to be judged erroneously high in space, and low-pitched sounds erroneously low in space. But the fact that sounds can be placed at all in the vertical plane needs explaining. All these problems mean that there is still scope for research into the physiology, biophysics and psychology of hearing.

Vision

Vision is the most important sense for man and the other primates, and indeed for many species of vertebrates active in the daytime. The eyes receive light waves reflected from the surface of objects and focused by the cornea and lens onto the photosensitive cells of the retina. Here photochemical reactions initiate sensory impulses conducted via several orders of neurones to the lateral geniculate bodies of the brain, and thence to the visual cortex in the occipital region at the back of the brain. This process causes the formation of a mental image of the objects. The size, shape, position, distance and (for some species) colour of objects can thus be identified. But the recognition of objects requires more than this. It needs experience, provided partly by information from the other senses, especially the sense of touch; and it is also necessary that the whole visual field should give to the brain a consistent meaning.

Structure of the eye, the eye muscles, accommodation and movement

The eyes are almost spherical and are inserted into the two hemispherical cavities of the skull, the orbits. Their front surfaces are protected by the eyelids, moveable flaps of skin, of which most species have two for each eye and some have three, the third one moving across from the nasal side.

The rigid outer case of the eyeball (sclera) is modified in front to form the transparent cornea (Fig. 12.16). The front surface of the cornea is constantly lubricated by fluid secreted by the lacrimal gland at the top; this fluid drains away through a small tube (tear duct) with an outlet at the back of the nasal cavity. Attached to the inside of the sclera around the cornea is an annular projection, the

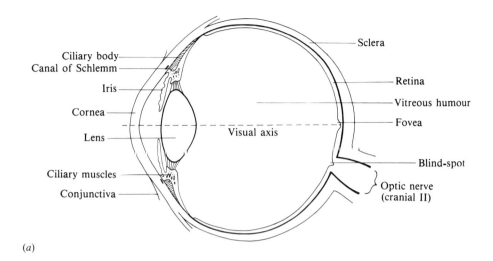

(a)

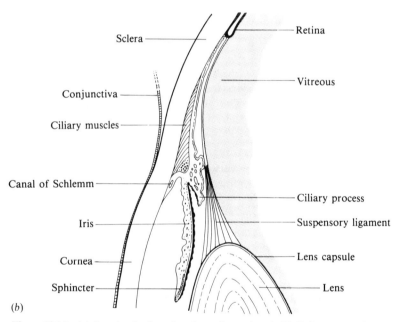

(b)

Figure 12.16   (a) Longitudinal section through eye (man). (b) Enlargement of a part of the longitudinal section, to show upper edge of lens and related structures. (a and b: Reproduced by permission from Young, J. Z., *The Life of Mammals: Their Anatomy and Physiology*, 2nd edn, Oxford University Press, London, 1975.)

ciliary process, which can be moved slightly by the small muscles within it. To the outer edge of the ciliary process there is fixed the thin suspensory ligament, which holds the biconvex crystalline lens of the eye. Movement of the ciliary process alters the tension on the suspensory ligament, and thus slightly alters the shape (and the focal length) of the lens. The space between the lens and the cornea is filled with aqueous humour (often called simply the 'aqueous'). The space between the lens and the retina is filled with the more viscous vitreous humour ('vitreous'). The aqueous is derived from blood plasma and has a composition similar to that of a protein-free plasma. There is a rapid turnover rate of aqueous (about once per hour, in humans), which is constantly being secreted and draining away along the small canal of Schlemn. (In old age this canal sometimes becomes partially blocked, causing a build-up of fluid in this chamber, and undue pressure on the lens and cornea.) Neither lens nor cornea has a direct blood supply. This fact is convenient for eye-transplant surgery: corneal grafts can be carried out without fear of an immune reaction and tissue rejection. The refraction of light rays and the focusing of the image onto the retina is brought about by the cornea, aqueous and lens. Of these, the only alterable part is the front surface of the lens. In the relaxed position of the ciliary muscle, when the eye is adjusted for seeing distant objects, and parallel light rays are focused onto the retina, the front surface of the lens has less curvature than the back surface (Fig. 12.16).

When the eye is focused on near objects, the ciliary muscle contracts. The suspensory ligament becomes slightly looser, allowing the lens to take a more spherical shape, and its front edge bulges forward. This process shortens the focal length of the whole refractive system and allows the image of the near object to be formed on the retinal surface. The action of the ciliary muscles in adjusting the refractive system for distant and close vision is termed accommodation. In humans the physical properties of the lens alter rather suddenly some time between the ages of 40 and 50: the lens becomes harder and more viscous. This means that even the maximum exertion of the ciliary muscle cannot alter the shape of the lens enough to bring near objects into focus. People in this age group often need reading glasses, to supplement their eyes' focusing.

In front of the lens lies the iris. This comprises two sets of smooth muscles: circular (sphincter) muscles, which on contraction close the space (pupil) in the centre, and somewhat weaker radial muscles, which on contraction open the space and enlarge the aperture. These sets of muscles are innervated by parasympathetic and sympathetic nerves, respectively, which are both tonically active. Increase in intensity of the light falling on the retina increases the parasympathetic tone and decreases pupillary diameter, and vice versa (Chapter 10). The iris muscles also work in cooperation with the ciliary muscles: accommodation for vision of near objects is accompanied by decrease in pupil size. The iris-muscle reflexes are easily elicited and seen in normal individuals, and are therefore much used as a diagnostic sign in neurological examination. They are influenced by many drugs, including drugs of addiction. A number of chemicals either initiate or inhibit the effects of autonomic nerve stimulation, and can be applied directly to the iris in solution in eye drops. One such compound, the drug atropine, inhibits the parasympathetic, thus enlarging the pupil by allowing sympathetic tone to dominate; oculists use this procedure to help in examination of the retina.

The pigments present among the muscles of the iris in most species are supposed to have a protective function, absorbing light and so preventing excessive intensity of light from damaging the retina; but direct evidence for this function is scanty. All human eyes contain an inner pigmented layer of the iris, giving the effect of blue; and this is masked in many people by an outer brown layer. There is a slow turnover of the brown pigment (gradual formation and destruction); and the rate of formation decreases in old age: eye colour becomes less deep. The rate of formation also decreases in extreme cold. One of the members of an early expedition to the Antarctic set out with brown eyes and returned 3 years later with blue eyes.

The muscles which move the whole eyeball in the orbit (called extrinsic muscles) are striated muscles, six for each eye. Their origin is in the bone of the orbit, and they are inserted around the curve of the back of the sclera. Man and many other creatures have stereoscopic vision—forward-looking eyes with a large overlap in the fields of vision of the two eyes. In such species the eye muscles work synergistically (in cooperation), so that moving the eye, say, towards the right involves contraction of the right eye's lateral rectus muscle and relaxation of the left eye's lateral rectus (and also contraction of the left eye's medial rectus and relaxation of the corresponding right eye muscle) (see Fig. 12.17).

Besides the large and comparatively slow movements of the extrinsic eye muscles, which occur as the eyes fixate and follow a moving object, there are also continuous slight jerky and totally unconscious movements, called saccades, the effect of which is to bring the image of the visual field onto slightly different points of the retina from moment to moment, thus preventing adaptation of the sensory receptors. This adaptation would otherwise occur very rapidly. If by experimental devices the image is kept at one point on the retina, the object seen becomes invisible in a matter of

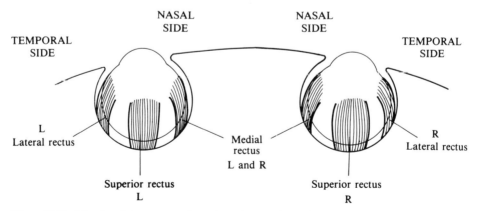

Figure 12.17 Muscles of the eye, seen from above (man). Three of the six muscles of each eye are shown; the inferior rectus and superior and inferior oblique are omitted.

seconds. These slight movements of the extrinsic muscles cease during deep sleep but are still present in light sleep, which is often called REM (rapid eye movement) sleep.

In summary, the eye, directed by its extrinsic muscles towards an object in the field of vision, receives light rays through its pupil, appropriately adjusted in size by the iris muscles. The rays are refracted by the lens system and, by appropriate accommodation of the ciliary muscle, brought to a focus on the retina.

The retina: rods and cones

The retina consists of three (main) layers of cells, all of which are derived from the CNS; they are in fact modified nerve cells (Fig. 12.18).

The first layer reached by the light coming through the lens system and vitreous is a layer of ganglion cells, the axons of which travel over the retinal surface and are bundled together and pass to the back of the retina, leaving the back of the sclera as the optic nerve (cranial II). Next comes a layer of bipolar cells; then finally a layer of rods and cones, which contain the photosensitive pigments. Behind this, right against the inner wall of the sclera, is a very thin almost structureless layer of pigmented epithelium. It is remarkable that in vertebrates the rods and cones should appear to be pointing the 'wrong' way: one might have expected these photosensitive elements to be at the front, receiving the light as soon as it has been transmitted through the vitreous.

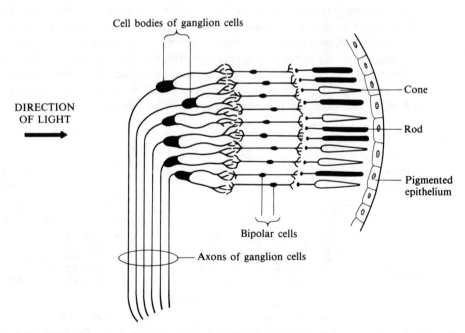

Figure 12.18   Layers of cells in the retina. Axons of all ganglionic cells course over the retinal surface and pass through the thickness of the retina at the blind spot. (Adapted from Gregory, R. L., *Eye and Brain: The Psychology of Seeing*, Weidenfeld & Nicholson, London, 1966.)

Instead, the light rays must traverse at least two layers of nerve cells before reaching the point where they start the photochemical reaction. At the retinal surface there occurs the formation of the image, and consideration of geometric optics shows that this retinal image must be inverted. Objects are of course 'seen' as upright; the reorientation of the objects in the visual field, like so much else in the visual process, must occur in the course of the central processing of retinal information.

The structure and function of the retina has been most thoroughly studied in primates and cats, but broad similarities of structure suggest that the retina in other mammalian species functions in much the same way. The rods and cones, the light-sensitive cells, are of slender cylindrical shape the cones being of slightly larger diameter, and tapering to a point at the inner end. In primates, cones are densely packed at a spot, the fovea centralis, directly opposite the centre of the lens. Outside the fovea there is a mixture of cones and rods, the proportion of cones decreasing with distance away from the fovea; in the peripheral parts of the retina, the photosensitive cells are almost entirely rods.

The functions of the two types of receptor are different. The cones function in bright light and in primates also operate in colour vision. Their close packing at the fovea gives great precision to the image formed at this point on the retina. A person or animal viewing a small object adjusts the eye to focus the image directly on to the fovea; when threading a needle, one uses a bright light and looks directly at the needle's eye. The rods function only in dim light—twilight, moonlight or any other type of semi-darkness. In bright light their photosensitive pigment is bleached and non-functional. Rods are extremely sensitive in conditions of semidarkness. It has been calculated that a rod gives a response to about 10 quanta of light; even one single quantum will initiate a photochemical reaction. Obviously for effective vision in semidarkness the image must be formed at the periphery of the retina where rods are abundant. Astronomers looking at dim stars, and people such as night-flying pilots using control panels in darkened rooms, train themselves to use peripheral vision by looking, not directly at the object, but slightly to one side of it.

The respective connections of cones and rods with the bipolar cells and ganglion cells give a further indication of these two types of function. A cone near the centre of the fovea connects with only one bipolar cell, which in turn connects with one ganglion cell, so effectively the cone has a 'private line' to the brain, a situation which makes for great precision and visual acuity, provided that there is sufficient light to activate the cone. For the rods there is considerable convergence of connections: a number of rods converge on one bipolar cell, and several bipolar cells on one ganglion cell. At the periphery there may be as many as 200 rods all contributing to the stimulation of one ganglion cell. This provides the possibility of spatial summation: a light source which would be below threshold visibility if only a few rods initiated impulse transmission becomes visible by the convergence of many impulses simultaneously on the ganglion cell.

The axons of the ganglion cells run through the thickness of the retina in forming the optic nerve (cranial II). Obviously at this point of the retina, slightly to the nasal side of the fovea, there are no rods or cones, and this is the blind-spot: objects from which the light rays form an image here would be invisible. Axons on the retinal surface, and retinal blood vessels also, course *around* the fovea, not across it; and this detouring also contributes to the acuity of foveal vision.

Retinal pigments and colour vision

There are four photosensitive pigments in the sensory elements of the retina of man and other primates. The rods contain the pigment rhodopsin, which is present in fairly large quantities and can be readily extracted after death from excised peripheral parts of the retina. The other three pigments are present in the cones, each cone containing only one of the three types. These pigments (called the red/yellow-sensitive, the green-sensitive, and the blue-sensitive photopigments) are difficult to extract and isolate, and little is known about them except the wavelengths of their photosensitivity. As seen in Fig. 12.19, these three photopigments have their maximal absorption at different wavelengths, but with considerable overlap in their range: in light of wavelength 559 nm, for instance, the red/yellow-sensitive cones would give a maximal response, the 'green' cones considerable response and the 'blue' cones none at all. It can be surmised that the colour as seen by the observer depends on the relative number of cones of each type involved and the extent of their stimulation; and the blending of

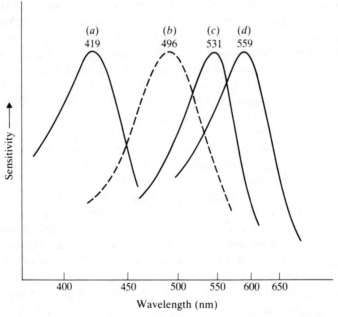

Figure 12.19   Sensitivity of four types of receptors of eye (man). (*a*) Blue cones. (*b*) Rods. (*c*) Green cones. (*d*) Red cones. Numbers give wavelength, in nm, of maximum sensitivity. (Adapted from Vander, A. J., J. H. Sherman and D. S. Luciano, *Human Physiology: The Mechanisms of Body Function*, 4th edn, McGraw-Hill, New York, 1986.)

colour sensations would be analogous to the mixing of paints or coloured lights to produce intermediate colours. (In humans a common type of colour blindness is 'red/green blindness', in which there is deficiency or absence of either the red/yellow-sensitive pigment (protanopia) or the green-sensitive pigment (deuteranopia).) Colour sensation, however, does not originate solely in the cones; it seems that the ganglion cells may contribute to it. Some ganglion cells respond to a bipolar cell and thus to a cone, and convey to the brain information about wavelength and brightness of the light; other ganglion cells (opponent colour cells) respond to, say, blue light with a high-frequency burst of impulses (superimposed on the steady background frequency) and to red light with a *decrease*, or inhibition, of the background frequency.

Colour sensation is clearly of value in helping recognition of objects in the visual field. Its extent differs in different species: colour vision is more restricted in range in dogs and cats as compared with primates. Certain humans who have defective colour vision find that this is of little disadvantage in ordinary life. They can usually recognize and even name colours 'correctly'—that is, like people with normal colour vision—and it may be only by chance or after specific testing that their defect is revealed.*

The precise sequence of chemical events occurring during photoreception has been worked out fairly well for rhodopsin, the only pigment which can be conveniently studied. The rhodopsin is contained in a series of discs arranged in a pile along the length of the rod. At the base of the pile is the part of the cell containing the mitochondria and nucleus, and then comes the tapering portion making the synaptic connection with the bipolar cell. The rhodopsin molecule is a protein (opsin) covalently linked to a pigment-containing portion, the chromophore, retinene. On exposure to light the chromophore changes shape but remains linked to the opsin. The distortion of the chromophore makes the whole molecule unstable; it spontaneously breaks down, breaking the covalent bonds. This breaking has the effect of shutting down Na^+ ion channels in the surface membrane; and this *hyper*polarization of the membrane is the electrical signal to the bipolar cell, thence to the ganglion cells and so on. In the dark a series of enzymes catalyse the regeneration of the rhodopsin. Retinene is related chemically to the carotenoid pigments and vitamin A, which is formed during the steps of resynthesis.

In bright light the rhodopsin will remain in the broken-down 'bleached' state and the rods will remain hyperpolarized. On passing from bright to dim light the eyes require several seconds to become dark-adapted, during which time rhodopsin is regenerated. Perception is then possible of light of quite low intensity, but not colour: objects appear black or shades of grey, or (in twilight) shades of blue, since there is overlap between the absorption spectra of rhodopsin and the blue-sensitive photopigment (see Fig. 12.19). A dark-red rose would appear black in dim light and a light-red rose pale grey. The poet who wrote of 'Two red roses across the moon' could not have perceived their redness by moonlight, and must have had prior information about their colour.

---

* Some types of defective colour vision are inherited as sex-linked Mendelian recessives and are therefore of great interest to human geneticists.

Visual pathways in the brain

Activity of each ganglion cell in the retina, as we know by recording their action potentials, is related to stimulation by a small point light-source of an area of the retina, roughly circular, called the receptive field. Some of these ganglion cells increase their rate of firing when the light spot is in the centre of the receptive field: these are 'on-centre' cells. Other ganglion cells—'off-centre' cells—*decrease* their rate of firing when the centre of the receptive field is illuminated, and increase firing rate when the periphery but not the centre is illuminated (see Fig. 12.20).

The axons of the ganglion cells from the retina form the optic nerve (cranial II). Different bundles or tracts are formed by axons from different regions of the retina: for

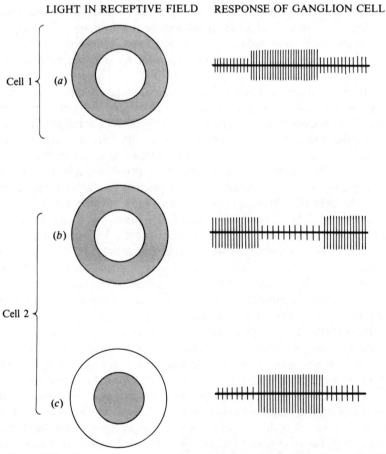

Figure 12.20 Response of two types of ganglion cell to illumination of receptive field. Cell 1 increases its activity (action potentials, right) when the centre of its receptive field is illuminated as shown, left (*a*). Cell 2 decreases its activity when the centre of its receptive field is illuminated (*b*), and increases its activity when the centre is darkened (*c*). (Adapted from Vander, A. J., J. H. Sherman and D. S. Luciano, *Human Physiology: The Mechanisms of Body Function*, 4th edn, McGraw-Hill, New York, 1986.)

instance a large bundle of small axons, the maculopapillary tract, emerges from ganglion cells of the fovea. At the optic chiasma on the base of the brain, there is a crossing-over of all axons from the nasal side of the retina of each eye, but not of those from the temporal side. The imaginary line of division runs vertically through the fovea, so the maculopapillary tract of each eye is itself split into nasal and temporal portions, the former crossing to the contralateral side, the latter continuing on the ipsilateral side (see Fig. 12.21). Beyond the optic chiasma the axons continue on each side of the base of the brain as the optic tracts, which reach a part of the thalamus of the brain, the lateral geniculate bodies (LGBs).

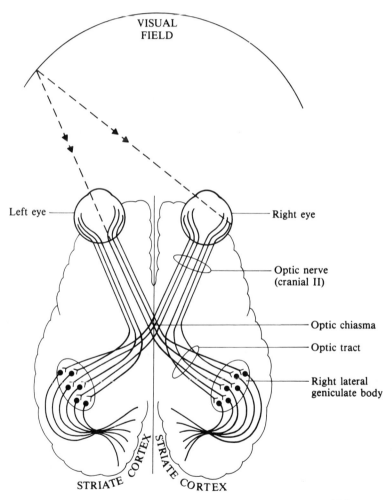

Figure 12.21 Optic tracts, from eyes to striate (visual) cortex (man). Main nerve tracts as if seen from *above* the brain; in fact these tracts run close to the *base* of the brain, and the optic chiasma is clearly visible on the basal surface when the brain is removed from the skull.

Before reaching the LGBs, branches of the axons have already separated out, in the region of the optic chiasma and optic tracts, to:

1. centres controlling the correlation of visual information with information from other sensory sources, notably those concerned in balance;
2. centres controlling the pupillary and ciliary muscles;
3. centres controlling circadian rhythms, closely connected in some species with the pineal body.

Within each LGB there are six well-defined layers of cells, separated by layers of fibres. The two afferent inputs (contralateral nasal and ipsilateral temporal axons) are kept separate among these layers (the nasal fibres end on cells of layers 1, 4 and 6, the temporal on cells of layers 2, 3 and 5). Recordings of action potentials from cells in the LGB have shown a similar point-by-point relationship to portions of the retinal fields as shown by the ganglion cells: there are similar 'on-centre' and 'off-centre' cells, as revealed in experiments where light spots are directed to points in the retinal receptive fields.

For mammals the final recognizable stage of visual processing occurs in the visual cortex at the back of the brain, also called the striate cortex. The striate cortex has been studied intensively since the early 1960s and it has become clear that many of the cell bodies here do not have a simple point-by-point relationship to areas of the retina. Certain cells of the striate cortex respond to the retinal image of an edge between light and dark; the line edge may have a preferred direction for different cells: vertically across the visual field for some cells, horizontally for others, obliquely for others. A group called 'hypercomplex' cells respond to angles or corners in the field of vision. So it is possible to imagine how the electrical responses of a certain pattern of simultaneously firing cells would enable the brain to encode the *shape* of an object in the visual field.

The mammals used for observations on the visual cortex have mainly been cats and monkeys, species which, like man, have stereoscopic vision (forward-looking eyes). It is perhaps unfortunate that test objects in such experiments have nearly always comprised patterns of straight lines. Straight lines are extremely common among man-made objects but almost unknown in Nature. So one may well speculate about the behaviour of cells in the striate cortex of wild animals, which, unlike experimental cats and monkeys, are not surrounded by man-made objects such as cages with vertical sides and corners.

It has been clearly shown that connections in the visual cortex have to be established by use, and that neurones rapidly degenerate if unused. An ingenious experiment was carried out in which kittens which had been reared in an environment of light and dark horizontal stripes were found to be unable to see shapes of objects having mainly vertical lines. It is certain that a rich visual experience in early postnatal life is essential for proper development of the visual cortex (Blakemore, 1974).

Binocular and stereoscopic vision, and perception of distance

Most animals which have eyes at all have two, one each side of the head or face. This may greatly increase the extent of the visual field. In many birds and in mammals with narrow skulls the fields of vision of the two eyes do not overlap very much, and the total angle of the visual field is enormous. For the rabbit the visual fields of the two eyes overlap in front, behind the head, and over the top of the head; the only objects out of sight of a rabbit are those immediately under its chin. The advantage of a large visual field for a predatory species, or for a species subject to predators, is obvious.

If the two eyes are forward-looking, as in man, the visual field is not greatly enlarged, but the possibility of distance and depth perception — stereoscopic vision — is increased. (A few birds such as owls also have stereoscopic vision.) In man the visual fields of the two eyes overlap, except for a narrow angle at each side. Part of the perception of depth and distance is given by the slightly different representation of the visual field on the retina of the left and right eye. However, it is still possible to judge depth and distance even if the sight of one eye is lost. Clues such as shadows allow the observer to differentiate, say, a sphere from a disc. The recognition of objects and comparison of their actual and apparent size is an important factor. An observer looking out of the ninth-floor window of a building and seeing cars in the street below is aware that he is far above them, since he knows that when he is close to a car it takes up the whole of his field of vision whereas at this distance he can see many in the same field. On a clear day with an uninterrupted view over the earth's surface, we can see as far as the visual horizon, a distance of 68 km, where the curvature of the earth cuts off visibility. But it is extremely difficult to judge distances, say, at sea or across a desert, where there are no recognizable objects of known size between oneself and the horizon. Clues about depth and distance are also given by the phenomenon of perspective—the apparent convergence of horizontal lines known on other evidence to be parallel; and by parallax—the apparent movement, as the observer moves, of stationary objects relative to each other, if they are at different distances from the observer. Perspective and parallax in interpretation of the visual world are learnt by experience and are somewhat sophisticated processes of interpretation. Some people are unaware of perspective; perhaps a large number of horizontal parallel lines in one's environment are needed to create such awareness. Many such lines are present among man-made objects, but few exist in non-human Nature.

Interpretation of the visual world

It is clear from this account that the formation of the image on the retina is only the first stage of the process of seeing; and that little is known about the central processes which must take place in the visual cortex as one sees the objects and interprets the field of vision. The correlation of visual information with information from other senses is of great importance; as an infant simultaneously looks at and handles objects, it is learning to correlate vision with touch. An important requirement for vision is that the whole visual field should be self-consistent: it must 'make sense' to the observer. The effect of trick-pictures and optical illusions reveals the unconscious

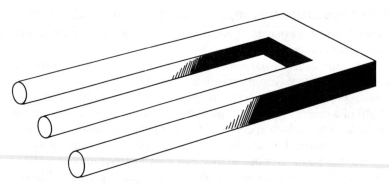

Figure 12.22 'The Devil's Trident': an optical illusion seen in perspective as either a three-pronged or a two-pronged fork. (Adapted from Gregory, R. L., *Eye and Brain: The Psychology of Seeing*, Weidenfeld & Nicholson, London, 1966.)

human desire to recognize objects and place them in appropriate contexts; and an inability to do so is somehow disturbing. The trick-picture in Fig. 12.22 suggests at its right-hand end a two-pronged fork with a space between the prongs, and at its left-hand end a three-pronged fork; by scanning the whole field one becomes aware of the internal inconsistency, and sees that the picture does not represent a real object; and one resents having been momentarily deceived in the interpretation of the visual world.

Again, as 'we hear what we listen for', so we see what we expect to see (or even what we wish to see). Proof-readers are well aware of the tendency to 'read' the word expected in the context, instead of the word actually written. A cat gazing sleepily at a television screen showing humans will suddenly leap up and rush towards the screen when the picture shows a bird fluttering across the field; the cat sees something which is recognizable and interesting, and it makes an appropriate response. It is likely that humans, too, see what interests them, and suppress whatever fails to 'make sense' in their visual world. For vision more than for any other sense the mental component plays a dominant role.

Pain

Pain differs from all other senses in that there is no single stimulus which gives rise to the sensation. There is no one receptor transducing one form of energy into another and so starting an action potential in a sensory nerve. The only common feature of the various factors producing the sensation of pain—cutting, bruising, burning and ischaemia (lack of blood flow), among others—is that they all cause damage to the tissues. It has been suggested that all injury-producing events release in the tissues a chemical which starts the sensory action potentials; and histamine and bradykinin have been suggested as the hypothetical substance. But evidence is scanty and hard to find, particularly for deep pain such as cramp.

The pain-sensory fibres are small unmyelinated C-fibres and small myelinated B-fibres (also called Aδ-fibres, see Chapter 13). A feature of pain fibres is that they do not show adaptation; unlike, say, touch fibres in which impulses cease even when the application of the stimulus continues, pain fibres conduct impulses for as long as the damaging stimulus remains. Pain fibres are abundant in the skin, in the muscles of the limbs and body wall, in the periosteum of bone and in the peritoneum around the abdominal organs; they are less abundant in the abdominal organs themselves, and they do not exist in brain tissue.

All sensations of pain have degrees of intensity, and have location. But it is difficult to classify pain sensations in any useful way. It is possible to distinguish 'sharp' pain, caused, say, by pricking, cutting, burning or bruising the skin, from 'deep' pain, which is often related to isometric activity of muscle (smooth, striated or cardiac), especially if the muscle is ischaemic; colic pain, leg muscle cramp and the pain of angina are of this kind. Both kinds of pain cause general sympathetic stimulation and adrenaline output, with consequent rise in blood pressure and quickening of the heart. Sharp pain in a limb causes an instant reflex movement of withdrawal, which may remove the limb from the source of the painful stimulus. Location of pain is learnt by experience, and individuals differ in the efficiency with which they can locate their pain. In damage to certain organs, particularly the heart and abdominal structures, we tend to locate the pain not in the organ itself but in some part of the body the pain-sensory nerves of which enter the spinal cord or brain stem very close to the point of entry of the pain fibres of the damaged organ. This is called 'referred pain': the pain is 'referred' to some place other than the correct one. The anginal pain of an ischaemic heart is often referred to the left arm or the neck; pain arising from damage to a part of the intestine is referred to the abdominal body wall; a tooth abscess can cause earache; and so on.

The region around the point of entry of pain fibres into the CNS (the upper strip of grey matter of the dorsal horn of the spinal cord or brain stem) has been called the 'gate'; it seems to determine whether sensory information shall be shut out or allowed through to cause the sensation of pain (Fig. 12.23). If there occurs large additional input from, say, pressure or touch fibres in the same region as the painful damaged tissue, the effect of the pain is masked: the 'gate' is partially closed. The squeezing of the hand when its fingers have been banged, and the rubbing of the skin around an insect-bite do indeed have the effect of reducing the pain. Furthermore, efferent impulses from higher parts of the CNS may also arrive at the 'gate' region and cause partial closure. Two particular regions in the medulla of the brain have been identified as sources of such gate-closing descending fibres, carrying impulses which reduce pain sensation.* It is not at all certain whether or how this efferent input from the medulla to the gating mechanism is used in real situations, and if used, what is the stimulus or trigger which initiates it.

---

* Patients suffering severe long-continued pain during an illness have been treated by the implanting of electrodes in the medulla; the patients gave themselves electrical stimulation for about half an hour per day and this process relieved the pain for 4 or 5 h.

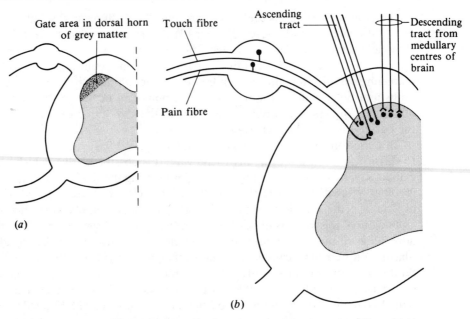

Figure 12.23 Gate area associated with pain perception. (*a*) Position of gate area in dorsal grey matter of spinal cord. (*b*) Possible mechanisms of masking of pain perception.

The discovery of a new group of neuropeptides has greatly stimulated research on pain and on other aspects of nerve activity, including neuroendocrine function. Morphine and other opiates were known to relieve pain by binding to specific receptors on nerve cells. Subsequently two natural pain-killers were found, and named enkephalins ('in the brain'); these two, both short-chain polypeptides, are called met-enkephalin and leucine-enkephalin. Later other morphine-like substances were discovered—the endorphins ('endogenous morphine'). All of these endogenous opioid peptides are now known to be derived from one of three precursor molecules, called pro-opiomelanocortin, pro-dynorphin and pro-enkephalin. These are distributed through the brain and spinal cord in specific tracts, the opioidergic neurones of the three precursor types generally being separate. It should be mentioned that pro-opiomelanocortin is also the precursor molecule for adrenocorticotrophic hormone (Chapter 14).

The opioid peptides may have a physiological role as natural pain-blockers; their effect in the brain may be similar to that of morphine, and it is interesting that the effect of some endorphins is blocked by naloxone, a drug known to block the effect of morphine. Some endorphins are closely connected with releasing factors of the pituitary hormones. High concentrations of the opioid peptides are found in the hypothalamus and pituitary stalk. In some species, opioids stimulate release of prolactin and growth hormone (see Chapter 14). In certain species, including man, opioids seem to inhibit the osmotically induced release of vasopressin (Chapter 7).

These effects when better understood in their physiological context may provide an interesting example of the overlap between nervous and endocrine systems, in that the opioid peptides, which could be classed as hormones, are released from nerves. Much biochemical research is in progress on endorphins and on the cell receptor groups which bind them—a necessary prelude to the study of the role of these substances in the whole animal.

Summary and problems

Sensory endings, sense organs and afferent nerves provide the brain with information about the external world and the internal state of the body, and their involvement is necessary before the body can initiate the appropriate response. Sensory endings and organs show a wide range of complexity, and there is corresponding complexity in the sensations produced. The 'modality' of different sensations is a useful idea, though it is not easy to see how it applies to pain sensation. In the case of hearing and vision much of the sensation appears to depend on central processing in the brain: one does not see unless one can 'make sense' of the visual field.

Discovery of one's world depends on all sources of sensory input. An infant playing with a rattle soon discovers that the rattle makes a noise, and that the harder he shakes, the louder the noise. This process involves the sense of touch (as he grasps the rattle in his hand); the proprioceptors of the muscles and joints of the arm (as he shakes the rattle); sight (as he watches its movement) and hearing (as he enjoys the noise). Knowledge of the world depends on correlation and comparison of simultaneous sensory inputs from many sources, and their synthesis into a self-consistent mental picture.

At several points in this chapter an indication has been given of the many problems about sensation and sense organs which await solution. In the case of hearing and vision we are beginning to understand how the brain encodes information received from the sense organs and how this encoding might be interpreted in the building of a picture of the outside world. However, there are in many animals sensations which cannot yet be related to any organ or nerve tract. Migrating birds appear to have a sense of direction, probably related to the earth's magnetic field; and there is evidence that humans too have this sense in some small degree. Many species, certainly including man, have some kind of sense of the passage of time. The working of 'biological clocks', and the influence on them of normal or experimentally manipulated external events, such as abnormal light and dark periodicity, have been the subject of many studies. Even when we know far more than at present about the physiology of the recognized sense organs, the functioning of these rather indeterminate sensations will still provide a rich field for research for the sensory physiologist.

13 Introduction to the central nervous system

Introduction

The central nervous system (CNS)—the brain and spinal cord—is the route through which nearly all the functions of the organism are coordinated, and by which they are controlled. It is probably the least thoroughly understood of any system of the body. This is mainly because of its complexity, and partly because of its inaccessibility to experimental study. The brain, including the brain stem, is firmly encased within the skull, and the spinal cord within the tube formed by the vertebral column. The peripheral nerves emerge from the brain either through small holes on the skull surface or through the larger hole at its base; and the spinal nerves emerge between the vertebrae.

For many years our knowledge of the spinal cord was built up by experiments involving electrical stimulation or cutting of the peripheral nerves emerging from it and by the electrical or chemical stimulation and recording of some of the cell bodies near the surface of the spinal cord itself; and a reasonably satisfactory picture of many spinal-cord processes has now been formed. But for the brain such manipulations, even in experimental animals, have been either impossible, or, if attempted, uninformative because of ambiguity in the interpretation of the results. For instance the crude experiments involving cutting the brain stem at different levels to study the brain's control of respiration gave rise to theories now seen as extremely flimsy. So study of the brain was until recently based largely on the observation of the results of disease, accidental injury, or congenital defects in man or other animals, and also by observing the effects of placing small carefully localized lesions in the brain of experimental animals. Much information was thus acquired. For example damage to the surface tissue at the back of the brain causes blindness, and this area is now identified as the visual cortex. Damage to the cerebellum causes interference with balance and posture. Damage such as a stroke (cerebral haemorrhage) on one side of the brain causes paralysis of the limbs on the opposite side, implying a crossing-over of nerve tracts somewhere on the route between the brain and the muscles. A lesion made in the hypothalamus below the fourth ventricle interferes with an animal's temperature control; and so on. But here again caution is necessary in the interpretation of results, because a localized lesion may interrupt a nerve tract (group of axons) from elsewhere in the brain, instead of destroying a group of cell bodies, and would thus give an erroneous idea of the location of the fault.

Another contribution to the study of brain function has come from neurosurgery—notably from the pioneer work of Penfield (see Penfield and Jasper, 1954). Neurosurgery involving exposure of the brain surface is frequently carried out under local anaesthesia, so the observer has the advantage of the cooperation of a conscious human subject. Electrical stimulation of particular regions of the exposed cerebral cortex elicits specific movements of groups of muscles; but more remarkably, stimulation of other regions producing neither movement nor sensation can elicit precise memories from the subject's past life, which he can describe in detail.

Much research is currently being carried out on the brain at the biochemical level, especially in the study of chemical transmission. Some 60 chemical transmitters, linking neurone to neurone, have been described, and much of this biochemical study has already had a valuable practical outcome. For instance researchers on drug addiction have found that certain hallucinogenic drugs function by blocking the normal transmission of neurones producing the transmitter serotonin. Again, the discovery that Parkinson's disease (a disabling condition of many elderly people which involves uncontrollable shaking of the arms and head) is associated with a disorder of the neurones which use dopamine as transmitter has allowed production of effective drugs to treat the disease. In the field of biochemical neurology, a probable practical value gives hope of rapid advance.

In spite of all this important work on the brain—electrical, surgical and biochemical—there is still a need and a search for ways of studying the normally functioning and minimally disturbed brain of man and other animals. One device requiring no intervention is the electroencephalogram, which by electrodes placed at points on the scalp records electrical impulses generated in brain cells; not, of course, in individual neurones, but the average voltage change in many cells. This has been of some use in revealing normal inherent rhythms and in locating clinical abnormalities. More recently a considerable advance has been made by the discovery that the movement of specific groups of muscles is accompanied by increased metabolism of particular regions of the brain, and increased blood flow to these regions; and methods of scanning the brain from outside the head can locate these areas of activity. The scan can be made with thermal sensors detecting a pattern of temperature change correlated with alteration in regional blood-flow rate; or by radiation detectors after injection of a radioactive isotope into the blood as a tracer. In this way, for instance, the area of the motor cortex associated with eye movements is located in the brain of a person reading; and, when he reads aloud, the area of lip and mouth movements also becomes active. The technique has confirmed and added detail to the knowledge of localization acquired by cruder methods. More significantly, study of regional blood flow has revealed increased blood flow in the *supplementary* motor area during the time when a subject is planning or anticipating a movement ('internal programming'), before any actual movement has occurred (Fig. 13.1). It is of great interest that a purely mental process, unaccompanied by any sensory input or motor action, can be associated with a consistent and highly localized pattern of brain-cell activity as

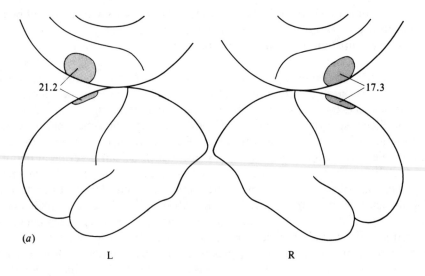

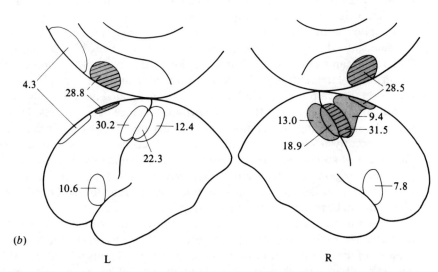

Figure 13.1 Supplementary motor areas in man. Area of brain showing increased blood flow (*a*) before and (*b*) during movements of the fingers of the left hand in a specified series of movements. Sketches show left (L) and right (R) cerebral hemispheres. The main part of the drawing shows the cerebral hemispheres as seen from the side; the upper strip shows the same cerebral hemisphere as seen from above. In (*a*), supplementary motor areas of both hemispheres show increased blood flow. In (*b*), supplementary motor areas are activated equally in both hemispheres; the finger areas of the motor cortex are also activated, but much more so on the right (contralateral) side than on the left (ipsilateral). Numbers give mean percentage increase in blood flow, corrected for non-specific increase. (*a*) L, 3 subjects; R, 5 subjects. (*b*) L, 5 subjects; R, 10 subjects. (Reproduced with permission from Roland, P. E., B. Larsen, N. A. Lassen and E. Skinhøj, *Journal of Neurophysiology*, **43**, 118–136, 1980.)

detected by these physical methods. This technique, non-invasive and non-damaging, has shown where the active cells related to a given function are located, but not precisely what they are doing; and the search for better investigative methods and clearer insights must continue.

In this chapter on the CNS much is deliberately omitted. Omissions include many of the functions of the brain, and all the so-called 'higher functions' of the CNS, such as consciousness and sleep, memory and the control of cognitive behaviour. Indeed most of the functions to be described in this chapter could be illustrated by examples from spinal-cord and brain-stem structures; but in the account of the maintenance of posture and initiation of movement, reference to structures in the higher centres of the CNS is necessary.

Reflexes in the nervous system

Definition

The reflex arc in the nervous system can be thought of as the simplest pattern of activity involving the CNS and peripheral nerves. It is composed of an afferent limb passing to the CNS from a sense organ or receptor, an efferent limb passing to the effector organ (muscle or gland) and a central processor within the CNS. At its simplest level, then, a reflex arc involves five structures: sensory receptors and effector organs, sensory (afferent) and motor (efferent) nerves, and some part of the CNS. At the very simplest there is just one synapse involved in the CNS: the sensory nerve makes synaptic connections directly onto the cell bodies of the motoneurones, and no interneurones are activated. An example is the stretch reflex originating in sense organs, the muscle spindles, lying among and in parallel with muscle fibres; on being passively stretched they cause a reflex stimulation of the muscle via impulses down its motoneurone. However, such monosynaptic reflexes are rare. Most reflexes involve many interneurones and interconnections. Readers may recall examples of reflexes given in previous chapters. For example in digestion a reflex started by the sense organs of taste and smell works through the salivary nucleus in the brain stem to stimulate salivary glands. Receptors in the wall of the carotid sinus on being stretched start a reflex which involves medullary centres and efferent vagus nerve (cranial X) fibres, slowing the heart beat. Bright light shining on the retina is the stimulus which, via optic nerve (cranial II) and midbrain cells, causes reflex closure of the iris. A stretching of the smooth muscle forming the wall of the urinary bladder initiates a group of reflexes which contract the bladder wall and relax the urethral sphincters, thus emptying the bladder at micturition. From these examples it is clear that:

1. the effector organ can be cardiac or smooth muscle or a gland, as well as striated muscle;
2. the efferent nerve can be autonomic as well as somatic;
3. the sense organs involved can be within the body cavity, not just on the surface or among striated muscles or tendons.

So much of the activity of the various physiological systems seems to be controlled by reflexes or analogous processes that we should remind ourselves that such control is not universal. Quite apart from willed behaviour, there are inherent rhythms in the CNS such as that which can maintain rhythmic activity of the respiratory muscles without apparently any sensory (afferent) input; and on a longer periodicity, the circadian fluctuations of deep body temperature, for instance, are presumably controlled by the CNS. Furthermore we may recall that there are organs, tissues and processes (haemopoiesis in bone marrow, for instance) capable of functioning without efferent nerves at all.

Three further points about the general properties of reflexes arise from the examples already given, and are worth pointing out at this stage.

1. The response in efferent nerves and muscles may be a *decrease* in their activity rather than an increase: as in the case of micturition, there is reflex *inhibition* of the external urethral sphincter muscle.
2. Certain reflexes can be brought under voluntary control, as is the group of reflexes concerned in defaecation and micturition in adult humans.
3. Reflexes can be conditioned: that is, an additional extraneous stimulus, if it invariably accompanies the stimulus initiating the reflex, can be made eventually to produce the response even in the absence of the normal stimulus. (The standard example is that of the dogs in the experiments of Pavlov, which could be induced to salivate on hearing a bell, even before they could taste or smell food.)

Both voluntary control and conditioning appear to be confined to reflexes involving autonomic nerves, and thus to glands and non-striated muscles.

The first reflex arcs which were studied intensively (by Sherrington, 1897) were those involving the spinal cord, the leg muscles, and receptors on the skin surface or among the muscle fibres, and the first recorded use of the word 'reflex' in the physiological sense is its occurrence in the title of a lecture given by Sherrington in 1897. The salivation reflexes and their conditioning and inhibition were carefully studied (by Pavlov, 1927) in the first 20 years of the twentieth century. There is some disagreement about how far the term 'reflex' can usefully be extended to other patterns of behaviour. Let us consider, for example, the secretion of pituitary and sex hormones which leads to mating and nest-building behaviour in birds, the secretion being stimulated by lengthening hours of daylight as perceived by the birds' eyes. Is this a reflex initiated by the eye? Or consider the stimulus to the secretion of vasopressin—a change in osmolarity of the plasma, affecting osmoreceptor cells in the midbrain; it could be argued that there is no fundamental difference between a receptor within and one outside the CNS, so this process could be reasonably called a reflex. Then again, in many mammals including humans, even newborn infants, a sudden loud noise produces quickening of the heart beat: could this be a reflex response? Or should the term be confined to responses (such as the stretch reflex) shown even by sleeping or unconscious animals? What about the dog which wags its tail on hearing its master's voice? Could this be considered a conditioned reflex? Are animals born with a set of rudimentary reflexes which can be developed into behaviour patterns by inhibiting some and enhancing or conditioning others? These are problems on the borderline of physiology and psychology, and the reader's attention is drawn to the danger of this grey area where one may find oneself discussing words instead of concepts. Most physiologists would agree on excluding from the term 'reflex':

1. a process starting from an inherent rhythm within the CNS;
2. a process, movement or behaviour pattern which shows signs of being 'willed'.

Like a piece of overstretched elastic, the term 'reflex' ceases to be useful if one tries to include too much within it, but there is not yet any agreement about how much is 'too much'. Most of the reflexes discussed in this chapter will be the spinal reflexes as originally described by Sherrington and others in the 1920s, and later studied by detailed biochemical and electrical methods.

Peripheral nerves and central synapses

This section describes first the general action of the peripheral spinal nerves and the behaviour of synapses within the CNS. Using this information some of the properties of reflexes are pictured. Certain particular spinal reflexes are used to illustrate these properties.

Fibres in a mixed spinal nerve

By stimulating a spinal nerve close to the spinal cord and recording impulses from leads placed at some distance away along the peripheral nerve, one obtains a recording of nerve action potentials spread out over a period of time as the fibres (both somatic and autonomic) conduct at various speeds. The action-potential record shows peaks and troughs as the nerve impulses arrive at the recording leads in bunches. Separate stimulation of the sensory and the motor roots has made possible the identification of these batches of nerve fibres conducting at different velocities. These groups of fibres in the peripheral nerve have been named alphabetically, as shown in Fig. 13.2.

The experiment illustrated in Fig. 13.2a, in which a large stimulus is applied near the roots of a mixed spinal nerve, involves stimulation of both sensory and motor fibres, the sensory fibres conducting antidromically: that is, in the direction opposite to that of their normal route. Accordingly both sensory and motor fibres contribute to the record of the compound action potential of the figure. The fastest impulses, the group labelled A and subdivided into α, β and γ, travel (in mammals) at about 100 m/s for α, 60 m/s for β and 40 m/s for γ. Then come B-fibres at 10 m/s and C-fibres at about 2 m/s.

Stimulation of only the sensory (dorsal) root of the spinal nerve elicits all the A-waves (that is, α, β and γ) and also the C-waves (Fig. 13.2b).

Stimulation of only the motor (ventral) root elicits α-, γ- and B-waves (Fig. 13.2c). The B action potentials have been found in other experiments to go only to the white ramus, so they are likely to be preganglionic sympathetic fibres; they are sometimes called the δ-subgroup of A. The fastest-conducting fibres (the α-fibres) are motor

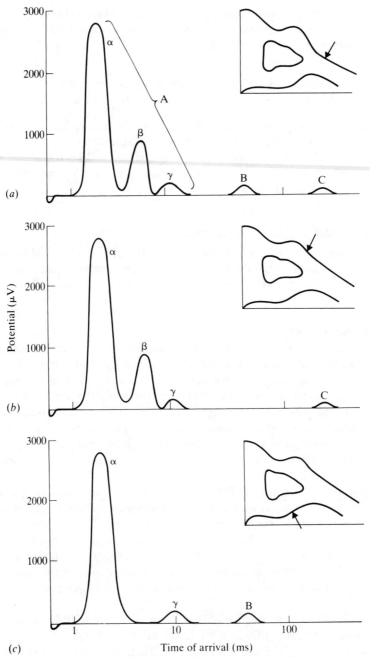

Figure 13.2   Action potentials in a mixed spinal nerve. Graphs show peaks of compound action potentials (μV) plotted against time of arrival (ms) at recording leads (not shown) placed on the nerve at a distance from the spinal cord. Arrows in insets show position of stimulating electrodes in relation to dorsal and ventral roots. (a) All fibres. (b) Sensory fibres only. (c) Motor fibres only. See text for explanation.

fibres to striated muscles, and sensory fibres from sense organs (muscle spindles) within these muscles.

The γ efferent fibres innervate (in mammals) minute muscle fibres (intrafusal fibres) forming part of the structure of muscle spindles. Their role is described in the section on Posture and movement. The β- and C-fibres are sensory, and some of the slow-conducting non-myelinated C-fibres convey pain sensation.

Myelinated *sensory* fibres have also been classified according to diameter (and thus conduction velocity) as Group I (the fastest), II and III. Group I fibres are found only in nerves from muscles, and convey impulses from muscle spindles (Ia) and Golgi tendon organs (Ib). Groups II and III carry impulses from other types of organs in both muscle and skin.

The motor nerves to muscles (called the lower motoneurones) have unusually large cell bodies situated in the ventral (anterior) horn of the spinal cord. Any activity of the muscle, whether reflex or voluntary, must be initiated by the depolarization of these ventral horn cells. Voluntary activity originates in the brain, and a series of fibres relay information to the lower motoneurones. Reflex activity can be initiated by sensory input to either the brain or the spinal cord at any level, since the sensory nerves form synapses with interneurones along the CNS; and this network of interneurones allows

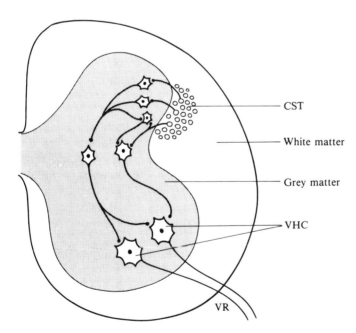

Figure 13.3   Cross-section of half spinal cord, showing position of corticospinal (pyramidal) tract (CST) in the white matter close to the dorsal horn of grey matter. At the level of each spinal nerve, branches of corticospinal axons terminate on cell bodies of interneurones in the grey matter. Their axons run through the grey matter from dorsal to ventral horn, terminating on ventral horn cells (VHC) the cell bodies of motoneurones of which the axons emerge at the ventral roots (VR). One, two or three interneurones connect the corticospinal tract with the motoneurone.

modification, enhancement or inhibition of the sensory signal. The main sensory (ascending) and motor (descending) fibres in the spinal cord run in identifiable bundles called tracts, comprising the white matter. For example fibres of the large corticospinal (pyramidal) tract from the sensorimotor cortex of the brain run in a bundle which terminates in the white matter close to the dorsal horn of grey matter whence, via one or two small interneurones, the ventral horn cells of the appropriate spinal segment are stimulated.

Figure 13.3 shows a cross-section through the spinal cord, and indicates the distribution of grey matter—mainly cell bodies—and white matter—mainly myelinated axons.

CNS transmitters, EPSP and IPSP

As in the case of transmission at the neuromuscular junction or synaptic transmission in autonomic ganglia, the depolarization of the cell body of one neurone is brought about by the release of a chemical transmitter from the terminal buttons of another. As in peripheral nerves acetylcholine and noradrenaline are two of the CNS transmitters; and many others have been proposed, including 5-hydroxytryptamine (serotonin) and dopamine. But in contrast with peripheral nerves, the CNS includes neurones producing *inhibitory* transmitters, the effect of which is to *hyper*polarize the membrane on which they impinge. Several of these inhibitory transmitters are fairly simple amino acids: γ-aminobutyric acid and possibly also glycine (α-aminoacetic acid). These may work by making the membrane more permeable to K^+ ions, thus bringing the membrane potential closer to the K^+ equilibrium potential; or perhaps by increasing the permeability to Cl' ions, thus allowing inflow of extracellular Cl', which would make the cell interior more negative.

Against the surface of every cell body in the CNS there are terminal buttons from hundreds of other neurones, and there may be some 10 000 buttons on a single cell body. Some of these synapses are excitatory and some inhibitory, and it is obvious that if a cell body receives an excitatory and an inhibitory volley of impulses simultaneously, causing a (depolarizing) excitatory postsynaptic potential (EPSP) and a (hyperpolarizing) inhibitory postsynaptic potential (IPSP) at the same time, the result might be no change at all in membrane potential. It is only when the excitatory stimulus is sufficient to override any simultaneous firing of the inhibitory neurones that the threshold is reached and an impulse started down the axon, or to dendrites of adjacent cells. An EPSP (or IPSP) once established dies away gradually in about 10 ms. Like the local excitatory state in peripheral nerves, the EPSP is a graded response which must attain a certain threshold level to start an action potential; and it has a finite time of decay. Its size (voltage) seems to depend on the amount of transmitter released, and on the size and position of the area of cell surface affected.

Properties of spinal reflexes

Some general properties

Many properties of reflexes can be explained in terms of:

1. the amount of EPSP on the ventral horn cells;
2. the network pattern of interneurones bringing excitation to these motoneurones from the sensory input;
3. the number of motoneurones involved.

These properties are illustrated in Fig. 13.4. They can be exemplified (as they were originally by Sherrington) by the use of the flexor reflex in the leg muscles of a dog, the tension in which is easily measurable. Reflex contraction of the flexors can be produced by stimulation of a pain-sensory nerve on the toe. Recruitment and after-discharge, facilitation, occlusion and summation at the subliminal fringe are explained in Fig. 13.4.

Inhibition

The properties of reflexes so far described can be understood in terms of the morphological arrangements of interneurones (the 'wiring diagram' in the spinal cord), together with parallels between the behaviour of EPSP at motoneurone membranes and the properties of the local excitatory response during conduction of an impulse in a single nerve axon: threshold, time of decay, subliminal area of excitation in advance of active region and so on. The feature of the CNS which has no analogy with any property of mammalian peripheral nerves is inhibition: the attainment of *hyper*polarization at a cell body (IPSP), which renders the initiation of an action potential in the axon or dendrites *less* probable; so the passing on of the effect of stimulation through a neural path or network depends on the relative amount of EPSP and IPSP at each cell body on the route.

Inhibition is of several kinds. Direct (or postsynaptic) inhibition (sometimes called lateral inhibition), illustrated in Fig. 13.5a, is achieved by the interposition of an inhibitory neurone, presumably secreting a hyperpolarizing chemical, on the route of the reflex path. In Fig. 13.5a, input A is excitatory to the motoneurone M, and input B is inhibitory, because of the insertion of the inhibitory neurone I, although input B may be excitatory to other motoneurones such as motoneurones M' and M". The inhibition lasts about 10 ms.

Direct inhibition is extremely sensitive to the drug strychnine, which poisons inhibitory synapses. In consequence all *excitatory* synapses of the CNS, which continue to function, are unopposed and unmodified; striated muscles in the back and limbs twitch and contract in an uncontrollable manner and the animal goes into convulsions. The implication is that in normal conditions even in the resting animal there is continuous slight activity of both excitatory and inhibitory pathways through the CNS; if the essential inhibition is eliminated, excitation gets out of hand.

Presynaptic inhibition (Fig. 13.5b) occurs where a dendrite from a second neurone,

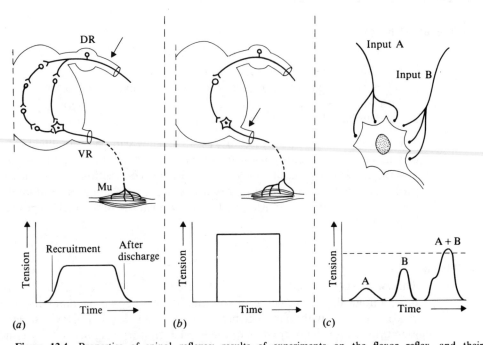

Figure 13.4 Properties of spinal reflexes: results of experiments on the flexor reflex, and their interpretation. DR: dorsal root; VR: ventral root; Mu: muscle. (a) Recruitment and after-discharge. When reflex contraction of flexor is initiated via direct stimulation of the axons of the sensory nerve, maximum tension in the muscle is reached gradually (recruitment) and the tension dies away gradually (after-discharge) when stimulation ceases. The effect of the stimulus reaches the motoneurone pool by several paths through the interneurones. There is a gradual build-up of EPSP over time at the start of the response, and similarly, a gradual dying away of EPSP at the end when the short-route interneurones have ceased to affect the motoneurones while impulses are still arriving by the longer routes. (b) If flexor muscle is stimulated directly through the axons of its motor nerve, the tension rises and falls instantly as the stimulus starts and stops. Also, the tension developed is much greater than that attained with reflex stimulation. Direct stimulation of the motor nerve produces action potentials in all the motoneurones whereas any sensory nerve has access to only a small group of the cells of the total motoneurone pool. (c) Facilitation. This depends on the graded nature and slow decay of EPSP. If two sensory inputs (A and B), both slightly subthreshold, reach the same motoneurone in quick succession, the second may reach the motoneurone while some of the EPSP due to the first is still present, and summate with this residual EPSP to attain threshold; thus the second stimulus becomes effective and sets off an action potential in the axon. (d) Occlusion. Two separate sensory nerve fibres are stimulated, and the response to each is recorded; if the nerves are then stimulated simultaneously, the total response may be less than the sum of the two separate responses (occlusion). Some of the motoneurones available to the two sensory inputs would be the same. Two such motoneurones are shown. (e) It is also possible to obtain a greater effect from two stimuli simultaneously given than the sum of the separate effects. Around each pool of motoneurones in which EPSP has reached threshold there is a subliminal fringe of motoneurones in which EPSP has been increased by the stimulus but not quite to threshold. If two simultaneous sensory volleys are placed in such a way that the subliminal fringes of their motoneurone pools overlap, some of the motoneurones in the overlap region might reach threshold EPSP, so an action potential could be set off in their axons. Two such motoneurones in the subliminal fringe are shown.

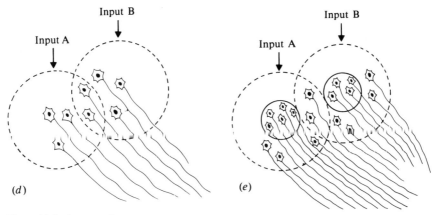

Figure 13.4 (*continued*)

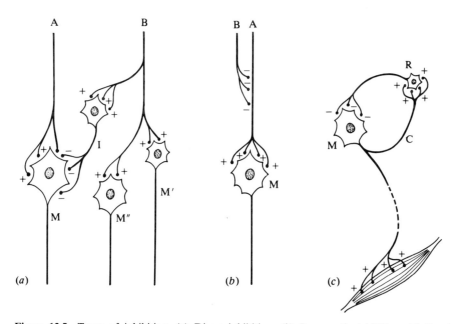

Figure 13.5 Types of inhibition. (*a*) Direct inhibition. (*b*) Presynaptic inhibition. (*c*) Renshaw-cell inhibition. For explanation see text.

B, forms a synapse (axo-axonic synapse) on another neurone, A, close to the synapse of A on the cell body of a motoneurone M. If B is activated slightly before A, the excitatory effect of A on the motoneurone is reduced, or it may be abolished altogether. There is no actual IPSP (or hyperpolarization) of the surface of the motoneurone, but the magnitude of the EPSP set up by stimulating A may be reduced, perhaps to a point below threshold. The effect of B could be interpreted as reducing the amount of excitatory transmitter released from the terminals of A. Presynaptic inhibition has a much slower time-course then direct inhibition: it decays over a period of about 200 ms. It is not destroyed by the drug strychnine.

Renshaw-cell inhibition (Fig. 13.5c) is an interesting type of inhibition, which was discovered by putting antidromic volleys of impulses (i.e. the reverse of the normal direction of transmission) up a motor nerve towards the CNS, and recording changes of membrane potential on a ventral horn cell. The motoneurones, M in Fig. 13.5c, in addition to the main axon leaving the spinal cord in the motor nerve, have also small branches called recurrent collaterals, C, which run back into the tissue of the ventral horn, and (like the main motor axon) release acetylcholine at the terminal. These collaterals end on the cell bodies of small neurones called Renshaw cells, R, which are thereby stimulated. Their terminals produce an inhibitory transmitter, on the surface of the same or adjacent motoneurones. So the discharge of a motoneurone down its axon simultaneously contributes via the recurrent collaterals to its own inhibition. The significance of Renshaw-cell inhibition is not quite clear, and it seems surprising that the activity of a cell should lead to the checking of its own action. One idea is that this type of inhibition is in some way protective, limiting the frequency of impulses going to the motor endplates of muscles; indeed there is evidence that during normal muscular activity the frequency of impulses in motor axons is nowhere near the maximal frequency which the axon is capable of conducting. (Maximal muscle tension is attained by the involvement of large numbers of axons rather than by a high frequency of impulses in any one axon.) It could be by Renshaw-cell inhibition that frequency is kept low.

Reciprocal innervation

At most joints in limbs, muscles are placed in opposing pairs, called antagonistic pairs, in such a way that when one member of the pair contracts, the other must be relaxed. There are several examples of reflexes in which a given stimulus produces excitation and shortening in one member of the pair and at the same time relaxes the other (Fig. 13.6).

This type of 'wiring' arrangement is present in all the joints involved in movements such as walking: when a foot is raised by bending the hip and knee joints, flexors at these joints contract and the corresponding extensors are inhibited. The 'knee-jerk' reflex shown in Fig. 13.6 is often used clinically as a test for the presence, speed and magnitude of spinal reflexes. It has no particular biological advantage for the animal, and is in fact rather untypical of a stretch reflex, which in extensor muscles normally results in *isometric* action, not isotonic contraction.

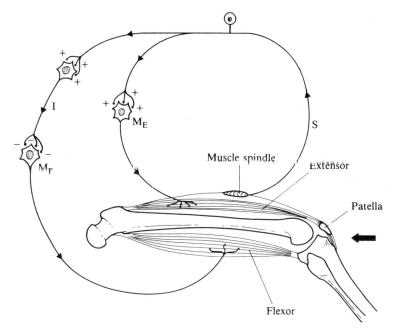

Figure 13.6 Reciprocal innervation. A tap on the patella at the knee joint (thick arrow) gives a short stretch to the muscle spindles among the fibres of the extensor muscle along the top of the thigh. Via the sensory nerve (S) this reflexly excites motoneurone (M_E) which causes (isotonic) contraction of the muscle (the monosynaptic stretch reflex). At the same time the inhibitory interneurone (I) is excited, and affects the cell body of the motoneurone (M_F) to the (flexor) muscle below the thigh, increasing its IPSP (or decreasing its EPSP) and so allowing it to relax. (Adapted from Davson, H. and M. B. Segal, *Introduction to Physiology*, Vol. 2, Academic Press, London, 1975.)

Examples of spinal reflexes

Stretch reflex

The stretch reflex originating in muscle spindles has already been mentioned as an example of a monosynaptic reflex. It is of fundamental importance in the maintenance of posture. The muscle spindle, lying between and in parallel with the muscle fibres, is in fact quite a complicated sense organ, which will be described in the next section of this chapter. The spindle serves mainly to control the *length* of its own muscle, opposing a passive stretch by increasing isometric activity. For example when a man standing with hand and arm hanging loosely by his side uses that arm to pick up a heavy weight (but does not flex the elbow), the extensor muscles along the length of the arm are stretched by the effect of gravity. The muscle spindles are activated and immediately cause an increase in isometric action, increasing the tension along the length of the muscle. This opposes the gravitational pull of the weight, and maintains the length of the muscles. The afferent fibres from the muscle spindles in this reflex conduct very rapidly and are known as Group Ia fibres.

Tendon-organ reflex

Tendon-organ reflexes originate in the Golgi tendon organs, which are found among the fibres of the tendon close to its junction with the muscle, and arranged in *series* with the muscle fibres. Increase in tension in the tendon, whether produced by external stretching or by isometric action of the muscle, stimulates the Golgi tendon organ, which starts a reflex inhibiting the muscle concerned but exciting its antagonist. The sensory nerves from Golgi organs are only slightly slower than the Group Ia fibres and are called Ib fibres. It is likely that reflexes from Golgi organs are involved in stance and walking movements, and that they give the CNS information about rate of change of tension in the tendon as well as the absolute tension. Muscle spindles and tendon organs are classified as proprioceptors: sense organs which supply information to the CNS about the position of limbs and joints.

Flexor and crossed-extensor reflexes

The flexor and crossed-extensor reflexes are seen when a painful stimulus is received on the skin of the sole of the foot. The leg is flexed and there is increased *extensor* activity in the muscles of the opposite leg. This results in removal of the foot from the source of pain, and the weight of the body can be supported by the other leg.

Plantar reflex

The plantar reflex is initiated by touch or firm pressure against the sole of the foot, and produces increase in extensor tone (in man) at the knee and hip hoints. If, say, the pressure on the feet is due to the weight of the body on the ground, a whole group of muscles become involved and this leads to a process called the 'positive supporting reaction', in which the ankle joint is flexed and the legs, by simultaneous increase in activity of both flexors and extensors, are made into firm columns supporting the weight of the body.

These reflexes illustrate some of the possibilities of the paths through the spinal interneurones, between sensory input and motor output; the result is dependent on the balance of EPSP and IPSP at the cell bodies of the motoneurones, the final common path to the particular muscle involved. Most of the reflexes mentioned have an obvious biological value, and form components of a behaviour pattern, whether supporting an animal's weight or helping it to take a step, or making it withdraw a limb from a source of possible damage to the skin.

The final section of this chapter will attempt to answer the questions: How does a person (or other animal) stand upright? How does it change its posture? And how does it start a voluntary movement? The answers to these questions involve reference to a number of different sense organs, to parts of the CNS other than the spinal cord, and to various nerve tracts connecting parts of the CNS.

Posture and movement

Maintenance of posture

The study of posture and movement requires reference to something more than the spinal reflexes already described, because structures in the brain stem and other parts of the brain are also involved. So it is necessary to understand the connections between these several parts of the CNS. Figure 13.7 shows the main tracts, in diagrammatic form.

Figure 13.8a and b show a man and a cat standing upright. The man manages to stand supported on two legs because the antigravity muscles of his legs, trunk and neck have brought the centres of gravity of each of these three major components of the body into a single straight line which reaches the ground in the area between the soles of the feet, so the feet support the body in a balanced stance. If the man suddenly becomes unconscious, the antigravity muscles cease to operate (Fig. 13.8c). The major part of the head is in front of the vertical line joining centres of gravity, so the head tends to fall forward. The knees, too, will move forward and the buttocks backward, and the man will fall down in a heap, as illustrated. This shows that in normal standing, the effect of gravity is, for instance, to pull on the muscles at the *back* of the neck, stimulating their muscle spindles and maintaining their steady isometric tension; similarly, extensor muscles at the knee and hip joints would be having their tension maintained by the pull of gravity on their spindles. Now suppose that the (conscious) man starts to sway sideways, as many people do in darkness when they must balance without help from the sensory input from their eyes. The centre of gravity will move, say, further to his left; there is additional stimulus to the extensor muscle spindles in his left leg and extensor tension is increased in this leg. His weight is still supported; proprioceptors from other parts give him information about the position of his body in space and he will bring himself upright. Incidentally, people who have difficulty in balancing when standing or walking in darkness give themselves additional sensory information by lightly touching with their fingertips the walls or other nearby objects. Cold reduces proprioceptive sensation, and this reduction of sensory input from the soles of the feet causes difficulty for (blindfolded) people in standing upright in cold water.

A quadruped such as a cat covers a larger floor area in proportion to its size. If one draws an imaginary vertical line through its centre of gravity, the line could reach the floor at any point over a large area, and thus, in spite of some movement of its centre of gravity, the cat remains in balance.

In Fig. 13.9 the man has altered the position of his head, trunk and thighs in relation to his feet. The centre of gravity is brought slightly forward onto the front edge of the feet. The backward position of the thighs balances the forward position of the upper trunk and right arm, and the head, tilted slightly backward on the neck, is close to the vertical line through the feet. The upper part of the trunk is supported also by extension of the left arm, with the left hand on the knee. The cat's head has moved upwards and backwards (from the position in Fig. 13.8), and its neck is stretched.

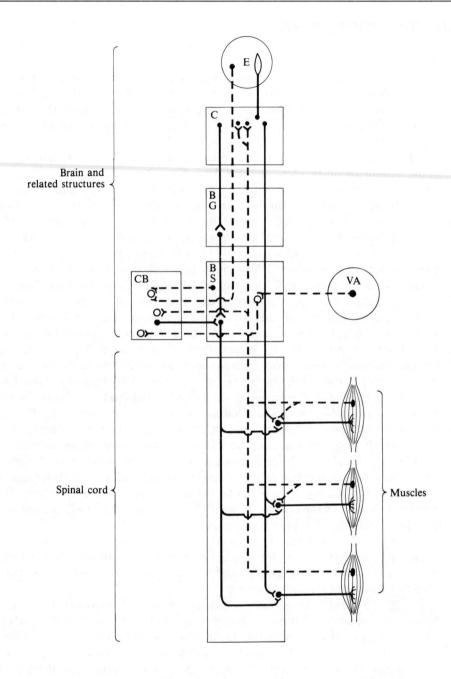

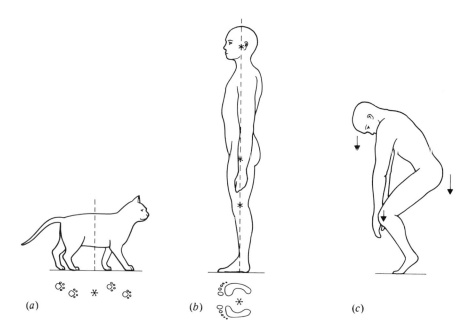

Figure 13.8 (*a*) and (*b*) Balanced position of cat and man. Centres of gravity of each main component of the man's body (asterisks) lie on a vertical line extrapolated to the ground between his feet. In (*c*), where in unconscious man the postural reflexes are lacking, the head and knees fall forward and the hips backward.

◀ **Figure 13.7** Tracts in the CNS: a highly simplified diagram of some of the main tracts in the CNS connected with postural reflexes. The skeletal muscles at every level down the spinal cord are under the control of a closed loop: sensory neurones from the muscle are connected with motoneurones transmitting impulses back to it. Though these loops can function autonomously in simple reflexes (such as the stretch reflex), they are more often controlled (in either reflex or voluntary activity) by impulses coming from elsewhere in the CNS. One such tract, bringing impulses direct from the sensorimotor area of the brain down to each spinal level, is the corticospinal tract (pyramidal tract). All other motor tracts (collectively known as extrapyramidal) start in the brain stem, and are themselves controlled by the sensorimotor cortex with a relay point in basal ganglia, and the cerebellum, with relay points in brain stem. Many of the (pons and medulla) postural reflexes, and reflexes involving movements such as orientation and walking, are controlled via the cerebellum which collects information about the position or movement of the body from the sense organs, including muscle and joint receptors, eyes and vestibular apparatus. By these tracts also, sensory information from one group of muscles can affect muscles elsewhere. The crossed-extensor reflex is a simple device connecting left and right limbs via the spinal cord. More complicated circuitry leads to connections between, say, fore limbs and hind limbs, or neck muscles and limb muscles. BG: basal ganglia; BS: brain stem; C: cortex; CB: cerebellum; E: eyes; VA: vestibular apparatus.

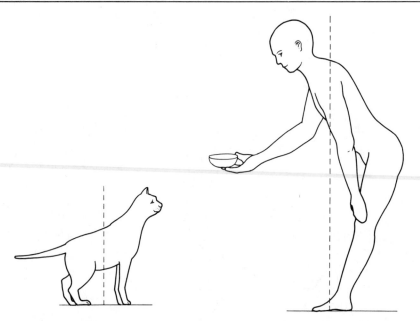

Figure 13.9 Balanced position of man and cat. Compare with Fig. 13.8*a* and *b*.

Sensory information from proprioceptors in the neck muscles in this posture have the effect of increasing extensor tone in the front limbs.

Righting reflexes

In the steady maintenance of a given posture, input from the eyes together with that from proprioceptors of the limbs and neck muscles is adequate. But in preventing oneself from falling, or in righting oneself from an abnormal position, one uses an additional source of sensory input, the vestibular apparatus of the inner ear described in Chapter 12. The vestibular apparatus (semicircular canals, utriculus and sacculus) sends impulses to the vestibular nuclei in the brain stem, whence information reaches the cerebellum, the centre through which the reflexes of posture, balance and movement are controlled.

Figure 13.10*a* shows a man standing upright. In Fig. 13.10*b* the man has started to fall forwards. This has moved the image on the retina of the eyes, causing a visual fixation reflex, and the eyes move upwards. This in turn leads to an adjustment of the head in such a way that the eyes look straight forward in their sockets (Fig. 13.10*c*). This movement of the head stimulates the vestibular apparatus and also places the neck in an abnormal position. Vestibular-apparatus reflexes and impulses from proprioceptors of the neck muscles cause movement of the trunk and limbs in such a way as to bring the head and trunk back into alignment and prevent the fall (Fig. 13.10*d*).

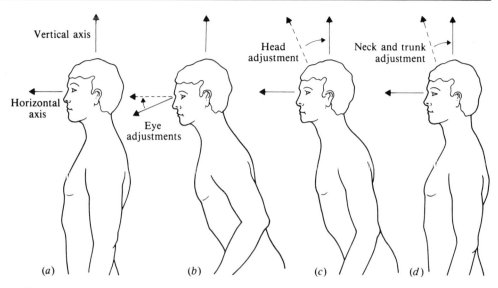

Figure 13.10 Righting reflexes. (*a*) A man standing upright. (*b–d*) He starts to fall forward and saves himself by reflexes from (*b*) his eyes, (*c*) his head, and (*d*) his neck and trunk. (Adapted from Davson, H. and M. B. Segal, *Introduction to Physiology*, vol. 4, Academic Press, London, 1978.)

A similar series of reflexes can be seen in a quadruped placed on its side. A cat so placed first moves or jerks its head into the upright forward-looking position. This movement excites the vestibular apparatus and also gives a twist to the neck muscles. This in turn is the stimulus causing the movements of the limbs which bring the whole body upright.

It is not always easy in experiments to distinguish the effect of neck-muscle proprioceptors from that of the sensory input from the vestibular apparatus. In real situations there is cooperation of the various reflex responses. If a piece of meat is shown to a cat and gradually raised in front of its head, the neck muscles are flexed backward, giving rise to neck and vestibular reflexes, causing strong extensor tone of the forelimbs. In the hindlimbs, however, the *de*creased extensor tone due to neck-muscle proprioceptors and the *in*creased extensor tone due to vestibular sensors cancel out, and the position of the hind limbs is unchanged. A cat lying on its side in a relaxed posture nearly always has its head upright and eyes forward-looking, even though this gives a twist in the neck: clearly the sensory input from the eyes is overriding that from the neck proprioceptors. Small dogs when lying similarly relaxed usually place the head on the ground in line with the trunk.

The eyes or head of a person or animal whose whole body is being passively moved or turned perform a series of characteristic movements, called nystagmus. This is a slow horizontal movement of the eyeballs or head in one direction, followed by a quick jerk in the opposite direction. The phenomenon of nystagmus could be considered as a righting reflex involving the eye muscles. The eye muscles of the orbit, by sensory input through the optic nerve (cranial II), keep the eye almost steady in such a way as to maintain an almost constant field of vision and thus a stable retinal image (fixation reflex). If the head or the whole body is passively moved, horizontally or in a horizontal circle, the eyes are made to move in the opposite direction and the same pattern of objects is thereby kept in view. As movement continues, the eyes cease to look forward; their abnormal position initiates vestibular reflexes which stimulate the eye muscles to bring back the eyes with a quick flick to the forward-looking position, when a new visual field will be fixed. Observation of the eyes of a person gazing out of the window of a moving train reveals these processes clearly: the slow movement of the eyes as an object in the view is fixated, and the quick eye movement back to the forward-looking position. Nystagmus is the whole process, and if the quick eye movement is towards the left, this is called 'left nystagmus'.

Nystagmus is initiated by a turning motion in a horizontal plane, and the sense organs concerned use the semicircular canals. Another part of the vestibular apparatus, the utriculus, is responsible for a reflex started by a sudden downward movement, which causes increased extensor tone of the limbs. This is seen in the limbs of animals at the start of a free fall. Many humans are aware of increased extensor tone in the legs when in a lift at the start of the descent.

Control of movement and action of spindles

So far we have considered how man and other animals can maintain a steady posture, save themselves from falling and right themselves from an abnormal position; and it is apparent that the muscle spindles lying parallel with the striated muscle fibres have an important role in this, especially in the antigravity muscles. The effect of passive stretch by gravitational pull reflexly causes isometric activity of the muscle, in such a way as to oppose the pull and to maintain its length. Muscle spindles also have a role in isotonic contractions, when the muscle fibres shorten in moving limbs at the joints.

A diagram of a muscle spindle is shown in Fig. 13.11. The stimulus to the spindle, and thus to the Group Ia afferent, is *either* passive pull on the whole muscle *or* contraction of the intrafusal fibres via γ-efferent nerve fibres. The Ia-afferent conveys information to the brain (though not to consciousness) about the position and length of the muscle. Impulses are being sent all the time: more pull on the muscle leads to more impulses in the Ia-fibre; less pull to fewer. A branch of the Ia-afferent goes to cell bodies (ventral horn cells) of the motoneurones giving α-axon impulses to the same muscle, initiating the isometric action which resists the pull and stabilizes the length of the muscle (stretch reflex) (Fig. 13.12).

Now suppose that the muscle shortens isotonically as a voluntary movement is initiated. It appears that the motor cortex stimulates the α-motoneurones to the extrafusal fibres and the γ-motoneurones to the intrafusal fibres *simultaneously* (see Fig. 13.12). If there were only α-motoneurone stimulation, the consequent shortening of the muscle would cause the intrafusal fibres to go slack. But, since these intrafusals are made to shorten in parallel with the main muscle fibres, they are prevented from going slack; the spindle would be kept in a state of readiness during the muscle

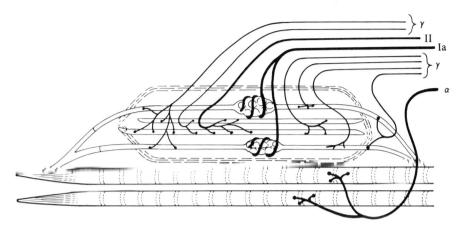

Figure 13.11 Muscle spindle. The spindle is in embryological origin a group of modified muscle fibres, *intrafusal* fibres (in contrast with the normal striated muscle fibres called *extrafusal* fibres). Some intrafusal fibres have all the nuclei closely packed together in a swollen central region: nuclear-bag fibres. Two such fibres are shown. Others have their nuclei arranged in a single central row: nuclear-chain fibres. Two such fibres are shown. The sensory innervation is a Group Ia afferent, which ends on both types of intrafusal fibres. There may also be slightly slower-conducting Group II afferents, ending mainly on the nuclear-chain intrafusals. At each end, the fibres of the spindles are gathered into a bundle and attached to an extrafusal muscle fibre. The two ends of the spindle are joined to different but closely related muscle fasciculi, or (as in the diagram) to a muscle fibre and a tendon. The motor nerve supply to the spindle is by γ-efferent nerves, also called fusimotor fibres (see page 304). Six γ-efferent fibres are shown. One α-motoneurone to the extrafusal fibres is also shown. (Adapted from Bell, G. H., J. N. Davidson and H. Scarborough, *Textbook of Physiology and Biochemistry*, 7th edn, Livingstone, Edinburgh, 1968.)

shortening, so the range of length at which it can be useful is increased; it is always ready to initiate a further batch of impulses up the Ia afferent.

Let us suppose that the voluntary movement is the bending of the arm at the elbow as one picks up a heavy load. The possible mechanism of this is as follows. The motor cortex of the brain somehow makes a prediction about the weight of the load and sends appropriate impulses to activate both α- and γ-efferents; the muscle will shorten, and by flexion at the elbow the load is lifted. If the guess as to the weight of the load is correct, shortening of extra- and intrafusal fibres will match. If however the load is too heavy, so that the extrafusals cannot shorten enough, there will be an additional gravitational pull on the muscle, the intrafusal fibres will be stretched, giving rise to more Ia-afferent activity and thus, via the ventral horn cells, to more α-motoneurone activity; this further activity gives more muscle contraction and helps raise the load. If the load is *lighter* than predicted, there is a mismatch in the other direction: the muscle shortens too much, the intrafusals go slack, *fewer* impulses go up the Ia-afferent, there is *less* activation of the motoneurone pool and less α-motoneurone activity. So the amount of muscle contraction is reduced.

It is common experience to overestimate weights—to find, for instance, on lifting a jug anticipated to be full that it is empty; the isometric tension of the flexors of the elbow for which the brain has been prepared is quickly converted to an isotonic

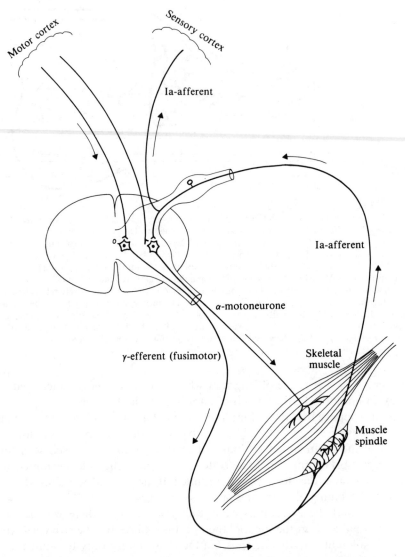

Motor cortex

Sensory cortex

Ia-afferent

Ia-afferent

α-motoneurone

γ-efferent (fusimotor)

Skeletal
muscle

Muscle
spindle

Figure 13.12 Conduction of efferent impulses (initiated in motor cortex of brain) from cells in the ventral root of the spinal cord to a muscle (extrafusal fibres) and also to the intrafusal fibres of its spindle. Afferent impulses from the sensory region of the spindle are sent (via the Ia afferent) both to the sensory cortex and to the cell bodies of the α-monotoneurones of the muscle concerned. Greater stretch of intrafusal fibres produces a larger Ia afferent volley and thus leads to more EPSP at the α-motoneurone. (Adapted from Davson, H. and M. B. Segal, *Introduction to Physiology*, vol. 4, Academic Press, London, 1978.)

contraction as the gravitational pull is unexpectedly small, and the forearm jerks upwards.

The muscle spindle is thus acting to sense the displacement between the lengths of extrafusal and intrafusal fibres, and keep them appropriately matching. (A device of this kind is called a 'servo-assist'.)

This idea of the role of the spindles in a voluntary movement seems plausible, but there are some unexplained points. The whole process must take time; by the time the displacement or mismatching has been sensed and impulses sent to correct it, it would have gone further in the wrong direction; so the system would be oscillating or jerky or unstable. How is it then that voluntary movements can in fact be made smoothly? One possible answer is that the spindle is in some way able to sense not only change of length but *rate* of change of length, so the brain unconsciously assesses not only where the muscle is now but also where it will be in 2 or 5 ms. When this information reaches the sensory cortex of the brain, the nearby motor cortex is made to adjust the α-motoneurone excitation accordingly. (A system of this kind is called 'phase-advanced'.)

In fact there may indeed sometimes be a certain degree of oscillation or instability in the system; it is called 'intention tremor' or 'effort tremor', and is seen, for instance, in a child learning to write, or a person picking up a load which is too heavy. The establishment of 'phase-advanced' processes might perhaps be the basis of the learning of movements, turning an unskilled or clumsy movement into a skilled one.

Patterns of movement and their significance

The foregoing rather oversimplified account of the control of a movement of a single muscle may provide a useful model, or way of thinking about muscular movements. It is of course an abstraction, because in real situations whole groups of muscles are working together or in a sequential pattern. The question of the starting point or initiation of a voluntary movement (or pattern of movements) is a matter for speculation and experiment. For a reflex movement the starting point can be found in the sensory ending, and the whole action might pass through the spinal cord, or brain stem and cerebellum, below the level of consciousness. But for a voluntary movement a starting point could be sought somewhere within the brain. The observation of increased blood flow to the 'supplementary motor area' of the brain (described in the Introduction to this chapter) during the planning of a series of voluntary movements may be of great significance here.

Certain sequences of movements may initially be learnt with some difficulty, as shown, for instance, by an infant learning to walk. Once learned and performed many times, a sequence is stored by a process described as 'motor memory', in which one movement leads on automatically to the next in the sequence. Learning to play a piece of music is an example of this: when the musician has reached the stage of storing the finger and hand movements in motor memory, he can give his conscious attention to the subtler aspects of tone and interpretation. But the stored behaviour pattern can be modified: if a certain finger becomes injured, the player can alter the movement sequence to use another finger. Not all species, however, have this ability to modify behaviour sequences already stored in motor memory. Adult birds which are feeding nestlings bring food repeatedly and place it in the open beaks of the young, at a particular place on a particular branch of a particular tree. If the whole nest containing the young birds is moved, say, 15 cm to one side of its original position, the parent birds cannot find it (even though the young may be cheeping), and are unable to continue feeding the nestlings. If there is no 'purpose' or 'motive' for the behaviour pattern, or if such 'purpose' becomes obscured, the storage of the routine behaviour pattern may lead to disaster.

The term 'motor memory' may be somewhat misleading, because it is quite different in nature from the recall to the mind of a unique series of events which happened some time in the individual's past life, which is what is normally meant by memory. This difference is well illustrated by the account of a man who after a blow on the head suffered from retrograde amnesia—the condition experienced by sufferers from mild concussion who forget the events of the period immediately preceding the blow, a period perhaps of only seconds or minutes, or perhaps of several days or weeks. This particular sufferer of retrograde amnesia had no recall of the period 2 or 3 weeks before the accident. During this 3-week period he had learnt touch-typing. After the accident he could touch-type as well as before, but was unable to recall the circumstances surrounding the learning of this manipulative skill.

The learning of a whole pattern of skilled movements, and its storage in the CNS, and subsequent performance below the level of consciousness, seem no different in principle from the establishment of a series of conditioned reflexes: the seeing of a certain group of letters on a written page is the stimulus which produces in the touch-typist a response in the form of a certain pattern of finger movements; the seeing of an arrangement of black dots on a stave causes the sight-reading pianist to press certain piano keys. Indeed the fact that so much of the active movement in the daily life of all animals including humans goes on below the level of consciousness leads one to ask the question: is *all* behaviour of man and other creatures the carrying out of a series of reflexes, unconditioned and conditioned? We have an inherent distaste for answering this question in the affirmative, at least in respect of humans. There are questions here about motivation, emotion, learning and willed behaviour, in oneself, in other humans, and in other species of animals. These important questions are worth asking, but discussion of them is beyond the scope of this book.

Many of the apparently inborn and instinctive behaviour patterns of animals have an obvious biological value for the individual or the species: the search for food or a mate, the escaping of danger from predators or natural hazards, the courtship displays which lead to successful mating, and so on. Even the spontaneous playing seen in young animals and human infants could be said to have survival value in exercising the limbs and in practising the movements required by many mammals in hunting prey or escaping predators. Man, of course, has intricate psychological requirements in addition to the fundamental biological needs: the avoidance of boredom, the satisfying of curiosity, and the exercising of body and mind. Playing back-garden tennis and going to concerts have no survival value but are a normal and necessary part of life for many humans. But perhaps man is not after all unique in showing behaviour patterns which have no obvious biological value. Young pigs will stand for hours beside a fence, watching the movement of a plough up and down the furrows in the next field, just as people stand watching a crane on a building site. Adult birds will fly, soar, swoop, plunge and tumble in the air currents above a cliff-face, apparently 'for fun', just as humans romp about in a swimming pool. It could be said that the pigs' behaviour is the outcome of the biologically advantageous instinct to explore and examine anything novel or unfamiliar in the environment; and that the bird is practising movements which may subsequently be of value to it when facing a tempest. But as far as we can tell at present from watching other species, humans are the only creatures which have insight into their own motives for actions and behaviour. Self-examination seems a uniquely human trait, and the Delphic inscription 'Know thyself' could be identical with the instruction 'Be human'.

Summary

Many of the unconscious and involuntary activities of the CNS can be understood in terms of reflexes connecting sensory input with motor output. Actions of reflexes passing through the spinal cord could be interpreted in terms of the connections of the interneurones (which may be simple or highly complicated) together with the properties of action potentials in peripheral nerves and the formation (by chemical transmitters) of EPSPs and IPSPs at central synapses. The central synapses are continuously active and it is the algebraic sum of the postsynaptic potentials that determines whether or not an impulse starts in the next neurone along the path.

The position of the limbs and joints is signalled to the CNS by proprioceptors (muscle spindles and tendon organs). The stretch reflex, particularly in antigravity muscles, is of fundamental importance in maintaining length against gravitational pull. Posture is maintained by reflexes initiated in these proprioceptors, in the vestibular apparatus, and (especially humans) in the eyes.

At the start of a voluntary movement, postural reflexes are overridden by the motor cortex, which sends impulses both to the α-motoneurone innervating the main (extrafusal) muscle fibres and to γ-efferent nerves innervating the intrafusal fibres of muscle spindles. The stimulation of the spindle afferents during the muscle's response may be a factor which allows precisely the appropriate amount of α-motoneurone activity required for the carrying out of a smooth movement.

Many muscular movements are carried out in coordinated sequences or patterns, the intricate control of which by the CNS has to be learnt and practised before being performed unconsciously. Such learning of patterns of muscular activity may be equivalent to the establishment of conditioned reflexes. One may speculate about the extent to which other behaviour patterns are analogous with reflexes, and about whether man is unique in performing actions which have no apparent biological significance.

14 Endocrine system

Introduction

The endocrine glands are a heterogeneous collection of glands scattered throughout the body, being found in the head, neck and abdomen of mammals, as shown in Fig. 14.1. Their function is the production and secretion of hormones. Originally a hormone was defined as a substance produced in an endocrine or ductless gland and secreted directly into the circulation to act on a second organ. The term was first applied by Bayliss and Starling (1903) to secretin, the active principle of an extract of intestinal mucosa, which stimulates pancreatic secretion. The steps in establishing whether an organ has an endocrine function are to demonstrate the changes on its removal, and their reversal on transplantation of the organ or injection of an extract of the tissue. The active principle can then be isolated, purifed and the structure identified. Assays can be established for the hormone and the arteriovenous difference in hormone concentrations across the gland established to verify the source of the hormone. A further test of endocrine function is a study of the histology of the gland, which should be characteristic of actively secreting glands (with secretory granules in the cells, for instance), but without ducts.

In the light of recent work, however, the original definition is seen to be too restrictive. Hormones may be produced in organs other than endocrine glands, such as for example the intestinal mucosa, for secretin, and the kidney, which produces erythropoietin. Hypothalamic releasing hormones are synthesized in nerve cells and released into the hypothalamic portal system. The hormone need not even be released into blood vessels. In the gastrointestinal tract the hormones act on surrounding cells. Thus, in addition to the classical function, hormones may have a paracrine function, producing effects on adjacent cells, or a neurocrine function, acting as neuro-modulators and neurotransmitters, or even an autocrine function, being self-regulatory.

The endocrine system forms part of the control system of the body and is closely integrated with the nervous system: the hypothalamus controls the pituitary gland and the adrenal medulla has a nervous supply. Some hormones, such as growth hormone (GH) and insulin, have widespread effects throughout the body, while others such as thyroid-stimulating hormone (TSH) and calcitonin, which influences calcium balance, have more specific target organs. Hormones may be grouped in many ways according to their action, but a convenient classification is to place them in one of three categories:

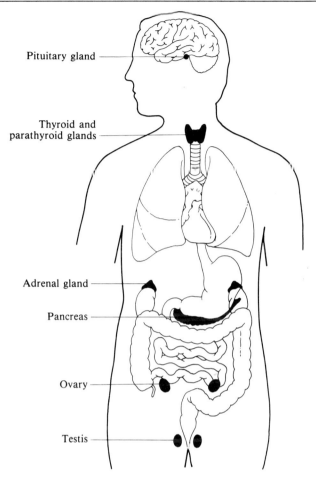

Figure 14.1 Location of the endocrine glands in human. (Both male and female reproductive endocrine glands are shown.)

1. hormones which keep physiological parameters, such as blood sugar and calcium, constant;
2. hormones which control growth and sexual development;
3. hormones which contribute to physiological adjustments to the changing environment.

The chief endocrine organs are listed in Table 14.1 and their locations are shown in Fig. 14.1. Much of our knowledge of endocrine function has come from the study of man. Clinical conditions associated with either under- or overproduction of a given hormone have taught us much. For example the clinical features of diabetes mellitus were known as long ago as 1500 BC. Whereas clinical observations laid the

Table 14.1   Endocrine organs and their secretions

Gland/organ	Location	Hormone	Molecular structure	Target
Hypothalamus/ median eminence	Base of brain	Thyrotrophin releasing hormone (TRH)	Peptides	Anterior pituitary
		Somatostatin		
		Luteinizing hormone releasing hormone (LHRH)		
		Corticotrophin releasing factor (CRF)		
		Growth hormone releasing factor (GHRF)		
		Prolactin inhibiting factor	?Dopamine	
Pituitary (hypophysis)	Cavity in sphenoid bone at base of skull (sella turcica)			
—Anterior pituitary		Prolactin	Protein	Mammary gland
		Growth hormone (GH)	Protein	General body cells
		Adrenocorticotrophic hormone (ACTH)	Peptide	Adrenal cortex
		Thyroid-stimulating hormone (TSH)	Glycoprotein	Thyroid gland
		Luteinizing hormone (LH)	Glycoprotein	Ovary / Testis
		Follicle-stimulating hormone (FSH)	Glycoprotein	Ovary / Testis
—Pars intermedia		Melanocyte-stimulating hormone (MSH)	Peptide	Melanocytes of skin
—Posterior pituitary		Vasopressin (antidiuretic hormone, ADH)	Peptide	Kidney, blood vessels
		Oxytocin	Peptide	Uterus / Mammary gland
Thyroid	Neck, anterior to trachea	Thyroxine (T_4) Tri-iodothyronine (T_3)	Tyrosine derivatives	General body cells
		Calcitonin	Peptide	Skeleton

Gland	Location	Hormone	Chemical nature	Target organ
Parathyroids	Neck on each side of thyroid	Parathyroid hormone	Peptide	Skeleton Kidney Gastrointestinal tract
Adrenals	Rear peritoneal cavity on rostral border of each kidney			
—Adrenal cortex		Glucocorticoids (cortisone; cortisol; corticosterone)	Steroids	General body cells
		Mineralocorticoids (aldosterone)		Kidneys
—Adrenal medulla		Adrenaline and noradrenaline	Catecholamines	Smooth muscle Metabolic effects
Islets of Langerhans	Scattered throughout the pancreas	Insulin	Protein	Liver, muscle, adipose cells
		Glucagon	Protein	Liver
		Somatostatin	Protein	Pancreas
Ovaries	Peritoneal cavity below the Fallopian tubes	Oestrogen	Steroid	Reproductive tract, mammary glands
		Progesterone	Steroid	Endometrium and mammary glands
Testis	Suspended in scrotum by the spermatic cord	Testosterone	Steroid	Reproductive and secondary sex organs
Stomach		Gastrin	Peptide	Stomach
Duodenum and jejunum		Secretin	Protein	Pancreas
		Cholecystokinin/pancreozymin	Protein	Gall bladder, pancreas

foundation of endocrinology, advances in other disciplines including biochemistry have provided tools for development of the subject.

Measurement of hormone concentration

Progress in understanding of the endocrine system has depended on ability to measure concentration of hormones in blood and tissues. The first method for such measurements was the use of biological assays on animals or isolated organs. A quantifiable action of a hormone such as increase in heart rate or reduction of urinary flow rate could be calibrated by means of a series of known concentrations of the hormone, and unknown solutions could then be applied to the same animal or organ, their action measured and the corresponding concentration calculated. Bioassays can now also be carried out using isolated living cells in culture media.

Biochemical assays are now in common use. An antibody to a specific hormone, formed in the plasma of an animal by repeated injection of the hormone, is used as a binding agent for that hormone when samples of the hormone and the plasma are mixed to form a complex. If a fixed amount of hormone and antibody are allowed to react together, at equilibrium they will form a hormone-antibody complex, a proportion of antibody and labelled hormone remaining free. If unlabelled hormone is now introduced into the system, some of the labelled material will be displaced so that more will be in the free form. The free material can be separated and its radioactivity counted. With increasing concentration of added non-radioactive hormone, the quantity of bound hormone decreases and the quantity of free radioactively labelled hormone increases. So the system can be calibrated by a series of solutions of known hormone concentrations and the unknown material measured in the same system. This procedure is called radioimmunoassay (Fig. 14.2).

Chemistry of hormones

Hormones fall into one of three chemical structures:

1. polypeptides and proteins;
2. steroids;
3. derivatives of tyrosine.

Polypeptide and protein hormones

Polypeptide and protein hormones have a great range of molecular weights, from tripeptides such as thyrotrophin releasing hormone (TRH) to GH with 190 amino acids and the large glycoprotein hormones such as TSH. They may comprise a single peptide chain or may be more complex. There are no mechanisms for synthesizing peptides as such. Instead peptide hormones are formed as prohormones or pre-prohormones. The first identified prohormone was proinsulin. The C- (connecting) peptide is cleaved from this single-chain peptide, leaving insulin, which is a peptide comprising two chains (A and B) connected by two disulphide bonds (Fig. 14.3).

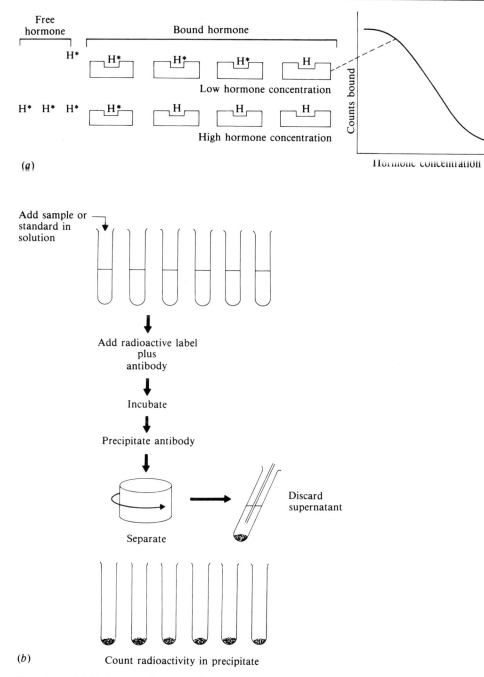

Figure 14.2 (*a*) Basic principles of a radioimmunoassay. At low concentrations of antigen most of the radioactively labelled antigen (H*) is bound to antibody. The concentration of hormone in an unknown sample can be read off a standard curve. (*b*) Procedure for carrying out a standard radioimmunoassay.

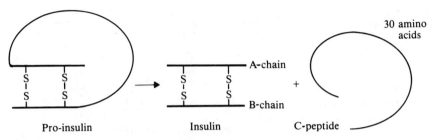

Figure 14.3 Formation of insulin from pro-insulin.

Peptide hormones are synthesized on the ribosomes and the prefragment removed as the product passes into the cisternal space. Carbohydrate residues may be added and the hormone transferred to the Golgi complex, where it is packed into vesicles. The hormone may then be released by exocytosis.

Steroid hormones

Steroid hormones are not stored in large quantities like peptide hormones, but are formed as needed. Steroid hormones comprise three six-carbon rings and a five-carbon ring, fused together as indicated in Fig. 14.4. The carbon atoms are numbered as indicated. Methyl groups may be added at C10, C13 and C17. The biochemical pathway for steroid synthesis starts at acetate and proceeds via norvalonate and squalene to cholesterol, the precursor of all steroid hormones. The cholesterol is first converted to pregnenolone in the mitochondria under the action of cholesterol desmolase, and then either progesterone or 17-hydroxypregnenolone are formed in the smooth endoplasmic reticulum. Cortisol, an adrenal hormone with effects on carbohydrate metabolism, is formed from pregnenolone by 17-hydroxylation, and aldosterone, a hormone affecting salt balance, by successive hydroxylation and dehydrogenation. The side-chain of 17-hydroxypregnenolone may be cleaved to form the sex-steroid dehydroepiandrosterone which is dehydrogenated to androstenedione (Fig. 14.5).

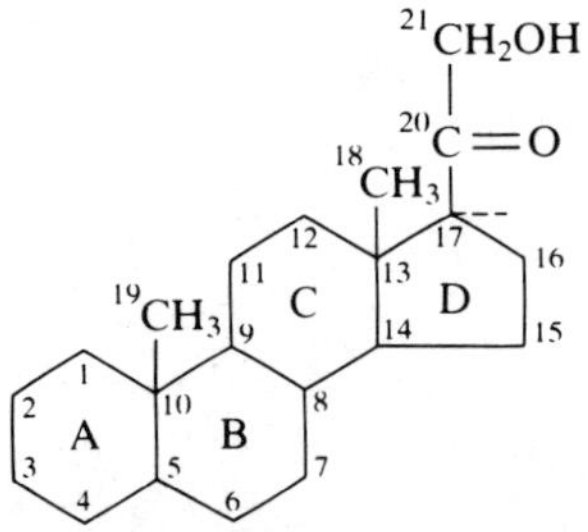

Figure 14.4 Structure of the cortisol molecule showing the scheme for labelling the rings and numbering the carbon atoms.

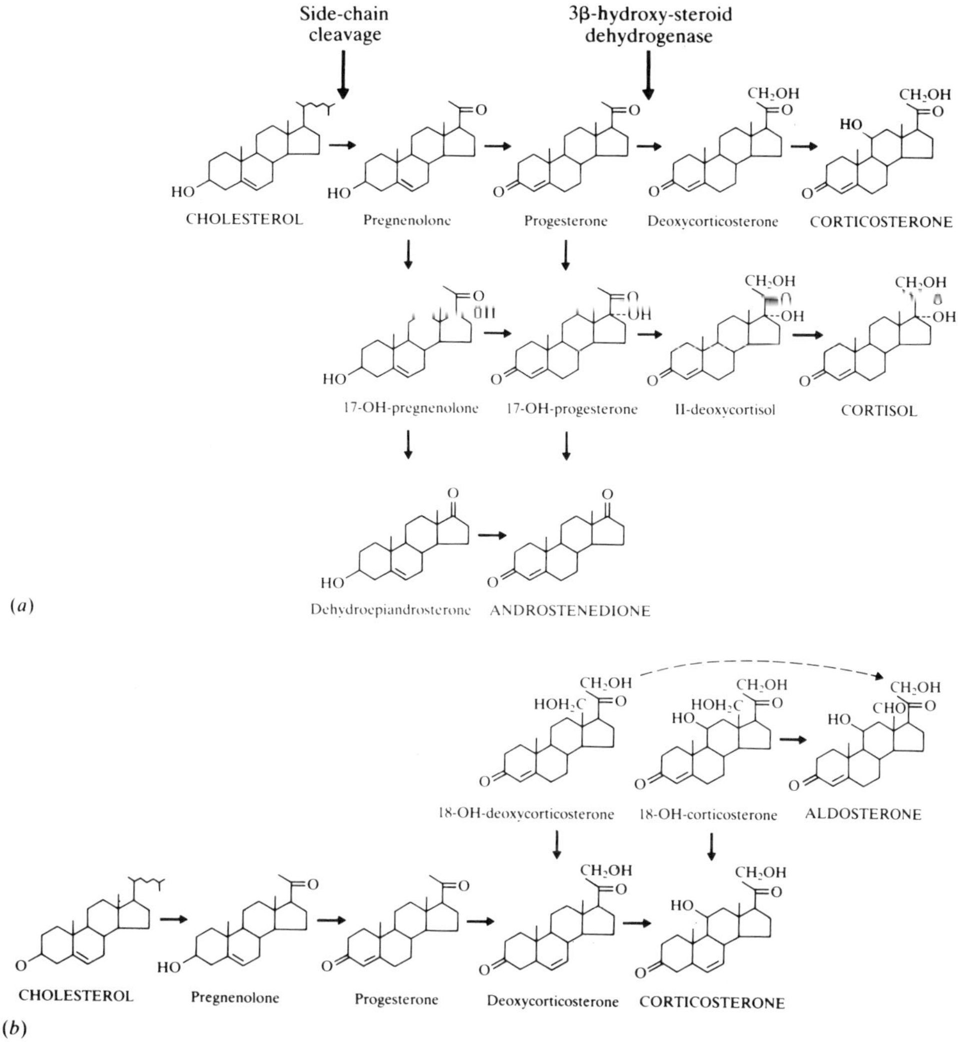

(a)

(b)

Figure 14.5 Pathways for the synthesis of steroid hormones from cholesterol in (a) the zona fasciculata and reticularis and (b) the zona glomerulosa of the adrenal cortex.

Tyrosine-derivative hormones

The derivatives of tyrosine (Fig. 14.6) include the monoamines adrenaline, noradrenaline and dopamine, and also the thyroid hormones thyroxine (T_4) and tri-iodothyronine (T_3). Dopamine is formed from tyrosine via 3,4-dihydroxyphenylalanine. Subsequently noradrenaline is formed and then adrenaline by the action of phenylethanolamine N-methyltransferase. The thyroid hormones are formed from two molecules of iodinated tyrosine linked through an oxygen molecule.

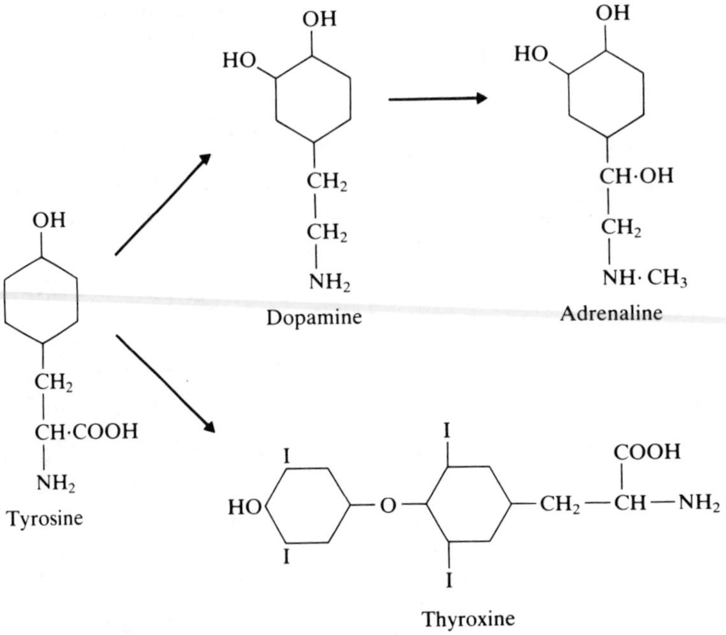

Figure 14.6 The structure of hormones derived from tyrosine.

The rate of clearance of a hormone from the plasma depends on its chemical nature. Some hormones are carried in the plasma in the bound form. Binding may be to albumin or to specific carrier proteins such as cortisol-binding globulin and thyroxine-binding globulin. Plasma binding helps to prevent filtration of the hormone at the kidney and hence increases the half-time of disappearance from the plasma. It is the free hormone which is biologically active, so changes of the quantity of hormone binder in the plasma can be quite important. Hormones are largely removed from the circulation in the liver and kidney. Steroid hormones which are not readily water-soluble are conjugated in the liver before excretion in the urine.

Mechanisms of action

The mechanisms of hormone action at the cellular level are also dependent on the chemical nature of the hormone. The first step in the sequence of events leading to the response is binding of the hormone to a receptor. It is this step which contributes to the specificity of the hormone's effect. Hormones circulate throughout the body, yet produce a given effect only in specific tissues. This is due to the 'lock and key' fit of hormone and receptor, and to the basic function of the cell itself.

Peptide hormones

Peptide hormones do not penetrate the cell, but react with receptors in the cell membrane. These receptors are large oligomeric proteins, a relatively small proportion of which are embedded in the membrane. Hormone binding may produce clustering of the receptors in the cell membrane, which are then taken into the cell (Fig. 14.7). Internalized receptor sites may be degraded, leading to a reduction in the number of receptors, which renders the cell less responsive. Alternatively they may be recycled back for reinsertion into the plasma membrane. Although the hormone binds to the outer cell membrane, its effects are produced intracellularly; so a second messenger in the cell is required, the hormone being the first messenger. A number of second-messenger systems have been proposed, including those for cyclic AMP (cAMP) and for calcium.

Cyclic AMP is formed from ATP, which contains high-energy phosphate bonds, through the action of the enzyme adenylate cyclase. The receptor unit which binds the hormone is just one of three functional units which make up the hormone-sensitive adenylate cyclase, the other two being the regulatory protein (G) and the catalytic moiety (C). On binding of the hormone with its receptor, guanosine triphosphate

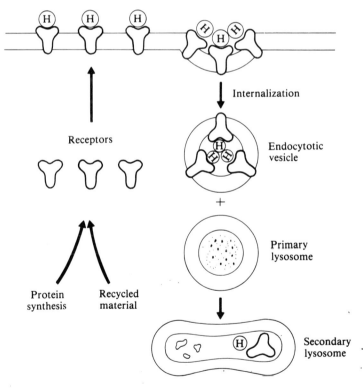

Figure 14.7 Postulated changes in hormone (H) receptors and subsequent internalization following hormone binding.

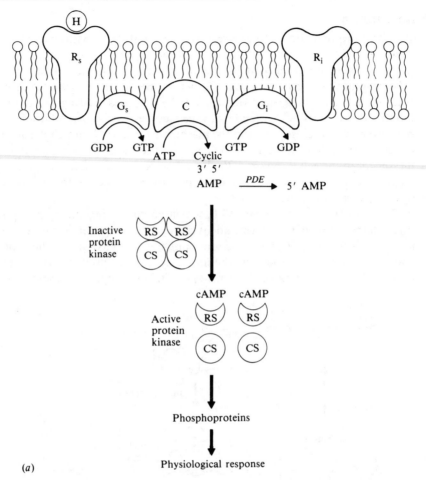

(a)

Figure 14.8 Outline of mechanisms of action of peptide hormones, showing the second messengers involved. (*a*) Hormone (H) binds with either a stimulatory (R_s) or an inhibitory (R_i) receptor, associated with a transducer unit or G-protein which can be either stimulatory (G_s) or inhibitory (G_i). This protein comprises three subunits, one of which dissociates and activates an enzyme adenylate cyclase (c) which converts ATP to cAMP; this in turn activates a protein kinase which in turn leads to the physiological response. RS: regulatory subunit; CS: catalytic subunit; PDE: phosphodiesterase. (*b*) Dissociation of the G-protein results in activation of phospholipase C (PLC), which hydrolyses phosphatidylbiphosphate (PIP_2) to give diacyl glycerol and activation of protein kinase C (PkC), as well as the formation of inositol trisphosphate and the release of Ca^{++}, both of which lead to a physiological response.

(GTP) binds to the G-protein, leading to activation of the C-protein, which catalyses the conversion of ATP to cAMP. It is proposed that all of the biological effects are mediated through the action of protein kinases, which catalyse transfer of phosphate from ATP to a proton acceptor. Protein kinases comprise two subunits, a regulatory and a catalytic subunit. Cyclic AMP binds to the regulatory subunit and causes the two subunits to dissociate, the free catalytic subunit being the active protein kinase.

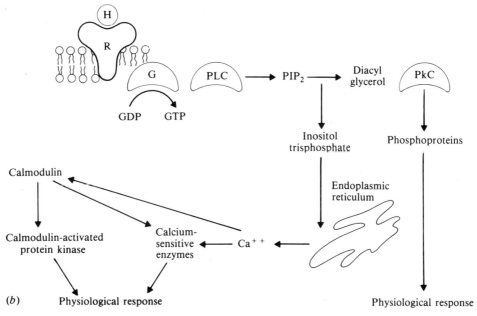

Figure 14.8 (*continued*)

The duration of the response is limited by the breakdown of cAMP by phosphodiesterase. The protein kinases formed have many important functions including an effect on protein synthesis, the phosphorylation of nuclear histones and perhaps other nuclear proteins. The wide range of effects which may be produced include one on RNA synthesis.

In contrast to the cAMP system, in which the generation of cAMP is due to direct coupling of the hormone to the receptor, the generation of the calcium signal may not be the initial consequence of hormone binding. Elevation of the cytosolic Ca^{++} ion concentration may mediate the response to many hormones. Cytosolic Ca^{++} ion concentration must be kept low, otherwise the high concentrations of intracellular phosphate would cause precipitation in the cells of hydroxyapatite, a form of calcium phosphate. Cytosol calcium may be derived from intracellular pools or through fluxes across the cell membrane. On binding of hormones to plasma-membrane receptors, phospholipase-C activity may be stimulated, leading to the formation of inositol trisphosphate. This acts as a second messenger to stimulate the release of Ca^{++} ions from intracellular pools. The intracellular action of Ca^{++} ions is mediated by activation of calcium-sensitive enzymes and via calcium-binding proteins including calmodulin, protein kinase C and troponin C, this last being one of the components of the thick filaments of skeletal muscle. The calcium binder, calmodulin, is able to bind and thus activate a variety of enzymes including several protein kinases, a cyclic nucleotide, phosphodiesterase and a neuronal adenylate cyclase. Figure 14.8 summarizes mechanisms of action of the peptide hormones.

While the response to most peptide hormones seems to involve cAMP, or calcium, this seems not to be true for insulin, prolactin, GH and growth factors. Insulin acts *inter alia* to increase cell permeability. Its actions, like those of growth factors, depend on its ability to activate tyrosine kinase, an enzyme responsible for catalysing the phosphorylation of tyrosyl residues in proteins. Growth hormone also acts by altering membrane permeability and hence the availability of amino acids and energy substrates. In addition, it acts on protein synthesis to modify the ability of ribosomes to translate messenger RNA (mRNA) into protein in a manner involving an increase in the production of mRNA.

Steroid hormones

Steroid hormones, being rather smaller than most peptide hormones and being also lipid-soluble, are able to penetrate the cell and exert their effect at the nucleus. Binding of steroid hormone to the nuclear receptor results in a change in the activity of the DNA-dependent polymerase and hence a change in the rate of production of mRNA and subsequently specific proteins. Figure 14.9 shows the action of steroid hormones at the cellular level.

Thyroid hormones

The thyroid hormones (members of the tyrosine-derived group of hormones) act in a similar manner to the steroid hormones. There is an active transport mechanism in

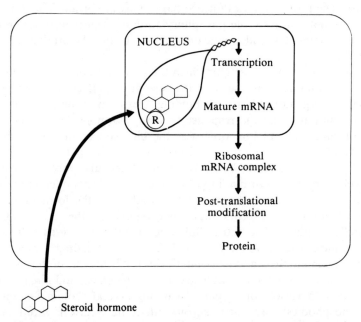

Figure 14.9 Outline of mechanism of action of steroid hormones. R: nuclear receptor.

the membrane for thyroid hormones, which subsequently enter the nucleus where they produce a switch to formation of a large group of catabolic enzymes required for increased cellular activity.

Control of secretion

The endocrine system is part of the control system of the body and in turn is subject to close regulation. The basic components of a control system (Fig. 14.10) are:

1. a detector system, sensitive to changes in the controlled variable·
2. an integrator which processes the information and passes on the signal to ...
3. an effector system, which brings about the appropriate changes.

The commonest form of control in biological systems is negative feedback. In this instance any perturbation of the controlled variable results in a response to return it to the pre-set resting level. An example of this is in the control of blood sugar concentrations. A rise in blood sugar concentration acts on the pancreas to stimulate insulin secretion, which in turn lowers blood glucose. A more complex response is seen in the case of maintenance of the osmolarity of the blood plasma. As described in Chapter 7, an increase in plasma osmolarity stimulates the osmoreceptors in the hypothalamus, which leads to stimulation of other neurones and the release of vasopressin which promotes water retention by the kidney so that the plasma osmolarity returns towards its former value. The other form of feedback is positive feedback, which leads to instability and rarely occurs in biological systems. Here any change in the controlled variable feeds back to increase the change, a response which

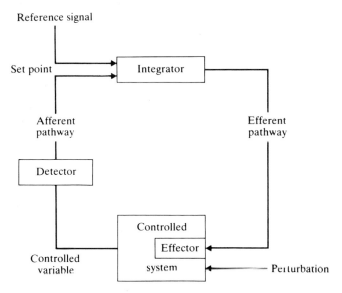

Figure 14.10 General scheme of a physiological control circuit.

can occur only if the situation is self-limiting. An example of this occurs during parturition. As the fetus enters the birth canal, oxytocin release is stimulated, leading to enhanced uterine contractions, which in return result in the release of more oxytocin. Thus delivery is speeded up, a process which obviously has a natural endpoint. Ovulation is similarly controlled by positive feedback. If concentrations of the hormone oestrogen are maintained at a certain level for a sufficient length of time, they exert positive feedback stimulating release of the anterior pituitary hormone, luteinizing hormone (LH), which stimulates the release of the ovum from the ovary.

Simple negative-feedback systems are sufficient to control a parameter such as blood glucose. Greater complexity is required if the endocrine system is to be integrated with the nervous system, enabling hormones to form part of the whole-body response to changes in the internal and external environment. Thus not only are there closed-loop systems, as in the control of blood glucose, but open loops are introduced. The concentration of a given hormone may also become the controlled variable. Thus one hormone may control the release of another hormone. The second hormone may have two effects—first, to feed back and control the release of the first hormone and, secondly, to produce a response in other target tissue(s). This response will probably not give rise to a feedback action. The series of steps may be extended by including nervous control over the release of the first hormone (open loop). This is the case in the control of some pituitary hormones. Nervous impulses control the secretion of a releasing hormone, influencing release of the pituitary hormone, which controls the function of another endocrine gland. The products of this target gland can feed back to influence the control pathway and produce responses in the specific target tissues (Fig. 14.13).

Neuroendocrinology: the hypothalamus and pituitary

Structure, development, general function, and releasing factors

The hypothalamus is the region where integration of endocrine and neural control occurs. It makes up the ventral half of the diencephalon and forms the lateral walls of the third ventricle. It is below and anterior to the thalamus from which it is separated by the hypothalamic sulcus. The pituitary gland (Fig. 14.11) lies just beneath the hypothalamus in the pituitary fossa. Below and rostral to the hypothalamus is the optic chiasma, which is a useful landmark. The hypothalamus is divided into the following regions:

1. preoptic, ahead of the chiasma;
2. supraoptic, over the chiasma;
3. tuberal connected with the hypophysial stalk, and the mamillary bodies.

The hypothalamus controls the maintenance of the internal environment, namely the restorative and reproductive functions and the readiness of the body to respond to external stimuli. It is able to accomplish this as it receives inputs from all areas of the periphery and from the cerebral cortex. It also has receptors located within its structures (see Chapter 10): thermoreceptors important in evoking compensatory

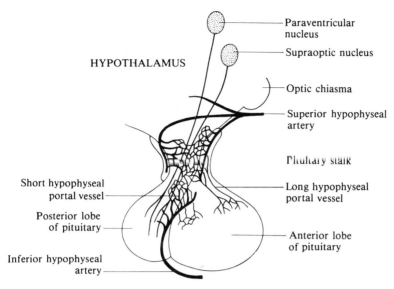

Figure 14.11 Pituitary gland and surrounding region (in man).

mechanisms for changes in body temperature, osmoreceptors important in controlling thirst and fluid excretion, and possibly glucose receptors important in controlling food intake. Outputs from the hypothalamus control the activity of the sympathetic and parasympathetic systems, and the activity of the pituitary.

The pituitary acts to control many endocrine functions in the body and for this reason was at one time termed 'the conductor of the endocrine orchestra'. In view of more recent discoveries this description has now to be modified, so that the pituitary becomes the leader of the orchestra and the hypothalamus the conductor. The pituitary comprises an anterior and a posterior lobe, and in some species, but not in man, an intermediate lobe between the two is present. The pituitary is derived embryologically from two different sources. The anterior pituitary derives from an upward growth of the buccal cavity—Rathke's pouch. The pituitary stalk and the posterior pituitary develop as a downgrowth of the neural tissue which forms the floor of the third ventricle (Fig. 14.12). The posterior pituitary thus comprises nerve terminals, the nerve bodies lying in the two hypothalamic nuclei: the supraoptic and the paraventricular nuclei. In contrast, the anterior pituitary has no nervous supply; instead the control is hormonal. The anterior pituitary, however, has no direct arterial blood supply either. Nutritional and hormonal signals arrive via the portal vessels which arise from a primary plexus in the median eminence, which lies at the start of the pituitary stalk. The anterior pituitary secretes six hormones, and separate cells exist to synthesize each one of the hormones so that there are mammotrophs, thyrotrophs, etc.

Control of anterior pituitary secretion is summarized in Fig. 14.13. The hormones

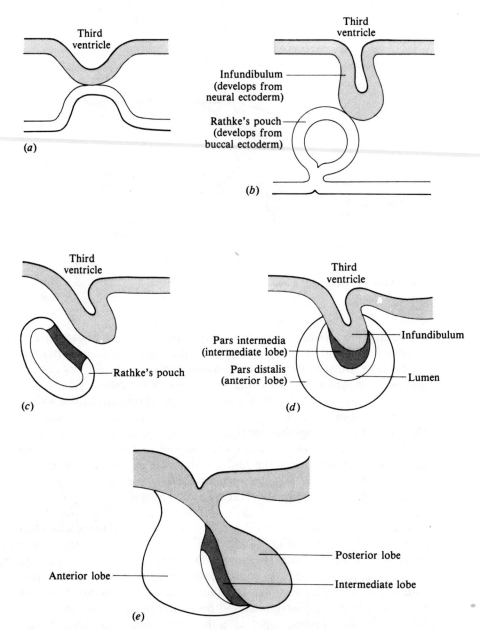

Figure 14.12 Embryological origins of the pituitary gland. (a)–(e) Chronological development.

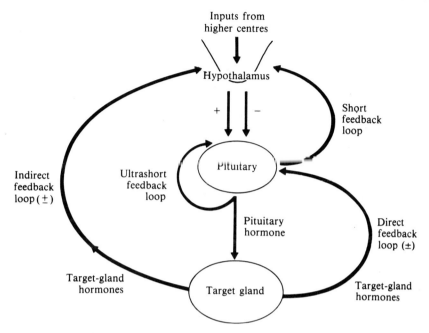

Figure 14.13 Feedback loop involved in the control of pituitary hormone release. Growth hormone and prolactin do not have target-gland feedback, nor have all pathways been proved for every hormone.

controlling anterior pituitary hormone secretion are synthesized in the cell bodies of neurones in the hypothalamus. The hormones are released from the nerve terminals into the portal circulation and pass to the anterior pituitary. The six hormones secreted by the anterior pituitary are:

1. GH
2. LH
3. TSH
4. adrenocorticotrophic hormone (ACTH)
5. follicle-stimulating hormone (FSH)
6. prolactin

Most of these hormones are under the control of hypothalamic releasing hormones, all of which are polypeptides. Prolactin is controlled by an inhibitory factor, and for GH there are both releasing and inhibiting factors. One may surmise that inhibitory factors exist for prolactin and GH because these hormones have no specific target gland or organ, and so no possibility of hormonal feedback limiting release. Separate releasing hormones do not appear to exist for LH and FSH: just the one gonadotrophic releasing hormone (GnRH or LHRH). Hypothalamic releasing and inhibitory factors were postulated over 30 years ago, but they have been isolated and characterized only quite recently. Once such a factor has been isolated and its amino-acid sequence determined, it may be termed a hormone.

The hypothalamic releasing factors are controlled by inputs from higher centres and also by feedback from the peripheral target organs; they are possibly also controlled by a short feedback loop involving the anterior pituitary hormone secretions. Secretion of the anterior pituitary hormones and presumably of the releasing factors is pulsatile. Secretion, as in the case of ACTH, may show a diurnal rhythm, the concentrations being highest in the early morning and lowest at midnight. Secretion of other hormones such as GH, prolactin and TSH reaches a peak during sleep. Hence there may be truth in the old wives' tale that one grows in one's sleep. There are rhythms of hormonal secretion of greater duration than 24 hours. The duration of the cycle may be as long as the oestrous or menstrual cycle for LH and FSH. In the case of seasonal breeders such as sheep, the secretion of prolactin is controlled by the day length and hence shows a pattern changing over an entire season.

Posterior pituitary hormones

Control of hormonal release from the posterior pituitary is via nervous inputs to the supraoptic and paraventricular nuclei in the hypothalamus. The two posterior pituitary hormones oxytocin and vasopressin are synthesized in these nuclei in the form of precursor molecules, which also contain the amino-acid sequences of the so-called 'carrier proteins', the neurophysins. The precursors are packaged within neurosecretory granules and transported to the posterior pituitary. The active hormones, both nine amino-acids long (Fig. 14.14), are formed during this process and may subsequently be released into the circulation by exocytosis. The hormones have a short half-life in the circulatory system.

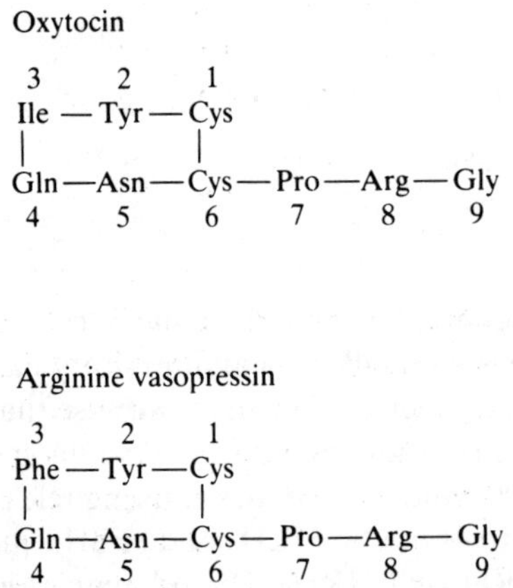

Oxytocin

```
 3      2      1
Ile — Tyr — Cys
 |             |
Gln —Asn —Cys — Pro —Arg—Gly
 4      5      6      7     8     9
```

Arginine vasopressin

```
 3      2     1
Phe —Tyr —Cys
 |            |
Gln —Asn —Cys — Pro —Arg — Gly
 4      5     6      7     8     9
```

Figure 14.14 Structures of oxytocin and of arginine vasopressin.

Vasopressin

Vasopressin has a number of actions; the main one on a day-to-day basis, as indicated in Chapter 7, is an effect on the kidney, which promotes water retention. The hormone increases the permeability of the collecting duct so that water passes down its concentration gradient into the renal interstitium. Vasopressin is also a vasoconstrictor agent (hence the name), and may contribute to the long-term regulation of blood pressure. Other actions which have been claimed for vasopressin include effects on memory, on ACTH secretion, on fibrinolysis and on glycogenolysis. Consistent with its action in retaining water, vasopressin release is stimulated by an increase in plasma osmolarity. It is postulated that changes in osmolarity are detected by osmoreceptors in the hypothalamus, but their location has not yet been established. Vasopressin release is stimulated also in response to a fall in blood volume detected by the stretch receptors in the atria of the heart and, if there is a fall in blood pressure also, by the baroreceptors. Thus a fall in blood pressure leads to vasopressin release, which in turn leads to vasoconstriction, which helps to return the blood pressure to normal.

Lack of vasopressin results in diabetes insipidus, which in man results in the production of up to 20 litres of urine per day, instead of the normal daily volume, 1.5 litres. Sometimes the condition results not from a lack of vasopressin, but from failure of the kidney to respond to the hormone (nephrogenic diabetes insipidus). Excess vasopressin may be produced in a number of conditions including surgical operations. Secretion of vasopressin which is inappropriate for plasma osmolality (syndrome of inappropriate secretion of vasopressin) results in retention of water; plasma osmolality falls to dangerously low levels and water intoxication may result.

Oxytocin

Although oxytocin has only two different amino acids from vasopressin, it has rather different actions. It acts on the oestrogen-dominated uterus to increase the contractions, which is important in parturition. In the female the other important action is to cause contraction of the myoepithelial cells surrounding the alveoli and ducts of the mammary gland, thereby expelling milk. Oxytocin is present in the pituitary of male animals in similar amounts to those in the female, but it is not clear what is its function. It may aid in sperm transport during mating and could have an effect on salt excretion. The stimuli for release are consistent with the actions of the hormone. It is released in response to vaginal stimulation. Thus during parturition when the fetus enters the birth canal there is stimulation of oxytocin release, so uterine contractions are increased and the fetus passes further along the birth canal. Oxytocin is also released in response to suckling. Release is not continuous but occurs in spurts. There are no disorders known to be associated with disturbances of oxytocin secretion.

Anterior pituitary hormones

Most of the hormones of the anterior pituitary are trophic hormones affecting other organs with endocrine function. These trophic hormones increase blood flow to the gland, promote growth and, most important, stimulate hormone synthesis and secretion. As implicit in the names, ACTH acts on the adrenal cortex and TSH on the thyroid. In the female, as will be discussed in Chapter 15, FSH brings about ripening of the ovarian follicle and LH contributes to rupture of the ovarian follicle. In the male, FSH influences spermatogenesis, while LH controls the rate of synthesis of testosterone. The two remaining anterior pituitary hormones have properties in common, but GH mainly acts to promote growth, and prolactin to stimulate synthesis.

Adrenocorticotrophic hormone (ACTH)

Of the trophic hormones, ACTH is some 39 amino acids long, the first 24 amino acids contributing to biological activity and the remainder to the species specificity. The first 13 amino acids are identical with the α melanocyte-stimulating hormone molecule of all species, a hormone involved in pigmentation of the skin. Adrenocorticotrophic hormone is formed from a much larger molecule, pro-opiomelanocortin, which may be split to form a large number of polypeptides including endogenous peptides with morphine-like activity—the opioid peptides (Fig. 14.15). Secretion of ACTH is under the control of corticotrophin releasing factor (CRF), a 41 amino-acid peptide, and is also influenced by vasopressin. Secretion may be modulated by cortisol, which feeds back negatively on the pituitary. As already mentioned, ACTH secretion exhibits a circadian rhythm in most animals studied; a morning peak is seen in man and probably in other species active in daylight. The main action of ACTH is on the adrenal gland, where it stimulates the synthesis and release of cortisol and can also stimulate tissue growth. In addition ACTH has a number of extra-adrenal effects including possible stimulation of lipolysis, inhibition of thymic growth, and behavioural effects. Excess secretion of ACTH (Cushing's disease) or of cortisol (Cushing's syndrome) leads to a disorder characterized by poor wound-healing, fragile skin, and weakened bone structure (osteoporosis). There are also alterations in the lipid metabolism, resulting in a moon-shaped face, centripetal obesity and a buffalo hump. Cortisone is sometimes given for treatment of the inflammation of rheumatoid arthritis, and patients receiving this treatment must be made aware of the dangers of these possible side-effects.

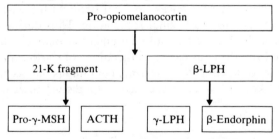

Figure 14.15 Products of processing of pro-opiomelanocortin in the anterior pituitary. The precursor first yields a pro-ACTH intermediate (molecular weight 21 000) and β-lipotrophin (β-LPH). This is broken down to release ACTH and pro-γ-melanocyte stimulating hormone (pro-γ-MSH), and β-LPH is partially cleaved to γ-LPH and β-endorphin.

Growth hormone (GH)

Growth hormone is a single-chain polypeptide of molecular weight 22 000. The molecule is species-specific, so that only human GH is effective in man. Secretion, in addition to being associated with sleep, may also be enhanced by stress and exercise. Release is inhibited by elevated plasma glucose concentrations and may be modulated by hormones such as oestrogen.

As the name implies, the hormone stimulates growth, characteristically in the young. It stimulates growth of the long bones, not directly, but through the action of somatomedins or insulin-like growth factors. Released from the liver in response to GH, these factors have a number of actions including cartilage-stimulating activity, which contributes to the growth of long bones, and insulin-like activity. In addition to stimulating growth of the long bones, GH has widespread metabolic effects, both anabolic (building up) and catabolic (breaking down). The anabolic effects are related to growth promotion, enhanced formation of proteins and nucleic acids, and retention of other constituents of lean body mass. The effects on fat and carbohydrate metabolism are largely catabolic and support growth.

Lack of GH in the young results in dwarfism, and excess in gigantism. Altered secretion of GH is less important after fusion of the epiphyses of the long bones but, in the human, excess secretion, as from a pituitary tumour, results in acromegaly, a condition in which there is enlargement of the jaw, coarsening of the features and enlargement of the hands and feet. It may be treated by surgical removal of the tumour. Since GH exhibits 'spurt' release, it is not possible to make a diagnosis on the basis of the determination of hormone concentration in a single sample; instead dynamic tests are employed. An insulin-tolerance test is used in the case of suspected GH deficiency to see if the hyperglycaemia induced is capable of stimulating GH release, as in a normal subject. To determine if GH can be suppressed in a suspected case of acromegaly, a glucose-tolerance test is used. Suppression will not be seen in acromegaly.

Prolactin

A hormone with a structure very similar to that of GH is prolactin. Indeed at one time it was believed that human GH could account for all the actions which we now know are due to prolactin. Prolactin is important for the initiation and maintenance of lactation, and elevated concentrations can reduce fertility. Its presence is necessary for the development of the mammary gland during pregnancy, and high concentrations are needed for the initiation of lactation. During lactation, prolactin concentrations are elevated in response to suckling. In seasonal breeders such as sheep, prolactin concentrations in plasma vary according to the time of the year, increasing as day length increases. The nature of prolactin inhibiting factor is not yet unequivocally established, but it appears to be dopamine. Excess prolactin secretion can therefore be reduced by administration of the dopamine agonist bromocriptine.

Glycoprotein hormones

The remaining trophic hormones—TSH, LH and FSH—are all glycoproteins, consisting of two subunits, α and β. The α-chain is common to all hormones but is species-specific; the β-chain confers the characteristic activity of the hormone.

Hormones influencing intermediary metabolism

Many hormones have effects on intermediate metabolism. The interplay of the hormones maintains an adequate supply of the three groups of energy-supplying molecules—glucose, free fatty acids and amino acids—both in situations of starvation and after meals. Maintenance of blood glucose is of particular significance as it is the main substrate for brain activity. Postprandially, insulin is the important hormone controlling turnover of the three groups of foodstuffs: fats, carbohydrates and proteins. Insulin facilitates the absorption of foodstuffs from the gastrointestinal tract, and subsequently promotes storage of glucose as glycogen in muscle and liver, and of triglycerides in adipose or fat cells. In the fasting state the actions of a number of hormones including glucagon, adrenaline, glucocorticoids and GH dominate, so that blood glucose concentrations are maintained by a number of processes. Amino acids are mobilized from protein in the muscles and transported to the liver, where they are converted to pyruvate and then glucose. Glucose is also produced by the liver by the breakdown of glycogen. Fatty acids are mobilized from adipose tissue and provide a substrate for liver and muscle metabolism. Ketone bodies produced in normal fat metabolism are also used as a substrate for muscle metabolism. The key position of the liver in these changes depends on a number of factors including the fact that it is the only site of the enzyme phosphatase, necessary to break down liver glycogen to glucose. The liver is acted on by the pancreatic hormones, which arrive by the portal vein bringing blood returning from the gastrointestinal tract.

Central to the control of intermediate metabolism is the pancreas, which produces insulin, the only major hormone known at present which lowers blood glucose, and glucagon, one of the many hormones which can elevate blood glucose. The pancreas comprises two types of tissue: the exocrine tissue, which produces digestive juices released into the duodenum, and the endocrine or hormone-producing tissue found in the islets of Langerhans. The α-cells produce glucagon; the β-cells, insulin; and the δ-cells, somatostatin, which is the GH-release inhibiting hormone. Insulin is synthesized in rough endoplasmic reticulum in the form of pre-proinsulin, a long polypeptide chain. Hydrolysis results in the formation of proinsulin, which is packaged into vesicles. Enzymes within the vesicles act on the molecule to release insulin, which comprises two peptide chains linked by a disulphide bridge, and a C-peptide. Interestingly, as already mentioned, there are a number of peptides (the somatomedins) with insulin-like activity, some of which have a similar structure to insulin.

The rate of synthesis and release of insulin is determined largely by blood glucose concentrations, a rise causing augmented insulin secretion (Fig. 14.16). However, secretion of insulin involves other control mechanisms. First there is hormonal control: somatostatin is inhibitory; and glucagon and gastrointestinal hormones such as gastrin, secretin, cholecystokinin and glucose-dependent insulinotrophic peptide are stimulatory. Second, the hypothalamus controls islet-cell secretion during the

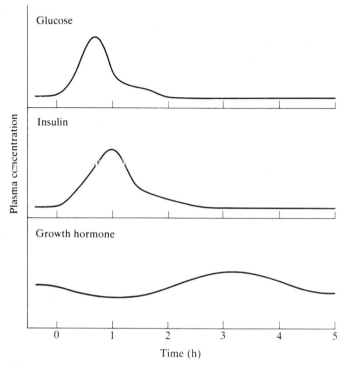

Figure 14.16 Relationship of insulin and GH to blood glucose concentrations. When blood glucose is elevated, insulin release is stimulated and GH is inhibited. As blood glucose concentrations fall, insulin level falls and GH is stimulated.

early phase of digestion, via the autonomic system: the vagus nerve (cranial X; parasympathetic) releases acetylcholine, stimulating insulin secretion in the presence of glucose. β-adrenergic agents are also stimulatory; in contrast, α-adrenergic activation by sympathetic stimulation inhibits insulin secretion.

Insulin lowers blood glucose by promoting tissue uptake and storage of glucose. It also reduces protein breakdown, gluconeogenesis (synthesis of glucose from amino acids) and glycogen breakdown. One way in which it produces its effects is to increase the number of glucose carriers or transporters. These are large proteins which span the membrane of the cell and facilitate the movement of glucose across it.

The importance of insulin is illustrated by the effect of lack of the hormone as seen in diabetes mellitus. There is a high plasma level of glucose, and consequently a high level in the glomerular filtrate. The reabsorptive mechanism in the cells of the nephron is completely saturated, so much glucose remains in the kidney tubules and appears in the urine. There is an increase in urine flow because the osmotic effect of the glucose causes a large volume of water to be retained in the nephrons. As a result the patient is thirsty and drinks much fluid. Despite an increased appetite there is loss of body weight. Fatty acids are heavily used as a source of energy, and this results in excess production of acetyl coenzyme A and of ketone bodies. These ketone bodies include aceto-acetic acid and hydroxybutyric acid which can liberate H^+ ions, so causing acidosis. This in turn stimulates respiration (see Chapter 6) and patients with untreated diabetes mellitus show overbreathing (hyperventilation).

Opposing the action of insulin is glucagon (Fig. 14.17), a single-chain polypeptide of 29 amino acids. Glucagon elevates blood glucose by enhancing glycogen breakdown and gluconeogenesis in the liver, a process which involves an increase in the intracellular concentrations of cAMP. Although it antagonizes the action of insulin, it also stimulates insulin secretion. Its own secretion is stimulated by a fall in blood glucose and by adrenaline.

Hormones influencing glucose metabolism are also released from the paired adrenal glands. These glands, essential for life, are small and triangular in shape, and lie at the top of the kidneys (Fig. 14.1). They comprise an inner medulla, synthesizing catecholamines, and an outer cortex, synthesizing steroid hormones in each of its three zones; the zona glomerulosa, fasciculata and reticularis. The main steroids

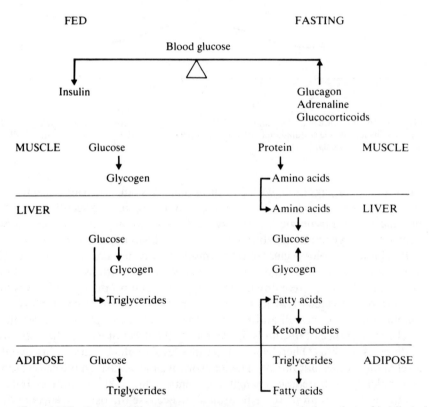

Figure 14.17 Control of blood glucose concentrations through the actions of insulin and the counter-regulatory hormones, which include glucagon, adrenaline and glucocorticoids. Insulin, a hormone for times of plenty, lowers blood glucose by promoting uptake into cells and storage. The counter-regulatory hormones elevate blood glucose by breakdown of fat and protein, as well as glycogen.

produced are the glucocorticoids such as cortisol which affect glucose metabolism, and the mineralocorticoids such as aldosterone which influence sodium balance, although as already mentioned, many intermediates are found including sex steroids. Glucocorticoids, of which the chief in man is cortisol, are synthesized in the zona fasciculata and reticularis. Cortisol circulates in the blood bound to cortisol-binding globulin, so that the concentration of this protein is an important factor in determining the free or biologically active concentrations of the hormone in plasma. The circulating concentration of cortisol is not constant over the day, but is highest in the morning, falling during the day as a result of changes in the concentrations of ACTH, which control release.

Cortisol has many actions, a characteristic one being to oppose the actions of insulin and thus to elevate blood glucose. This is achieved by stimulation of hepatic gluconeogenesis and inhibition of glucose uptake from plasma. It also affects protein and fat metabolism by stimulating protein breakdown and promoting fat deposition. While cortisol is normally defined as a glucocorticoid, it has a weak mineralocorticoid (salt-retaining) effect also, although its normal action on the kidney is to produce a diuresis. The hormone also contributes to the maintenance of normal blood pressure, and influences the body's defence mechanisms, having both anti-inflammatory and immunosuppressive effects. Finally, cortisol suppresses ACTH secretion.

The effects of cortisol are illustrated by a condition in which excess cortisol is secreted—Cushing's disease, some symptoms of which have been mentioned in the section on ACTH. The increased protein metabolism leads to muscle-wasting and easily bruised thin skin; the increase and redistribution of body fat leads to central obesity and a round face, the immunosuppressive effect causes increased susceptibility to infection, and the effect on the cardiovascular system causes high blood pressure. Lack of cortisol—giving rise to Addison's disease—is associated with weakness, loss of weight and low blood pressure. Another symptom, skin pigmentation, is due to the enhanced production of ACTH resulting from lack of suppression via negative feedback; it will be recalled that ACTH is chemically related to melanocyte stimulating hormone, which is involved in pigmentation.

The chief secretion of the adrenal medulla is adrenaline, which also elevates blood glucose concentrations. Secretion is by exocytosis from neurosecretory granules and is controlled by nerve impulses. It is brought about by many stimuli, particularly stress, including emotion, cold, hypoglycaemia and trauma, and also by certain drugs. Catecholamines have a very short half-life in plasma and are metabolized at many sites. The metabolic effects of adrenaline include promotion of breakdown of hepatic glycogen, which leads to hyperglycaemia. There is also lactic acidaemia due to the effect on muscle metabolism. Other actions of adrenaline are described in Chapter 10.

Yet another group of hormones influencing metabolic processes are the thyroid hormones—tri-iodothyronine (T_3) and thyroxine (T_4). In man the thyroid is a bilobed structure lying just in front of the trachea. A striking property of the gland is its ability to concentrate iodide, the concentrations inside the cells being 20 100 times greater than in plasma. The iodide enters via an energy-dependent pump. A number of anions of similar size, bromide and thiocyanate, for instance, can inhibit this pump. The iodide in the thyroid gland has to be oxidized to free iodine by an enzyme called peroxidase before it can be introduced into the thyroid hormones. As soon as free iodine is formed it attaches itself to a tyrosine ring to form mono-iodotyrosine (MIT). Further iodination of this molecule gives di-iodotyrosine (DIT). These two residues, MIT and DIT, then combine via an ether linkage to form T_3 and T_4. Formation of the iodotyrosines and iodothyronines occurs within a large protein molecule, thyroglobulin, of molecular weight 660 000 (Fig. 14.18). Microscopically, the basic unit of the thyroid gland is a colloid-filled follicle, lined with epithelial cells. Thyroglobulin is a major constituent of the colloid, the amount of hormone stored representing 3 months' supply of the hormone. Before the hormone is released, the thyroglobulin–hormone complex is engulfed by the cytoplasmic processes of the surrounding cells. Acid hydroxylases degrade the thyroglobulin, and the hormone is released.

Release of thyroid hormones is controlled by TSH, the secretion of which is in turn regulated by TRH and also by negative feedback exerted by T_3. The secretion of the latter is influenced by sleep, cold and non-specific stress, and by possible hormonal feedback. Greater amounts of T_4 are released than of T_3. The hormones circulate partially bound to globulin, relatively greater amounts of T_3 being found in the free form. It is T_3 which is metabolically active, and most of this derives from the deiodination of T_4 in tissue. If T_4 is deiodinated in the other ring, then the inactive reverse T_3 is formed. Formation of this inactive metabolite represents a further way of regulating the concentrations of T_3.

The principal effect of thyroid hormones on glucose turnover is to increase absorption of glucose from the intestine, but overall the only definite action of the

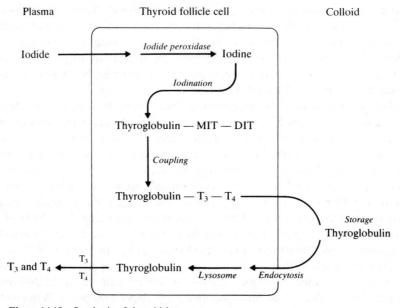

Figure 14.18 Synthesis of thyroid hormones.

thyroid hormones in the intact animal is said to be the increase of metabolic rate. However, the hormones are required for many functions such as the maintenance of body temperature and weight, and stimulation of heart contraction. They also stimulate protein synthesis and increase the turnover of cholesterol and triglycerides.

The actions of the thyroid hormones are best understood by looking at a hyperthyroid patient, who exhibits increased basal metabolic rate with increased heat sensitivity and increased protein catabolism, which may cause muscle weakness. The patient has an increased cardiac output, is restless, overanxious and irritable.

In summary, catecholamines mobilize energy reserves very quickly in situations of stress, while glucocorticoids make more gradual adjustments. Growth hormone, somatomedin, thyroid hormones and the sex steroids are all involved in the slowly adjusting demands of the growing animal.

Hormonal control of calcium metabolism

Glucose is not the only constituent of plasma of which the concentration is hormonally controlled. Calcium is maintained within the relatively narrow limits of 2.2–2.55 mmol/l. Of this, 0.7 mmol/l is bound to albumin, 0.25 mmol/l is complexed to citrate and the remainder is in the free form. It is this fraction which is biologically active. Calcium has a large variety of functions: it is involved in muscle contraction, nerve transmission, blood clotting and membrane structure, and is an enzyme cofactor. Hence the necessity for maintenance of the extra- and intracellular levels within narrow limits. Overall, the calcium balance depends on the equilibrium between the quantities absorbed from the intestine and the amounts lost in the urine and, to a minor extent, in the sweat. However, an additional factor contributes to the plasma levels and that is exchange with bone. Of the kilogram of calcium in the body of an adult human, 99 per cent is found in bone. Of this pool about 100 mmol is rapidly exchangeable, and in the course of a day some 500 mmol exchanges with the extracellular fluid. Calcium is also laid down daily in bone (accretion) and is lost by resorption, about 7.5 mmol being turned over daily in this way in man. The hormones controlling calcium balance could affect any of the three processes:

1. absorption from the gastrointestinal tract;
2. bone turnover;
3. loss from the kidney.

There are three hormones controlling calcium metabolism: calcitonin, which lowers plasma calcium, and parathyroid hormone and vitamin D, which raise it (Fig. 14.19). It may be surprising to find vitamin D called a hormone. However, since it is converted to the active form in the kidney and acts on a distant target organ, it may be classified as a steroid hormone. Calcitonin and parathyroid hormone are both polypeptide hormones. Parathyroid hormone is produced in the form of a pre-hormone in the chief cells of the parathyroid glands, of which in man there are four, embedded in the thyroid gland. The activity of the other cell type in the gland, the

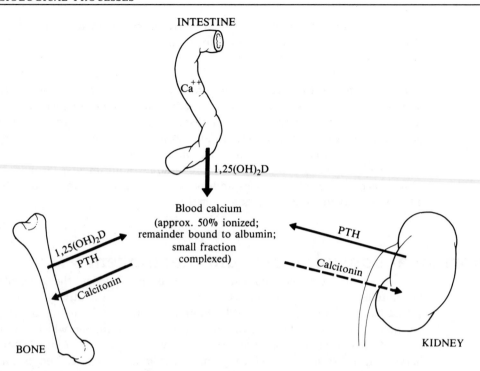

Figure 14.19 The hormones controlling Ca^{++} ion concentrations in plasma and their sites of action. PTH: parathyroid hormone; $1,25(OH)_2D$: 1,25-dihydroxycholecalciferol.

oxyphil cell, has not been determined. Parathyroid hormone elevates the plasma calcium in three main ways:

1. It stimulates reabsorption from bone, a process requiring vitamin D for its full effect.
2. It stimulates calcium reabsorption in the distal tubule of the kidney.
3. It stimulates renal synthesis of the active metabolite of vitamin D: 1,25-dihydroxycholecalciferol.

Secretion of parathyroid hormone is mainly controlled by the level of ionized calcium in the blood, a rising Ca^{++} ion concentration being inhibitory and a falling one stimulatory. Calcitonin is a 32 amino-acid peptide synthesized in the C cells of the thyroid gland as a precursor. It lowers blood calcium by inhibiting osteoclastic (bone-destroying) bone resorption and by decreasing renal tubular calcium resorption. Like parathyroid hormone its secretion is controlled by Ca^{++} ion concentrations. Its role in man is not clear, but it has been suggested that it helps protect the body against an influx of calcium such as occurs following suckling in an infant. In the evolution of the system, calcitonin may first have been concerned with cation regulation at cell membranes and perhaps with removal of excess blood calcium in fishes inhabiting very saline waters.

As well as being taken in the diet, vitamin D_3 is formed in the skin under the influence of ultraviolet light. It then undergoes two hydroxylations, one in the liver and one in the kidney, to form 1,25-dihydroxycholecalciferol. It elevates plasma calcium by stimulating Ca^{++} ion absorption in the intestine, probably via stimulation of a specific calcium binder and, together with parathyroid hormone, by enhancing calcium mobilization in the bone.

A note on growth

Growth depends not only on skeletal growth, in which calcium metabolism plays an important role, but also on an increase in the size and number of cells of other tissues including muscles and internal organs. The process depends on nutrition and the interplay of a number of endocrine factors including GH. Apart from GH, other hormones which play an important role in the process of normal growth are insulin, thyroid hormones, androgens, oestrogens and glucocorticoids. Insulin increases body weight and probably the width of the epiphysial cartilage. It is also required for the full anabolic effects of GH. The thyroid hormones are essential for skeletal maturation, which is also the major physiological action of testosterone. Androgens are responsible for the adolescent growth spurt in human males. Growth is fast during the first 2 years of life in the human and then decreases until the growth spurt, when maximum growth occurs. In boys an average growth rate of 5 cm per year is achieved in this period. Oestrogens, in contrast, inhibit growth by decreasing epiphysial cartilage width and antagonizing the effect of GH. Cortisol, too, inhibits growth, partly by a direct effect and partly by suppressing GH secretion and action. A great number of growth factors, some related to the somatomedins, have now also been described. They are probably produced and act within the same tissue.

Hormonal control of salt and water balance

Osmolarity and also volume of plasma have to be closely monitored and this is achieved by the interaction of a number of hormones (Fig. 14.20), including neurohypophysial hormones, adrenocortical steroids, atrial natriuretic peptides and prolactin. Although they have less direct effect, catecholamines and angiotensin II form part of this regulatory system. These hormones act individually or jointly on the various organs concerned with fluid balance in vertebrates, namely the skin, gill, gastrointestinal tract, kidney, urinary bladder, cloaca and salt-glands. In the human, water excretion is controlled by vasopressin and sodium excretion by aldosterone and atrial natriuretic peptide (Chapter 7). Maintenance of plasma volume also contributes to maintenance of blood pressure. Interestingly, two major components of the fluid-balance system, angiotensin II and vasopressin are also powerful vasoconstrictor agents and thus contribute to blood-pressure maintenance via this mechanism also. In

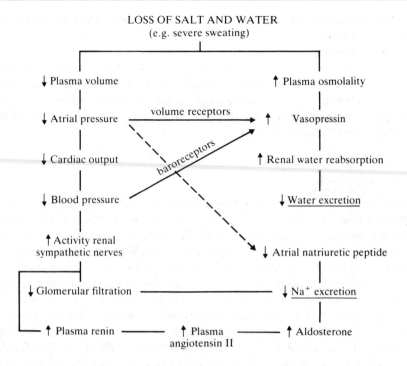

Figure 14.20 Involvement of hormones in the control of salt and water balance.

many mammals prolactin also influences fluid excretion by the kidney, and oxytocin has been postulated to have a role in sodium excretion. Vasopressin and oxytocin are members of a family of neurohypophysial peptides. Another important member of this family is arginine-vasotocin, the first five amino acids being identical to those in oxytocin, and residues 5–9 being identical to those in vasopressin. It is found in most non-mammalian vertebrates. It has been suggested that these hormones first evolved as vasopressor hormones and subsequently acquired the function of increasing the water permeability of the skin, bladder and kidney tubules.

Gastrointestinal hormones, the pineal body and the thymus

Hormones are also produced in a number of tissues not usually termed 'endocrine'. Such a tissue is that of the gastrointestinal tract, which produces a wide variety of hormones and is thus effectively a major endocrine organ. Those hormones concerned with digestion are elaborated by the mucosal cells in the walls of the stomach and intestine, and pass via the systemic circulation to the stomach, pancreas, gall bladder and liver, where they produce their effects. The hormone-secreting cells are scattered through the mucosa, not organized into compact glandular masses. The first gastrointestinal hormone to be described, and indeed the first substance to be termed a hormone, was secretin. In 1905, Edkins suggested that the stomach might also be the source of a hormone, gastrin. The gastrointestinal hormones which pass into the systemic circulation are gastrin, secretin, cholecystokinin (also called pancreozymin) and enteroglucagon. Most of these hormones have been discussed in Chapter 4. In summary, gastrin is secreted by the gastric mucosa in response to stimuli such as distension and the presence of food in the stomach, and acts to stimulate gastric-acid secretion. Secretin is produced in the upper small intestine and promotes secretion of a bicarbonate-rich fluid from the pancreatic acini. The primary stimulus for release is a low pH in the duodenum. Cholecystokinin is also produced by the duodenum. It stimulates an enzyme-rich secretion from the pancreatic acini and contraction of the gall bladder, the main stimuli for secretion being the presence of amino and fatty acids.

More recently discovered peptides include glucose-dependent insulinotrophic peptide, which is produced in the cells of the upper intestine and acts on the pancreas to promote insulin secretion; and also motilin, secreted by the cells of the mucosa of the duodenum and jejunum. As suggested by its name it acts on the smooth muscle of the stomach and upper small intestine. There are also hormones that occur both in the gastrointestinal tract and the nervous system. Thus cholecystokinin has been shown to be present in some neurones, and somatostatin, first isolated from the hypothalamus, has subsequently been demonstrated in endocrine cells in the pancreas and gastrointestinal tract. Neurotensin is another peptide found in the brain and also in the ileum, and is thought to help regulate release of food from the stomach. Also found in these two types of locations are substance P; vasoactive intestinal polypeptide, which stimulates hormone secretion and relaxation of blood vessels and smooth muscle; bombesin, which also stimulates hormone release; and the endorphins and enkephalins.

Another region which may have an endocrine function is the pineal body. However, the comparative anatomy of the pineal suggests profound functional changes during phylogeny. In lower vertebrates the organ is sensitive to light. It is involved in vision, circadian rhythms or responses involving chromaphores: specialized cells in which pigment can be moved around, affecting coloration of the animal. In mammals the pineal appears to be entirely glandular. Several amines are formed in the pineal complex but the most extensively studied is melatonin, a hormone concerned with melanophore blanching and with reproductive physiology. The pineal appears to be involved in regulating reproduction in seasonal breeders. With the short days of autumn the reduced exposure to light increases pineal secretion and this in turn reduces gonadotrophin secretion and action.

Like that of the pineal, the function of the thymus has been the subject of some speculation. Newborn mice deprived of their thymus fail to develop lymphocytes. If, however, the mice are implanted with a porous capsule containing a thymus from another mouse, they will survive and develop a lymphatic system, even though the cells could not leave the capsule. This shows that a chemical substance must be involved. The human placenta and kidney are also sources of important hormones.

Conclusion

Thus, the endocrine system provides a means of regulating metabolic processes so that development can occur and a constant environment can be maintained within the body. This is achieved through the complex interplay of a number of systems. Advances in our knowledge of endocrinology over the last few years have been extremely rapid. A large number of hormones have been identified, purified and synthesized. Recombinant DNA techniques have allowed great progress, including the synthesis of large hormones such as GH, which was not hitherto possible; previously human GH was obtained from postmortem tissue. Most of the recent advances have depended on technical developments in biochemistry. Understanding of the physiology of the hormones has tended to lag behind. A topic little understood at present, but which is exciting much interest, is that of local hormones—those having an effect within the tissue—such as growth factors.

15 Reproduction

Introduction

Sexual reproduction is the rule in all multicellular phyla, although many of the more primitive groups have the capacity for extensive regeneration and often reproduce asexually for longer or shorter periods in their lives. This may occur through parthenogenesis, which is the development of a new individual from an egg or sperm without participation of a germ cell from the opposite sex; through gynogenesis, in which a sperm activates an egg, but does not contribute any genetic material; or through hermaphroditism, in which both male and female gametes are found in the same animal. These unisex alternatives represent systems which have evolved in response to particular pressures. They may allow reproduction to occur where population density is low, or might allow for reduction in variability in small isolated populations where genetic drift might be a disadvantage. However, there is still considerable genetic variability even in unisex species.

Embryology of the gonads

In some primitive animals the gamete-producing tissues are diffuse, comprising many scattered loci for the proliferation of the sex cells. In the more advanced animals the gonads are localized, generally being found as paired organs. The primordial germ cells that are laid down in the ovary give rise to oogonia and those that will become testicular tissue give rise to spermatogonia. Like somatic cells these germ cells are diploid and divide many times mitotically. However, when they begin maturation divisions, they undergo meiosis to form haploid cells. At this stage they are called oocytes and spermatocytes, primary oocytes or spermatocytes being formed on the first meiotic division and secondary being associated with the second division. Subsequent transformations produce the mature eggs and sperm.

The sex of an individual is determined genetically (sex genotype). The physical translation of the genetic sex produces the sex phenotype. This depends on the interplay of a number of factors including genetic and hormonal factors. The X and Y chromosomes are called the sex chromosomes, the remainder the autosomes. In mammals the Y chromosome normally carries the genetic determinants for the development of masculine traits, while the female traits are carried in the X chromosomes or autosomes, or both. In the human the gonads start to develop at about the fifth week of gestation. Shortly afterwards, if the genetic constitution is male, the gonads differentiate into testes. In the female the undifferentiated gonads persist and ovarian structures do not appear until the twelfth week. By 8 weeks the human fetus contains both the Müllerian ducts, which can develop into female genitalia, and the Wolffian ducts, which can develop into male internal genitalia. During the following month, one pair of ducts completes its development while the other involutes. In the presence of ovaries (or even in the total absence of all gonads by a congenital defect), the female structures are formed. The uterine (Fallopian) tubes, the uterus and the upper half of the vagina develop from the Müllerian ducts. In the presence of testes, male development occurs, namely the virilization of the Wolffian duct through the action of androgens and the regression of the Müllerian duct. This latter process depends on Müllerian-regression factor, a glycoprotein produced by the fetal testes. The Wolffian duct develops to form the rete testis, epididymis, vas deferens and seminal vesicles (Fig. 15.1). Overall, the development of the female characteristics lags behind that of the male.

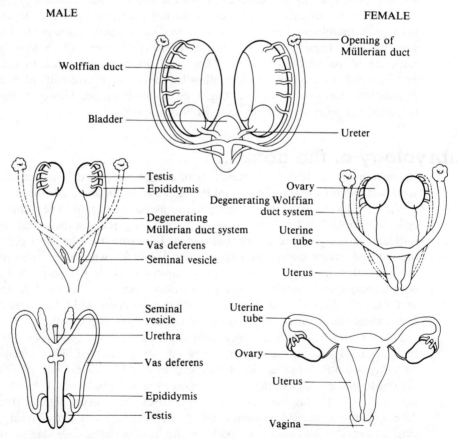

Figure 15.1 Development of the male and female reproductive systems from the Wolffian and Müllerian duct systems.

Male reproductive system

The testes have two main functions: the production of gametes (spermatogenesis) and the synthesis of male sex hormones (androgens). They thus play a less varied role than the ovaries and are structurally simpler, the complexity of the male reproductive system being associated with the accessory structures. Formation of the sperm occurs in the seminiferous tubules, the form of which varies greatly in different species. Often all stages of development are evident in cross-sections of the tubules: spermatogonia are located just inside the basement membrane of the tubule and the maturing stages occur towards the lumen. Secondary spermatogonia divide to form spermatids, which then mature to form spermatozoa. In the human it takes 74 days to form a mature sperm from a primitive germ cell. Other cells lining the basement membrane of the tubules are the Sertoli cells, which are believed to regulate the differentiation and to provide nourishment. The spermatogonia are extruded by the Sertoli cells into the lumen of the tubule. After discharge into the lumen the spermatozoa pass along finely coiled tubules and eventually into the epididymis, which is another coiled tube leading into the vas deferens. At the time of ejaculation they pass from there through the ejaculatory ducts into the urethra in the body of the prostate (Fig. 15.2).

A typical animal sperm as shown in Fig. 15.3 consists of two main components: the head and tail. The tail is further divided into the neck, middle piece, principal piece and end piece. The head is a condensed nucleus covered entirely by the acrosomal cap, which consists of hydrolysing enzymes associated with penetration of the membranes of the ovum and fertilization. The DNA is associated with protein in a ratio of about 1:1. In man the head is about 5 μm long and the tail about 60 μm long. The neck contains one of the paired centrioles concerned with the movement of chromosomes during cell division. The second centriole forms an annulus lying around the end of the middle piece. This region of the tail is surrounded by a spiral of mitochondria and is the major centre of energy production from both exogenous and endogenous carbohydrate. The axoneme, comprising doublets of microtubules, runs through the principal and end pieces. Thus in addition to a haploid complement of DNA, the sperm contains complex machinery for motility, release of energy, mitotic-spindle formation and penetration of the egg at fertilization. Although fully differentiated when they pass into the tubule, the spermatozoa are not capable of independent movement or fertilization until further maturation has occurred during the passage through the epididymis.

Between the seminiferous tubules lie the Leydig cells, which are the steroid-synthesizing cells producing androgens. These hormones are sometimes referred to as the C10 steroids because of the methyl group in the C10 position. Testosterone has a wide variety of actions, stimulating spermatogenesis, differentiation of male genitalia, anabolic (muscle-building) metabolism, thickening of the vocal cords, sexual differentiation of the brain, etc. The action of testosterone at most of these sites except muscle requires the formation of the metabolic product 5α-dihydrotestosterone. Androgens begin to function at a very early stage of life, *in utero*. Soon after birth the Leydig cells regress, but in man after the age of 5 years the tubules develop gradually until both tubules and Leydig cells mature at puberty.

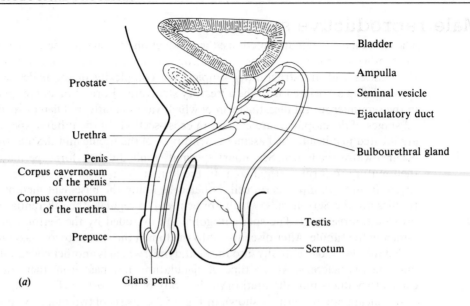

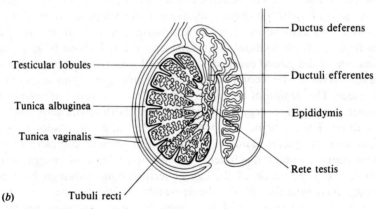

Figure 15.2 Male reproductive system. (*a*) General anatomy. (*b*) Testis. (Adapted, and reproduced with permission, from Junqueira, L. C., J. Carneiro and J. A. Long, *Basic Histology*, 5th edn, © Appleton-Century-Crofts, 1986.)

Testicular function is regulated by the two pituitary gonadotrophins, the mammalian hormones being follicle-stimulating hormone (FSH) and luteinizing hormone (LH). The LH stimulates synthesis of testosterone by the Leydig cells. Testosterone maintains spermatogenesis, but cannot initiate it; for this FSH is required. It is believed that the action of hormones on the process of spermatogenesis is not directly on the germ cells, but via production by the Sertoli cells of a substance necessary for sperm maturation such as androgen-binding protein. Secretion of gonadotrophins is

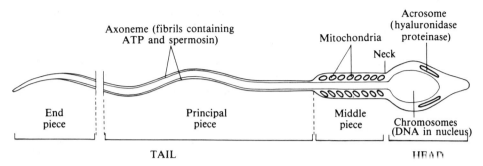

Figure 15.3 Principal parts of a sperm indicated for a human spermatozoon.

under the control of gonadotrophin releasing hormone (GnRH), which is released in a pulsatile fashion. Luteinizing hormone is also under the negative feedback control of testosterone, and FSH under that of inhibin, a polypeptide formed by the Sertoli cells.

Female reproductive system

The functions of the female reproductive system in mammals differ from those of the male in many ways. For example, often only one germ cell reaches maturity at a time and this event occurs intermittently. Furthermore production of germ cells continues for a limited time. The cyclical production of mature oocytes by the ovary is associated with cyclical changes in production of hormones by the ovary, resulting in cyclical changes in the uterus and vagina. The sexual cycles of vertebrates are extremely variable. The reproductive cycles which have been most extensively studied are the 4- to 5-day oestrous cycle of the rat and mouse, and the human menstrual cycle. Usually the female will receive the male only during the relatively brief period of oestrus or heat. Ovulation normally occurs spontaneously during oestrus but, in animals such as the rabbit and ferret, the stimulus of mating is required for ovulation and such animals are therefore called induced ovulators. Fertilization usually takes place within a few hours of ovulation, but can be delayed as in the bat, where mating occurs in the autumn and fertilization takes place in the following spring. Implantation of the blastocyst within the uterus usually takes place within 1–2 weeks but, in animals such as the weasel and badger, mating takes place in the summer and implantation late in the winter. Thus a wide variety of patterns is seen, many of which allow adjustment to environmental conditions.

The ovary and cyclical changes

The primary function of the ovary is to generate eggs. A second function is the synthesis of hormones needed for the chemical coordination of reproduction. A further function is the elaboration of nutritive materials for the early stages of embryonic development. A function in some viviparous animals is housing and nourishment of the developing young (follicular gestation).

The ovaries are surrounded by germinal epithelium (Fig. 15.4). Blood vessels and lymphatics enter and leave the ovaries via the hilum and are distributed throughout the dense connective tissue termed the stroma. Within the cortex of the gland, single oocytes differentiate within a ball of follicular cells: the granulosa. Its primary function is that of providing materials for growth of the ovum and provision of a yolk. The stroma surrounding the granulosa becomes organized into connective tissue layers called the theca. In higher forms including the human the theca interna becomes a vascular and glandular oestrogen-synthesizing layer distinct from the theca externa. In most species the eggs are shed into the peritoneal cavity and pass into the oviducts (uterine tubes).

Ovulation has been shown to occur as a result of a continuous cyclical process. In the submammalian species the ovarian cycle comprises only the development of the follicle: the follicular phase. In mammals there is also the luteal phase during which there is present a corpus luteum formed from the follicle after the shedding of the ovum. In laboratory rodents during oestrus, ovulation occurs and the uterus becomes enlarged and oedematous in preparation for implantation, the vaginal mucosa proliferates and the superficial layers are squamous and cornified in preparation for mating. During the following 10–14 h of metoestrus a small corpus luteum forms, producing some progesterone. This is associated with diminishing vascularity of the uterus and the appearance of leucocytes in the vaginal smear. In the absence of conception, the corpus luteum regresses during the 60–70 h of dioestrus and at this point the uterus is relatively small and anaemic. Preparation for the next oestrus occurs during the following 12 h of pro-oestrus.

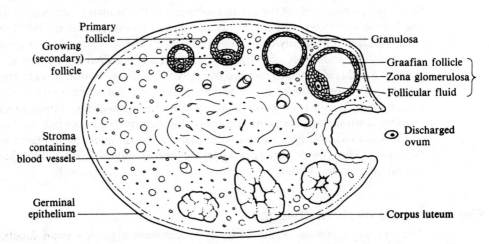

Figure 15.4 Outline of an ovary showing the different stages of development of follicles, the release of the ovum and formation of the corpus luteum.

The menstrual cycle of primates is characterized by menstruation, during which the inner portion of the endometrium or mucous membrane of the uterus collapses and is discharged with a certain amount of bleeding. Development of the follicles of the human ovary has been well studied recently by *in vitro* techniques, but a similar pattern of development occurs in all mammals, as shown in Fig. 15.4. At the beginning of the menstrual cycle a group of early follicles enlarge to form secondary follicles consisting of several layers of membrane-granulosa cells surrounding the oocyte. Usually only one follicle matures fully and the stromal cells become arranged to form the theca. The follicle enlarges to form a large cavity, the antrum, filled with follicular fluid, the oocyte being supported by a stalk of granulosa cells. At this stage it is known as a Graafian follicle. Prior to ovulation the granulosa cells, which were coupled by gap junctions, uncouple allowing liberation of the oocyte. The cells of the Graafian follicle proliferate and enlarge to fill the collapsed antrum of the follicle. This structure develops into the corpus luteum, which has a steroidogenic function. Initially it is red in colour, but then becomes yellowish. If there is no fertilization and blastocyst implantation, the synthetic activity disappears and the corpus luteum begins to involute and is replaced by scar tissue: the corpus albicans.

Associated with cyclical changes in the ovary of primates and other mammals, there is cyclical production of oestradiol and progesterone. In the early part of the cycle, FSH stimulates the development of the primary follicle and LH stimulates formation of the theca cells, which produce the precursors of oestriol and oestradiol. These precursors are then transferred to the granulosa to be transformed into the active forms of the hormones. Just before ovulation the granulosa cells develop receptors for LH and begin to synthesize progesterone. The corpus luteum synthesizes oestrogens and progesterone. These changes in steroid output produce changes in the uterus and vagina. In primates after menstruation, the oestradiol stimulates repair and proliferation of the endometrium including the endometrial glands. The rise in progesterone after ovulation produces the changes in the endometrium required for successful implantation. The endometrium becomes highly vascularized and slightly oedematous, and the glands become coiled and tortuous. In primates if fertilization does not occur the corpus luteum regresses, and the hormonal support of the endometrium is withdrawn so that it becomes thinner and breaks down and sloughs off; there is also necrosis of some small arteries, and menstrual bleeding occurs. These hormonal changes also alter the pH and consistency of the cervical mucus in all mammals. During the oestrogen-dominated follicular phase the mucus is watery and suitable for sperm penetration. During the luteal phase the high concentration of progesterone renders the mucus viscous and of low pH. The hormonal changes associated with the oestrous and menstrual cycles are shown in Fig. 15.5a and b.

Hormonal control of the menstrual cycle and puberty

Regulation of the menstrual cycle in primates results from the interplay of the hormones of the hypothalamo–pituitary–gonadal axis. At the start of the cycle the secretion of FSH stimulates the development of secondary follicles, which produce

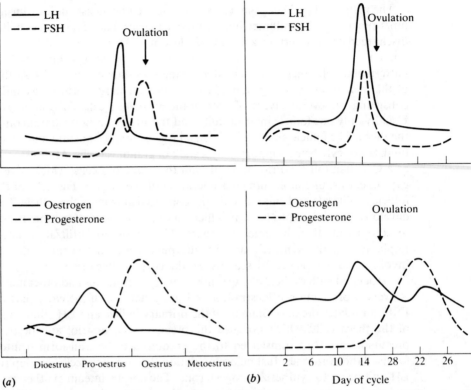

Figure 15.5 Changes in circulating hormone concentrations over (a) oestrous cycle; (b) menstrual cycle.

oestrogen. The release of FSH like that of LH is pulsatile, the pulses being seen every 1–2 h. This episodic release is controlled by the hypothalamus and is secondary to the phasic discharge of GnRH from nerves terminating in the median eminence. Under the influence of the oestrogens, FSH receptors are produced in the granulosa cells. When the FSH concentrations fall as a result of the negative-feedback effect of oestradiol, only those one or two follicles with adequate receptors develop; the rest atrophy. As the oestradiol secretion from the developing follicle increases, the rate of GnRH pulses increases and the maintained oestradiol concentrations augment the response (positive feedback) so that there is a massive discharge of LH and FSH resulting in ovulation. The corpus luteum then develops and the steroid it produces leads to reduced pulse rate of GnRH secretion and hence to reduced LH and FSH release, so pituitary stores of gonadotrophins build up. Luteinizing hormone is also required for the maintenance of the corpus luteum, so reduced secretion leads to luteolysis.

Puberty is characterized by somatic growth, sexual maturation, and the ability to reproduce, and is accompanied by hormonal as well as physical changes. In the human male the changes consist of a growth spurt, increased muscle mass, increased

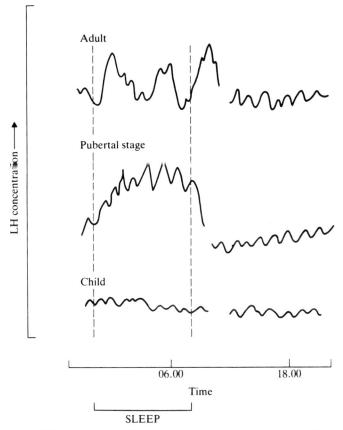

Figure 15.6 Patterns of LH secretion during puberty in the male. Elevation of LH concentrations results from elevated release of LHRH or GnRH and in turn leads to enhanced testosterone release.

testicular and phallus size, and development of facial, axillary and pubic hair. In females the physical changes involve growth spurt, development of breast tissue, onset of menses, growth of axillary and pubic hair, fat deposition, and uterine, endometrial and vaginal changes. In the prepubertal period the hypothalamic output of GnRH is in some way inhibited. The GnRH oscillator pulses at the same frequency as in the adult but with a much lower amplitude. The initiation of puberty is achieved by a night-time process that increases GnRH-pulse amplitude, and thus LH level, which maintaining invariant frequency (Fig. 15.6). In the rat this process probably involves a stimulatory adrenergic output, but this does not seem to be the case in the human.

Fertilization and pregnancy

The mechanism that brings the sperm into contact with the eggs and the subsequent processes must be absolutely reliable. This requirement of life has been satisfied through a host of special adaptations ranging from those acting at the cellular level to those at the level of social interaction. Such adaptations include mass spawning and internal fertilization, for example.

Many of the most successful groups of animals exploit the body of the parents as a nesting site for the fertilized egg. Some fishes incubate their eggs in the oral cavity and marsupial toads carry their eggs under a flap of the dorsal skin. In the case of viviparous animals (species which bear their young alive: *vivere* to live, *parere* to bring forth), the eggs are retained within the reproductive organs during development. In such species there is a reduction in the amount of yolk in the egg and there are elaborate mechanisms for the provision of the developing young. Most elaborate is the placenta, which reaches the highest degree of specialization in eutherian mammals (i.e. non-marsupial viviparous species), where it serves not only fetal nutrition, respiration and excretion but also as an essential endocrine gland regulating the physiology of both mother and fetus during gestation. In the human there is a complex placenta with vascular finger-like processes between pools of maternal blood.

In such mammals, for conception to occur a spermatozoon should fertilize an ovum in the uterine (Fallopian) tube. Although only one sperm is necessary for fertilization, the penetration of the ovum appears to require a sustained attack by many sperm, which release from their acrosomes hydrolytic enzymes that loosen the cells around the ovum and allow the sperm access. Once fertilized, the ovum is moved along the uterine tube by peristalsis and movement of the cilia in the lining cells. During the

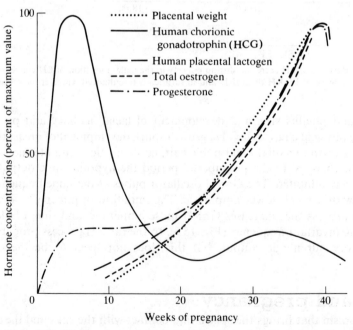

Figure 15.7 Changes in concentrations of circulating hormones during human pregnancy.

transfer the ovum undergoes division to form the blastocyst with about 16 cells. This then implants in the prepared endometrium of the uterus. In the human after successful implantation, the blastocyst continues to develop and the trophoblast begins to secrete (human) chorionic gonadotrophin (HCG), a glycoprotein with LH-like activity. This hormone is secreted into the maternal bloodstream, and its detection in the plasma or more usually the urine is used as a basis of early pregnancy testing. In the early stages of human pregnancy the production of HCG sustains oestradiol production by the corpus luteum and this supports the fetoplacental unit. At about 9 weeks of gestation the fetoplacental unit develops cholesterol desmolase activity and hence starts to synthesize pregnenolone and progesterone. The pregnenolone crosses to the fetus, where the adrenal forms a further intermediate which crosses to the placenta to be converted to oestriol. Oestriol production by the placenta starts around the twelfth week. In this way the placenta takes over the steroid production from the corpus luteum and by the twelfth week has usually become the principal site of synthesis. Many other hormones are synthesized by the placenta including chorionic lactogen or, as it is now more commonly called, chorionic somatomammotrophin. This appears to act as a growth hormone and brings about nitrogen, potassium and calcium retention, and decreased glucose utilization. Figure 15.7 illustrates the hormonal changes during pregnancy in the human.

The fetus

In the human the fetus *in utero* is surrounded by three membranes which are expelled together with the placenta after the birth of the baby. They are the amnion and the chorion, which are of fetal tissue, and the decidua, derived from maternal tissue. Contained within the vascular amnion is the amniotic fluid, which protects the fetus and allows it freedom of development and movement. The growth rate of the human fetus is rapid, being about 160 g per week just before term; at the end of the 9-month gestation the fetus weighs about 3.5 kg. During the third month of gestation the head of the fetus is about half the total length; at the end of the gestational period it is about one-quarter of the length.

During fetal growth, glucose is the major energy substrate. In addition to certain carbohydrates, amino acids and fatty acids are readily transferred across the placenta. The partial pressure of oxygen (Po_2) in the blood supplying the fetus is low as compared with that in the maternal arterial blood, but a number of factors improve the efficiency of oxygen transport to the fetal tissues. Fetal haemoglobin has a higher affinity for oxygen than adult haemoglobin (Chapter 6) and there is a greater haemoglobin concentration (higher red-cell count) in the fetus. Furthermore fetal tissue has a greater resistance to hypoxia than adult tissue and so a lower oxygen requirement. The pH in the placenta is low, so the maternal haemoglobin more readily gives up its oxygen (Bohr effect, Chapter 6). Fetal blood at this pH can hold more oxygen than that of the mother, and so oxygen is transferred from maternal blood to the fetal circulation. In the human fetus, adult-type haemoglobin first

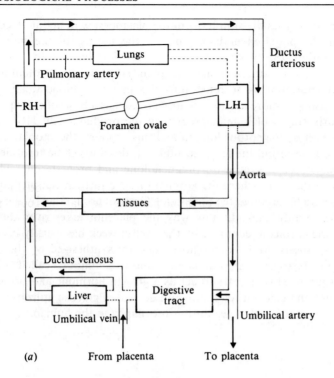

(a)

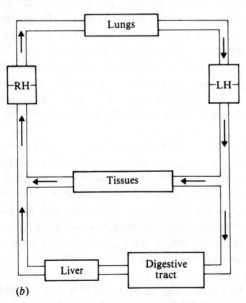

(b)

Figure 15.8 Circulation of the blood. (a) Fetus. (b) Adult. RH: right side of the heart; LH: left side of the heart.

appears in the fetal circulation at week 20 and by birth 30 per cent of the haemoglobin is in the adult form.

Because food and oxygen reach the fetus by the placenta, and carbon dioxide and other excretory products are lost via the placenta, the fetal circulation is necessarily different from that in the adult and a number of tissues including those of the digestive tract and the lungs are bypassed to a greater or lesser extent (Fig. 15.8). Blood returning from the placenta bypasses the liver in the ductus venosus and travels to the right atrium. Scarcely any blood passes through the lungs as the resistance of the collapsed lungs is high, the pulmonary pressure being 5 mmHg greater than that in the aorta. Blood reaches the left side of the heart via the foramen ovale, an opening between the right and left atria; and the ductus arteriosus transfers blood directly from the pulmonary artery to the aorta. At birth the placental circulation is cut off and the fetal peripheral resistance rises. The pressure in the aorta suddenly rises until it exceeds that in the pulmonary artery. Meanwhile, because the placenta has been cut off, the newborn animal becomes asphyxic and finally gasps several times, causing the lungs to expand. Important in the initiation of respiration in the newborn is the surfactant, the synthesis of which is promoted by cortisol (Chapter 6). Increasing blood flow through the lungs results in the closure of the foramen ovale. Subsequently the ductus arteriosus closes; and with the post-natal opening of intestinal tract and function of portal vein, blood flow through liver increases and the ductus venosus closes.

Parturition and lactation

Increasing levels of cortisol in the fetal circulation have been shown to play a role in parturition in the sheep, but it is not clear whether this is the case in the human. A fetal hormonal signal to trigger parturition is an appealing concept, as the fetus is best able to determine the conditions in the uterus. Maternal oxytocin, as described in Chapter 14, is important in the expulsion of the fetus, but it is not clear what is the initial stimulus for its release or whether fetal oxytocin plays a role (Fig. 15.9). Increasing oestradiol concentrations induce the formation of oxytocin receptors so that the uterus becomes extremely sensitive to the hormone.

The process of parturition varies from species to species. The problems associated with the delivery of a large number of small fetuses are different from those of the delivery of one or two relatively large offspring. Neonates are also of differing degrees of maturation, varying from the immature, blind and hairless rat pups to the young of herd animals or of marine mammals, able to walk or swim within a short time of birth.

Oxytocin also plays a part in lactation, contributing to milk ejection. Many hormones are required for the development of the mammary gland. Oestrogens are responsible for the proliferation of the mammary ducts, and progesterone is responsible for the development of the tubules (Fig. 15.10). During pregnancy, prolactin also contributes to full lobular duct development; insulin, cortisol and growth hormone are also required. After parturition and delivery the drop in circulating oestrogens initiates lactation. Although oestrogen and prolactin act

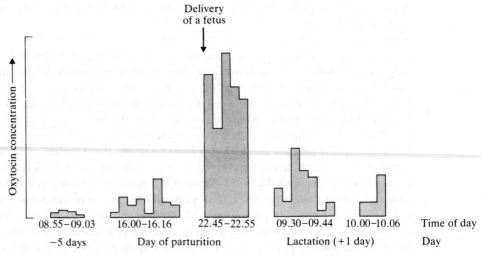

Figure 15.9 Release of maternal oxytocin during parturition and suckling in the pig.

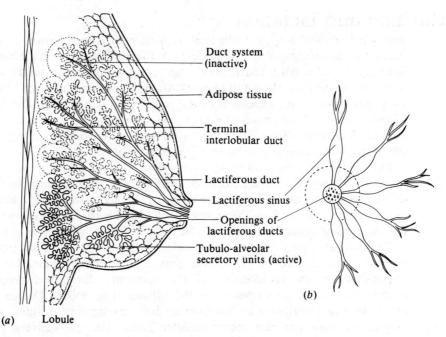

Figure 15.10 Human mammary gland. (*a*) General anatomy. (*b*) Arrangement of duct system.

synergistically in producing growth of mammary gland tissue, they are antagonistic with respect to milk production. Thus after birth the onset and maintenance of lactation is under the control of prolactin. This hormone also has an antifertility effect, thereby reducing the possibility of pregnancy while the young are suckling—a contingency which would put a large additional demand on the maternal resources. The mammary gland at first secretes colostrum. It has a higher protein content than milk, but contains less fat and carbohydrate. After 3–4 days, milk is produced, but this process does not continue unless the milk is removed. The composition varies from species to species depending on the individual requirements. Thus the milk of the seal is rich in fat, allowing rapid development of the pups. The patterns of suckling also vary from species to species, depending on a number of factors including the maturity of the offspring. Rat pups suckle at regular and frequent intervals throughout the day, whereas guinea-pig pups, which are able to eat adult food, suckle about once per day.

Recent and possible future developments

Management of fertility and infertility in domestic animals and the human have been influenced by developments over the last couple of decades. The contraceptive pill, usually comprising a combination of oestrogen and progesterone, has been used for some considerable time, although much recent effort has been put into the improvement of safety and minimizing of side-effects. More recently there have been great advances in the treatment of infertility. This has been made possible by greater understanding of the patterns of hormone secretion over the menstrual cycle, the ability to perform rapid estimation of hormone concentrations and the availability of synthetic hormone preparations such as GnRH. Once conception has occurred, fetal wellbeing can be monitored by estimation of maternal hormone concentrations, by amniocentesis and by ultrasound scanning. Many questions remain to be answered, especially about the way in which the cells of the early embryo are transformed into all the different tissue types and organs.

16 Defence mechanisms of the body

Introduction

As must have become clear in the previous chapters, most animals are well adapted to the environmental conditions in which they live. However, an animal rarely lives under constant conditions. Most species face not only nutritional uncertainties, but also, as described in Chapter 17, marked diurnal and seasonal oscillations which alter rates of metabolism and activity. There is also the possibility of invasion by bacteria and viruses, attack by other animals or damage as a result of knocks and falls. Damage to arteries in which blood circulates at high pressures is particularly dangerous. Mechanisms exist to prevent blood loss (haemostasis) as well as to repair damaged tissue. There is also the immune system, which inactivates or eliminates foreign cells, destroys pathogenic micro-organisms and removes ageing or damaged cells and destroys any abnormal or mutant cells that are in the body. These various defence systems reside largely in the body fluids, especially in the plasma and lymph.

Barriers for defence

The skin, the continuous outer layer covering the whole body surface, forms the primary defence against bacteria, fungi and viruses. Containing keratin, a tough water-insoluble fibrous protein, the skin prevents entry of organisms and loss of body constituents. A surface layer on the skin, comprising water, lipids, amino acids and polypeptides, has a low pH and forms an antiseptic barrier that retards growth of bacteria and fungi. The lipids also prevent the skin from drying and cracking. Sweat and sebaceous glands contain bacteriostatic substances. Cerumen in the ear discourages the growth of micro-organisms, and tears contain a lysosome that can lyse micro-organisms. Skin when tanned also protects from the effects of solar radiation.

Effectively, the lumen of the gastrointestinal tract lies outside the body, as the tract is a tube passing through it. Other body organs opening to the exterior are the lungs, vagina and bladder. Such hollow organs may have surfaces lined with mucous membranes. The mucus produced by glands or individual cells traps particulate matter. The organs may also secrete an immunoglobulin that can lyse bacteria on the organ's surface. Acidity provides additional effective protection. Saliva is mildly acidic (pH 5.8–7.1); it cleanses the mouth and retards the growth of organisms. The gastric acid with a pH of about 2 is extremely effective in killing organisms taken with the food. In the vagina the glycogen of the lining cells is broken down to produce organic acids, which gives a pH of 5.0. In the large intestine, where there is little movement of the contents, there are vast numbers of bacteria which not only contribute to the nutrition of the host but also prevent colonization by more harmful organisms. Similar harmless bacteria on the skin provide protection.

Haemostasis

When the skin is damaged by accident or attack, the immediate dangers to the body are loss of blood and invasion of bacteria. The simplest method for preventing blood loss is contraction of the body musculature and blood vessels as seen, for example, in marine worms and certain annelids. Such mechanisms are not suitable for hard-bodied animals or those with high blood pressures. In these forms the vascular fluids contain gelling proteins and cellular elements that plug the site of injury. In the most primitive groups, only blood cells are involved in clot formation, showing temporary aggregation following injury. The next step is to produce a fibrous protein material which serves to entangle cells. In many arthropods and all vertebrates blood clots contain tangled protein fibrils which develop from coagulogen (invertebrate) and fibrinogen (vertebrate). The mammals have numerous factors in the coagulation of blood.

Vasoconstriction

The first response to injury in muscular blood vessels is vasoconstriction. This results directly from mechanical stimulation and also from the action of vasoconstrictor chemicals, mainly serotonin, released from the platelets and as a result of cellular damage. It could also involve sympathetic reflexes largely triggered by the pain resulting from trauma. The reduced blood flow resulting from vasoconstriction lessens blood loss and allows accumulation of the factors required for coagulation. In addition the constriction process brings together the opposed endothelial surfaces of the vessels, which induces a stickiness which can effectively keep them stuck together. The endothelial cells also release coagulation factors such as factor VIII. Such blood-vessel responses prevent bleeding from only the very smallest vessels. When larger vessels are damaged, the higher pressure and rate of blood flow necessitate other steps, namely formation of platelet plug and coagulation.

Platelets

Platelets (as described in Chapter 7) are small discs of cytoplasm. An inactive platelet is about 10 per cent of the volume of a red blood cell, being 2–5 μm in diameter. Platelets in the circulation are about 5 per cent of the number of red blood cells. They

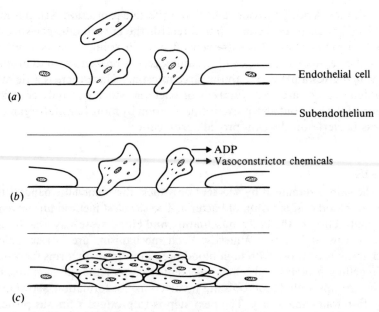

Figure 16.1 Outline of platelet function in haemostasis. (*a*) On damage of the blood vessel, platelets adhere to components of the subendothelium. (*b*) They then release vasoconstrictor agents and substances which attract surrounding platelets to form (*c*) microaggregates.

have a smooth outer coat, the glycocalyx, containing glycoproteins which are thought to play a role in the interaction with other cell surfaces. Platelets do not have a nucleus, but contain dense bodies which store ADP, serotonin and calcium, and granules containing a number of factors including fibrinogen. When there is incomplete coverage of the vessel wall with endothelial cells, as occurs on damage of a blood vessel, the platelets rapidly adhere to components of the subendothelium. On contact, the platelets rapidly change from a disc shape to a sphere; extension of pseudopodia follows, and then flattening of the platelets on the surface, so that they effectively cover a small break, rather like a plaster. Platelets react more vigorously when exposed to foreign materials and to the collagen fibrils of the tunica media of the vessel wall. Spreading of the platelets is followed by extrusion of ADP, serotonin and calcium. Arachidonate is mobilized from the cell membrane and metabolized to endoperoxidases and thromboxanes, which aid in platelet aggregation.

Aggregation is essential for the formation of the haemostatic plug. Platelets aggregate in response to thrombin, ADP, serotonin, arachidonate and platelet-activating factor, which is produced both by white cells and platelets. These factors all contribute to physiological haemostasis, whereas bacterial lipids, immune complexes and some fatty acids and viruses are more likely to initiate pathological platelet activation. Fibrinogen forms molecular bridges between adjacent cells, binding to a complex of glycoproteins IIb and IIIa which is exposed on the membrane during platelet aggregation. There are a number of inhibitors of platelet aggregation which prevent the spread of the platelet plug: in particular the platelet inhibitor prostacyclin produced by the vascular cells. Most inhibitors of aggregation stimulate the enzyme adenylate cyclase within the platelets, leading to an increase in intraplatelet cyclic AMP, which inhibits calcium mobilization and prostaglandin synthesis. Platelet interactions are shown in Fig. 16.1.

Blood coagulation

Clotting mechanism

Coagulation of blood is the ultimate process in haemostasis. A blood clot as seen under the microscope consists of a tangled closely enmeshed network of fibres (formed of the protein fibrin), with platelets and red cells in the interstices. When first formed it is jelly-like, but the clot later retracts and hardens, squeezing out a film of serum—plasma lacking the protein fibrinogen. As long ago as 1905 the classical theory of blood coagulation was proposed in which a postulated substance, prothrombin, is converted by the hypothetical enzyme, thrombokinase, to thrombin. This protease is capable of transforming fibrinogen to fibrin. During the 1940s the isolation of prothrombin was achieved, and this removed all doubts concerning this postulated precursor of thrombin. Investigations in the late 1940s and early 1950s provided evidence of a blood enzyme, factor Xc (thrombokinase), and a blood cofactor, factor V, which are required for the conversion of prothrombin to thrombin. It is now known that blood clotting represents a highly complex cascade process. The factors involved (see Table 16.1) circulate as precursors (non-active forms), which upon contact with a solid surface are activated in sequence. The sequence is maintained because the specificity of the binding sites means that each factor can act only on the next one, with a dramatic multiplicative enhancement. This ensures rapid sealing of the breach, through which blood may be flowing out under high pressure. Such a system requires containment by inhibitors and feedback loops, and enzymic dissolution of the clot to prevent blocking of the undamaged patent vascular channels. It has been calculated that, if unopposed, enough thrombin *could* be formed from 10 ml of blood to clot the entire vascular tree in a few seconds—an indication of the importance of such inhibitory processes.

Two biochemical amplification pathways, the intrinsic and the extrinsic, are activated by the contact of blood with damaged tissue and converge to generate thrombin (Fig. 16.2). Although these two pathways are often presented as separate, there is good evidence that physiological interactions occur at several levels between the two. Both are necessary for normal haemostasis and a deficiency in one cannot be compensated by normal function in the other. The enzyme cascade of the instrinsic pathway is triggered by the contact of blood with a negatively charged surface such as collagen fibrils. As shown in Fig. 16.2, factor XII in the presence of high molecular weight kininogen is absorbed first and can activate prekallikrein to kallikrein, which in turn activates factor XII to factor XIIa. This then activates factor XI to XIa.

Table 16.1 Properties of blood coagulation factors

Factor (International Committee designation)	Synonyms	Nature and function
I	Fibrinogen	A plasma protein produced in the liver—polymerizes to form a clot
II	Prothrombin	A plasma protein produced in the liver converts fibrinogen to fibrin; activates factors, V, VIII, XIII and Protein C
III	Thromboplastin tissue factor	Produced by the clotting process or released into fluids by injured cells. Cofactor for activation of factor X by factor VIIIa
IV	Calcium	Cofactor for many steps in intrinsic and extrinsic pathways
V	Labile factor	A plasma protein produced in the liver—cofactor for the activation of factor II by factor Xa
VI	Now considered identical to factor V	
VII	Proconvertin	Activates factor X
VIII	Antihaemophilic factor	Cofactor for the activation of factor X by factor IXa
IX	Christmas factor	Activates factor X
X	Stuart Prower factor	Activates factor II
XI	Plasma thromboplastin antecedent	Activates factor IX
XII	Hageman factor	Activates factor XI, also plasminogen
XIII	Fibrin-stabilizing factor	Cross-links fibrin to stabilize it

Two additional factors may be added: Protein C or antiprothrombin, which inactivates factor VIII and factor V and may activate plasminogen; and Protein S or IIa, which is a cofactor for Protein C.

Factors XII, XI and prekallikrein circulate as inactive zymogens, which are converted to active enzymes in a similar way to the conversion of trypsinogen to active trypsin (see Chapter 4 under Digestion). The next step, in which factor IX is generated, requires the presence of calcium, which is why calcium-complexing agents may be used as anticoagulants. Three cofactors are required for the next step: the activation of X by XIa, which occurs on the surface of adherent activated platelets. These cofactors are Ca^{++} ions, platelet membrane phospholipid and factor VIII. The next two steps—activation of prothrombin and fibrin monomer formation—are common to the intrinsic and extrinsic pathways. Factor Xa activates prothrombin to thrombin, the action taking place on the platelet surface. Thrombin removes two pairs of small polypeptides from fibrinogen, which changes the structure sufficiently to allow the fibrin monomers to polymerize immediately. The polymerized fibrin held together by hydrophobic and electrostatic bonds is stabilized by covalent cross-linkage induced by factor XIII.

The extrinsic pathway is triggered by a tissue factor (factor III) which forms a complex with factor VII that directly activates factor X. There is reciprocal activation between the two factors generated, factors VIIa and Xa. The earlier stages of the

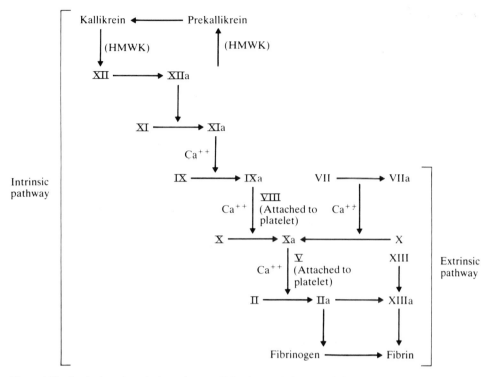

Figure 16.2 Intrinsic and extrinsic pathways of blood coagulation and their interactions. Coagulation is a surface-mediated phenomenon and is initiated by exposure to non-endothelial surfaces (intrinsic pathway) and tissue factor (extrinsic pathway). HMWK: high molecular weight kallikrein.

intrinsic pathway are bypassed, accounting for the apparently more rapid activation *in vitro* of the extrinsic pathway.

Anticoagulants

Any agent which blocks blood clotting is called an anticoagulant. *In vitro*, the easiest clotting factor to remove is calcium. Thus freshly drawn blood, as used for blood transfusion, may be mixed with anything which binds calcium, as for example, sodium or ammonium citrate. Heparin is a naturally occurring anticoagulant that facilitates the action of antithrombin factor. It is found in the granules of the mast cells: wandering cells found largely in organs rich in connective tissue. Heparin is used both *in vivo* and *in vitro*. Another anticoagulant used in patients with clotting disorders is dicoumarol or warfarin, an inhibitor of vitamin K which is required for the final stages of the synthesis of a number of coagulation factors. This agent was developed following the observation that spoiled lucerne produces bleeding disorders in cattle.

Fibrinolytic system

Blood contains a mechanism for fibrin dissolution and removal, which is activated during haemostasis. The process is essential for the remodelling of blood vessels following haemostatic plug formation and for removal of extravascular fibrin after wound healing. Fibrinolysis like blood clotting represents a cascade series of events. Plasmin is a two-chain molecule formed from plasminogen. It cleaves fibrin at multiple sites, releasing soluble fibrin-degradation products. Physiologically, fibrinolysis is almost entirely due to release of tissue plasminogen activators from endothelial cells. Two types have been identified—tissue-type plasmin activator, which bound to fibrin has an enhanced capacity to convert fibrin bound to plasminogen to plasmin, and urokinase-type activator, which does not bind to fibrin. Since both plasminogen and the tissue-type activator bind to fibrin, most plasmin is formed within the clot and little outside it. There is normally a low level of activator activity in the plasma, but it is increased by exercise, stress and venous occlusion. Fibrinolysis is checked by agents which inhibit both activators of plasminogen and plasmin itself. The most important antiplasmin in the blood is α_2-antiplasmin. Lack of α_2-antiplasmin is rare, but results in a severe bleeding disorder.

Disturbances of the coagulation mechanism

Events as complex and involving as many factors as blood coagulation and haemostasis may obviously fail at any one of a number of points. Even so, inherited coagulation disorders are rare. Pathological haemostasis includes disorders in which injury leads to prolonged haemorrhage, and also those in which there is an inappropriate or uncontrolled haemostatic response leading to intravascular thrombosis. The commonest disorder of coagulation, with an incidence of about $1:20\,000$ in the United Kingdom, is haemophilia A, in which factor VIIIc is deficient. The condition is mediated by a sex-linked recessive gene. Another disorder mediated by a sex-linked recessive gene is Christmas disease, or haemophilia B, which results in a failure of factor IX synthesis. Impaired blood haemostasis may also result from a low platelet count, liver disease with reduced synthesis of fibrinogen, and obstructive jaundice, in which the lack of bile secretion results in impaired reabsorption of the fat-soluble vitamin, vitamin K. On the other hand, blood may spontaneously clot within the vessel to give an intravascular clot or thrombosis. This is particularly prone to occur where blood flow in the vessels is sluggish, as for example in the veins after an operation and in the presence of roughened surfaces on a blood vessel as in atherosclerosis. This may be quite serious if it occludes the arterial blood supply and fatal if it occludes coronary or cerebral vessels. The term 'embolus' is used to describe a clot which has become detached from the site of formation and travels in the bloodstream to distant sites. It may lodge in a vital vessel and result in an embolism. Clots returning from leg veins may pass through the right side of the heart and obstruct the pulmonary artery or branches (pulmonary embolism).

Inflammatory response and wound healing

Tissue damage initiates haemostasis and, if there is bacterial invasion, the inflammatory response is also started. At a site of infection or damage there is increased blood flow, so the area can be seen to redden or darken, according to skin colour. (It also becomes swollen, and warm, tender to the touch and often painful.) The increased blood flow facilitates the destruction or neutralization of the agent responsible, and also repair of the injury. After the initial vasoconstriction, dilatation of the vessels occurs as a result of the release of histamine from damaged tissue and also from the action of a group of polypeptides called kinins. Lysosomes released from the damaged cells also clear the way for healing by digesting the products of cell death. The increased blood flow together with the increased permeability of the tissue to protein means that more fluid enters the tissue space, leading to oedema. The exudate may clot, thus limiting the spread of the chemicals of the reactions. Increased blood flow also allows more white blood cells to move to the area and begin the engulfing of the dead cells and any micro-organisms present. Bacteria exert a powerful chemotaxic effect, attracting phagocytic leucocytes, the neutrophils appearing first. Chemical mediators (chemotaxins) move out from the inflamed area, producing a gradient along which neutrophils can move. The neutrophils crawl towards the microbes, a process initiated by binding of the chemotaxins to receptors on the surface of the neutrophil. Within minutes, leucocytes adhere to capillaries in the region and granulocytes slip through gaps between the cells of the capillaries and migrate out into the tissue and engulf any bacteria. They may simply prise apart the connections between the capillary endothelial cells by force of amoeboid movement or they may secrete chemicals which disrupt the connections. Tissue macrophages are also stimulated and add to the defence response. A macrophage is a cell which functions in tissues as a phagocyte and contributes in many ways to the response of the body to infection. Later, monocytes move into the tissue from the bloodstream and become macrophages and aid in the fight. Plasma proteins that leak out into the tissues also add their specific effects as will be described later. The pus formed at the site of infection consists of white cells and cell debris, and is eventually cleared up by macrophages preparing the way for tissue repair. If the body's defences are unequal to the fight, the area is dammed up in an abscess, which has to be drained before the healing process can begin. The inflammatory response is summarized in Fig. 16.3.

Healing is promoted as mitosis of the remaining cells proceeds and new connective-tissue components are produced by fibroblasts. Recovery is faster in vascular tissue and also in younger tissues because of the greater rate of mitosis. If the injured tissue cannot replace the original cells by mitoses, then scar tissue is formed. If a peripheral nerve is severed, there is hypersensitivity of the postsynaptic receptors to the physiological transmitter. There is degeneration of the distal portion of the nerve (Wallerian degeneration, Fig. 16.4) and also retrograde degeneration of the axon stump to the nearest collateral. The Schwann cells surrounding the axon dedifferentiate and undergo mitosis, and thus the nerve sheath distal to the cut (i.e. further from the cell body) is filled. The cell bodies of the neurones involved undergo a process

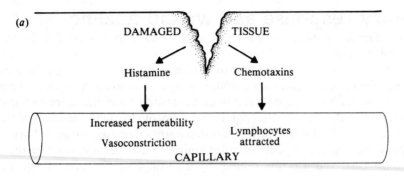

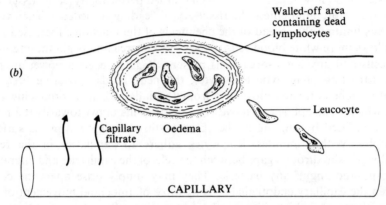

Figure 16.3 Inflammatory response and subsequent sealing off of the injured area. (*a*) Release of histamine leads to vasodilation and oedema. (*b*) Leucocytes are attracted to the area to ingest micro-organisms and cell debris.

involving dispersion of Nissl substance (cytoplasmic granules of nucleoprotein) and synthesis of new RNA. The coding for proteins involved in synaptic functions is lost and replaced by freshly synthesized RNA, which codes for the proteins required for regrowth of the axon. The proximal end of the nerve (the cut end nearer the cell body) starts to regrow with multiple small branches projecting along the path the axon previously followed. If, however, the more central portion of a sensory nerve is damaged, regeneration into the spinal cord does not generally occur. There is little specificity in the regrowth of the axons of peripheral nerves, so the normal relationship between nerve and innervated tissue is not accurately restored. The success of reinnervation therefore depends on the re-establishment of the original pathway. In contrast to peripheral nerves, neurones in the central nervous system of higher vertebrates have a very limited capacity for regeneration.

Specific immune responses

Phylogenetically, the oldest mechanism for dealing with foreign materials is phagocytosis and this response occurs in animal groups ranging from simple

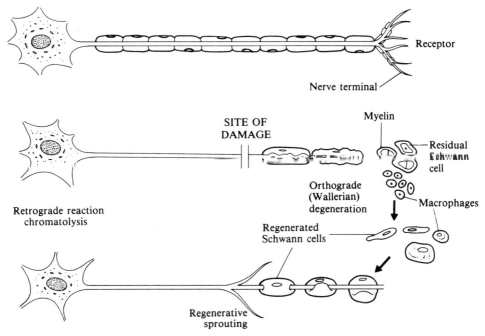

Figure 16.4 Sequence of events when an axon is cut or crushed. Wallerian degeneration is followed by peripheral nerve regeneration. After degeneration and removal of the axonal debris and myelin, by macrophages sprouts develop from the damaged end of the axon and may find their way into the tube of regenerated Schwann cells.

protozoans to mammals, as already described. Encapsulation is a related process in which matter too large to be engulfed is isolated by a large number of phagocytes. In complex invertebrates with circulatory systems are found certain chemicals called agglutinins, which inactivate foreign materials. These are all relatively non-specific mechanisms. A specific response is possible in vertebrates because of the evolution of lymphocytes. The specific molecules involved are antibodies, either membrane-bound or secreted into the circulation by B-lymphocytes (humoral immunity), and membrane-bound receptors on T-lymphocytes (cell-mediated immunity). The system of adaptive immunity of vertebrates differs from that of invertebrates in its specificity, its acquired nature and associated immunological memory.

Cellular immunity

As already described, on exposure to infection an important role is played by the phagocytotic actions of the polymorphonuclear leucocytes and monocytes in the blood and macrophages and histiocytes in the tissues. These responses are part of the effector mechanisms of the immune systems. The specific immune responses, as indicated above, are placed in two categories—cell-mediated and humoral or antibody-mediated.

Cellular immunity involves the T-lymphocytes (thymus-dependent lymphocytes). After birth, lymphocytes, like all leucocytes, are formed in the bone marrow. They are then discharged into the blood and pass to the lymph nodes, thymus and spleen and other lymphatic tissue, where, if appropriately stimulated, they undergo mitosis to form new cells. Those lymphocytes which become T-lymphocytes pass to the thymus, where they are processed to become effective or immunologically competent. This process is under the control of a hormone produced in the thymus (thymosin) and involves the acquisition of a new surface molecule. In the thymus there is not only maturation of the T-cells, but also selection (Fig. 16.5). The lymphocytes then enter the bloodstream. When they meet an antigen—in a lymph node or some other lymphoid tissue—they undergo blast transformation, giving rise to progeny, or a clone of cells, that have specific receptors for that antigen on their surface. When the molecular components of foreign cells or other foreign matter combine with these receptors, the responding attack is triggered.

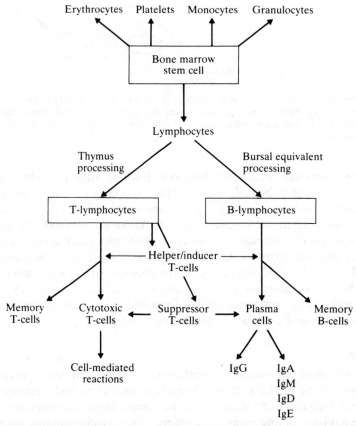

Figure 16.5 Products of the bone-marrow stem cells. The lymphocytes are processed to form T-lymphocytes, which on antigenic stimulation become involved in cell-mediated reactions, and B-lymphocytes, which may be transformed to form antibody-producing plasma cells.

There are several groups of T-lymphocytes and to date four have been described:

1. Cytotoxic T-cells. The binding of a foreign (target) cell to the surface of one of these cells triggers the release of chemicals (enzymes for example) which lyse the foreign cell so that it is directly destroyed without phagocytosis. (Cells with properties similar to cytotoxic T-cells are called natural killer or NK-cells; but unlike T-cells they do not need prior exposure to an antigen followed by a long maturation period before they can function.)
2. Helper T-cells. These enhance the humoral immunity (antibody production) and the cytotoxic T-cell function.
3. Suppressor T-cells. These act to suppress antibody production and cytotoxic T-cell function.
4. Memory T-cells. These are involved in the response to re-infection.

Cellular immunity is important in the defence of the body against infection by viruses, bacteria and fungi; and also in the defence of the body against neoplastic growths. It is also important in transplant rejection. Activity of lymphocytes may be suppressed by steroid hormones and by the drug azathioprine, which may be used to prevent such rejection. Cellular immunity is the basis of the tuberculin reaction. When the products of *Mycobacterium tuberculosis* are injected into the skin of someone who has previously been infected with the organism, a response (blister) occurs after 2–3 h at the site of the injection. Tuberculosis is also a disease which produces hypersensitivity resulting from overactivity of cell-mediated immunity. In contrast, congenital absence of the thymus in childhood results in a severe deficiency of T-lymphocytes and susceptibility to certain infections.

Humoral immunity

The cells concerned with humoral immunity are the B-cells, so called because in birds they are processed in the bursa. Thus, in the chicken, B-lymphocytes disappear and antibody production ceases after removal of the bursa of Fabricius, a mass of lymphoid tissue near the cloaca. The name B-lymphocytes is also applied in mammals even though they have no bursa; the transformation to B-cells occurs in the fetal liver and possibly the fetal spleen. In the adult the B-cells mature in the bone marrow. B-cells differentiate into plasma cells and memory B-cells. The proliferation and differentiation of B-lymphocytes is dependent on interaction with helper T-cells. As already observed, viruses, bacteria and other foreign proteins entering the body are ingested by macrophages, which process them. This appears to entail the exposure on the surface of the macrophages of part of the ingested antigen together with proteins of the major histocompatability complex (MHC)—a group of genes which codes for many proteins important for immune function. The macrophages then make contact with the lymphocytes. The helper T-cells are activated when they bind simultaneously to the antigen and to a protein produced by an MHC protein on the surface of the macrophage. The helper cells then make contact with the B-cells, activating them so that they proliferate and transform into memory B-cells and plasma cells. The most pronounced feature of the transformation into plasma cells is the increase in the volume of the cytoplasm, which is filled with endoplasmic reticulum. This enables the plasma cell to synthesize and secrete a large amount of antibody, which is released into the blood or lymph and carried to the site of infection, where it combines with the antigen. B-cells can themselves combine with free antigens in the blood if they are first modified by contact with helper lymphocytes. The memory cells are not fully differentiated, but are ready to respond rapidly should the antigen appear in the body again.

A few days after first exposure to a microbial antigen, antibody slowly appears in the plasma; its concentration then declines (primary response). The first antibody to appear is immunoglobulin M (IgM). Then IgG is produced and IgM disappears. On subsequent infection there is a pronounced rapid repsonse, the concentrations of antibody achieved being considerably greater and maintained for a longer period of time (Fig. 16.6). Most of the antibody is IgG. This secondary response is due to the persistence of the long-lived B-cells—the memory cells. Resistance built up as a result of contact with micro-organisms and other antigens is called *active immunity*. It may also be produced by vaccines—small quantities of living or dead microbes, or harmless antigenic materials derived from micro-organism.

There is a second type of immunity known as *passive immunity*, which entails transfer of antibody from an individual to a recipient. This occurs naturally when antibody is transferred across the placenta to a fetus, or via the milk to a neonate. The same principle may be used clinically when gamma-globulin is given to someone exposed to or suffering from an infection, as for example tetanus. Such a technique

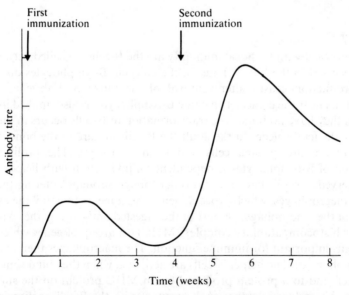

Figure 16.6 Antibody production following the initial contact with an antigen and subsequent contact with the same antigen.

Table 16.2 Types of immunoglobulin

Immunoglobulin	Heavy chain	Molecular weight	Function
IgG	γ	150 000	Complement fixation, can cross placenta
IgA	α	170 000	Provides localized protection as in tears and internal secretions
IgM	μ	960 000	Complement fixation
IgD	δ	184 000	Possible antigen recognition by B-cells
IgE	ε	188 000	Releases histamine from basophils and mast cells

may also be used on patients whose natural immune responses have been suppressed by treatment with drugs or hormones to allow the survival of an organ transplant. Protection derived in this way is short-lived.

Antibodies form part of the globulin fraction of the plasma proteins; more specifically they are immunoglobulins. Five classes of immunoglobulins are produced by the lymphocytes (Table 16.2). Basically, immunoglobulins are symmetrical molecules comprising four polypeptide chains linked by disulphide bonds (Fig. 16.7).

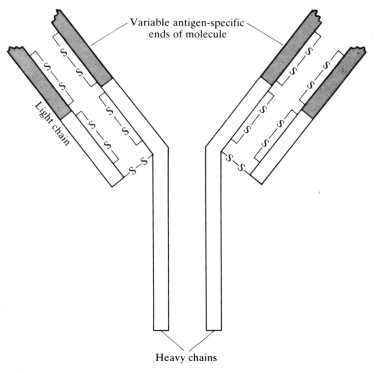

Figure 16.7 Structure of an antibody molecule: IgG. The shaded area indicates the region where the amino-acid sequence is variable.

The two long chains are called heavy chains and the two short ones, light chains. Only two types of light chain (kappa and lambda) have been described, but the heavy chains are specific for each of the four classes of immunoglobulin. In both heavy and light chains there are regions in which the amino-acid sequence is identical from one antibody to another and regions in which the sequences are variable. The variable sequences are unique for the myriad of antibodies which an individual can produce and they constitute the binding sites, which are situated on the so-called 'F(ab)' portion of the molecule. The constant sequences of the heavy chains constitute the Fc portion, which contains the non-specific binding sites for effectors such as complement, which mediates the reactions initiated by antibodies.

The most abundant immunoglobulin in man is IgG. The IgG antibodies are directed against a wide variety of antigens including viruses. This class of antibodies can cross the placenta, thus conferring immunity on the offspring. The IgM antibodies are unique in that they consist of five of the four-chain units linked together. They largely provide the specific immunity against bacteria and viruses in the primary antibody response. The principal role of IgA antibodies appears to be the protection of mucous membranes. They are secreted by plasma cells in the lining of the gastrointestinal, respiratory and urinogenital tracts. These antibodies are also found in milk. The class of antibodies termed IgE is involved in allergic reactions. The physiological role of IgE antibodies is uncertain, but they may contribute to the defence against certain protozoan and helminth parasites. The function of the IgD antibodies is also uncertain. It has been suggested that they may be important in early life as antigen-trapping determinants on the surface of the B-lymphocytes.

The interaction of antigens and antibodies can result in a variety of changes. Depending on the relative concentrations of the antibody and antigen and the nature of the immunoglobulin, the immune complex of antigen and antibody is precipitated, IgG being the most efficient antibody in the precipitating reaction. This response is particularly valuable in removing bacterial and viral toxins. Agglutination may also occur, a process in which cells including bacteria clump together. Another important activity of antibodies is to neutralize the attachment of micro-organisms to tissues. For example, the increased infectivity conferred on some viruses by the receptors which aid in their attachment is counteracted by antibody binding to these receptors. Some antibodies may combine with the cilia of bacteria, so reducing their effectiveness by immobilizing them. Finally, there is the process of opsonization, a term derived from the Greek *opsonin*—to prepare for eating. Coating of the bacteria with IgG antibodies provides a signal to the macrophages that such bacteria should be ingested.

The antibody–antigen reaction initiates the activation of the complement proteins. The complement system is yet another example of a cascade system in which activation of the first protein of the group results in the development of a sequential cascade of active molecules formed from inactive precursors. Complement was originally identified in serum as a heat-labile substance which causes the lysis of red blood cells and the destruction of certain bacteria when the appropriate antibodies are also present. The actions ascribed to complement result from the interaction of at least nine proteins. As well as the pathway initiated by the antibody–antigen reaction, complement may be activated by an alternative pathway involving the presence of a foreign substance. In addition to lysis of cell membranes the biological consequences of complement activation are opsonization; release of histamine and kinins, which cause vasodilatation and increased permeability of capillaries to protein; and general facilitation of every step of the inflammatory response.

Monoclonal antibodies

It is now possible to produce large quantities of antibody directed against a single entity. Such antibodies may be used in research or to treat disease. These antibodies are monoclonal antibodies. Animals are immunized with a given antigen or cell preparation. The antibody-producing cells are then extracted from the spleen. They are next fused with a myeloma or similar cell line that will divide and grow in culture media. Each cell starts a line or clone of cells. The antibodies produced are highly specific for a given antigen and may easily be harvested from the culture medium.

Summary

Many defence mechanisms exist within the body, protecting it from potential damage. First there is an outer barrier such as the skin or mucosa of the digestive tract. If this barrier is broken and blood vessels are damaged, haemostatic mechanisms are activated. First vasoconstriction is observed, followed by formation of a platelet plug in the region of the damage. Then the blood clot is formed, an essential component of which is fibrin formed in a cascade process. The two basic steps are formation from prothrombin of thrombin, which promotes the conversion of fibrinogen to fibrin. Later, dissolution of the clot occurs and wound healing. If in addition to vessel damage there is invasion by micro-organisms, the immune response comes into play. Attempts are made to eliminate the foreign matter by phagocytosis and by non-phagocytotic killing. Bacterial antigens also induce proliferation of specific B-cells and differentiation into clones and plasma cells, which produce antibodies which also contribute to the destruction of bacteria. Disturbances of the various defence mechanisms can lead to a number of diseases.

17 Adaptation to the environment

Introduction

Animals show a wide variety of adaptations to the environment to enable them to live in greatly differing environments from the cold of the South Pole to the heat of the equatorial deserts, from the heights of the Andes to the depths of the oceans. Not only are groups of animals adapted to various environmental conditions, but in addition changes are seen with the light–dark cycles and changing day lengths. Thus seasonal breeders and migrating species in temperate zones respond to changes in day length with altered rates of hormone secretion.

Temperature regulation

Introduction

Most habitats do not offer a constant environmental temperature and animals have developed ways to meet the normal temperature variations. Generally the temperature of tissues lies within the range 10–45 °C. Outside this range enzyme activity is inhibited and there are irreversible changes to certain proteins and lipids. Extremes of temperature lead to other problems including ice formation. There are a number of adjustments which prevent intracellular formation of ice, which damages cells through mechanical disruption and effective removal of water, producing very high solute concentrations. However, the tissues of some animals such as those which live in the intertidal zone can tolerate considerable extracellular ice formation. Mussels, for example, have been found to survive at about -20 °C for several months in the arctic. This may be related to the relatively large amount of water which is effectively 'bound'.

Some animals survive by the phenomenon of supercooling, which can occur when water is cooled without agitation: ice formation is avoided and water remains liquid at freezing-point and lower temperatures. Thus, arctic fish have been shown to survive in waters of -1.75 °C, while the freezing point of their body fluids is only -0.95 °C. In addition, the freezing point of body fluids can be reduced by increasing their osmotic pressure, i.e. by effectively using an 'antifreeze' solution. Glycerol and sorbitol are two solutes which contribute to this effect. There are a number of other chemical adaptations including the presence in the body of fats with a lower melting point than those in animals living in warmer environments, so there is no danger that intracellular or transcellular fat droplets might solidify.

Homeotherms

The body temperature of many invertebrates and lower vertebrates fluctuates with the temperature of their surroundings. These animals are said to be poikilotherms. Animals which maintain their temperatures within narrow limits are termed homeotherms. In eutherian mammals body temperature lies somewhere between 36 and 38 °C; in birds it is slightly higher (39–42 °C) and in marsupials, slightly lower. Stabilization of internal temperature removes one of the possible variables of the internal environment and allows a steady level of activity, both metabolic and locomotory. Maintenance of a constant body temperature requires a balance between heat gain (both endogenous and exogenous) and heat loss (Fig. 17.1). It demands a sensitive 'thermostat' in the brain and an ability not only to use heat formed as a byproduct of metabolism but also to increase metabolic energy in accord with demands. In addition, there is a need for appropriate anatomical structures, which facilitate heat exchange or provide insulation for example, and for behavioural adaptations which avoid extremes of temperature. Adaptations of behaviour include, for example, hibernation, migration to a favourable climate or, in the case of man, the use of clothing, shelter and fire. In addition to the metabolic heat production associated with the basal maintenance activities of tissues such as the heart, lung and kidney, heat may be produced by exercise, shivering or unconscious tensing of the muscles; by increasing metabolic rate; and through the specific dynamic action of food. Heat may be lost through conduction, radiation and evaporation. Convection contributes only via losses through conduction, radiation or evaporation; for instance a shell of warm air around the body is constantly rising, making an updraught of convection currents which aids evaporative loss. The relative contributions of the different routes of heat loss (or gain) depend on the environmental conditions and on the nature of the outer covering or integument. In aquatic animals the greater part of

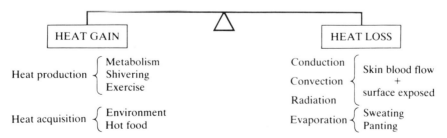

Figure 17.1 Balance between heat gain and heat loss. (Adapted from DuBois, E. F., *Lane Medical Lectures*, Stanford University Press, Stanford, 1937.)

heat transfer is via conduction, a route relatively unimportant in terrestrial animals. The amounts of heat lost by radiation and evaporation depend on the environmental temperature and humidity but, in man, radiation usually accounts for 55 per cent of the heat lost and evaporation for 40 per cent or less. Even so, heat losses in humid climates are restricted. Very few mammals live in tropical jungles and those that do are mainly slow-moving species, such as the sloths, and nocturnal.

Temperature control

In homeotherms it is only the core temperature which remains relatively constant. The temperature of the superficial shell of the body varies considerably and even the temperature of different tissues within the body shows some variation. Core temperature does not remain absolutely constant. In the human the temperature on waking is generally lower than on retiring and, in women, temperature rises slightly on ovulation and remains elevated until the next menstruation (Fig. 17.2). The centre for temperature regulation lies in the preoptic region of the hypothalamus, where the central thermoreceptors are located. Information is also provided by the thermorecep-

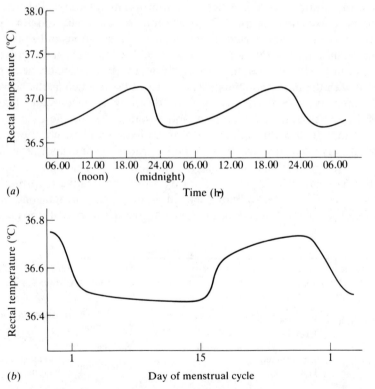

Figure 17.2 (a) Variation in body temperature over 24-h day (human). (b) Variation in temperature over 28-day menstrual cycle (human).

tors in the skin. For the sake of simplicity one can imagine a hypothalamic thermostat. In the development of a fever the thermostat is reset to a higher level through the action of pyrogens. These pyrogenic stimuli result in the release of interleukins, which act on the hypothalamus. The effect of aspirin, which in reducing body temperature inhibits prostaglandin synthesis, suggests that prostaglandins may also be involved. A feeling of cold is experienced and extra heat is produced until the new set point is reached. When the fever breaks, the set point is returned to the normal level and heat is lost from the body. The appropriate responses to bring about these changes are initiated in the hypothalamus.

Heat production

At rest, man produces about 170 kJ (40 cal) per square metre per hour, or roughly the output of a 40 W bulb. However, if placed in a bath of cold water at 4 °C, within 15 min this will have increased some 18-fold, an increase equivalent to that seen in maximal physical activity. The increase occurs largely as a result of shivering—shivering thermogenesis. In the cold, extra heat may also be produced from muscle as a result of conscious activity: 'jumping up and down to keep warm'. Various other organs contribute to the provision of heat—non-shivering thermogenesis. For example rats acclimatized to the cold have been shown to produce as much as 60 per cent of their heat in this way. Energy for increased heat production is provided by increased food consumption, and appetite is stimulated under these conditions. Energy is also supplied from adipose tissue. Increased sympathetic discharge results in increased lipolysis which makes glycerol and fatty acids available for metabolism by skeletal muscle and myocardium. There is also present in mammals tissue known as brown adipose tissue. This is seen particularly in newborn infants, including the human, and in hibernating animals at the time of arousal. Its main function is to produce heat and in the newborn it provides the principal means of increasing heat production, allowing metabolic rate to be increased by about 2.5 times in the infant. Brown adipose tissue is located close to major blood vessels with the result that the heat produced is transported to organs essential for survival such as the brain and heart. Histologically, it is a very vascular tissue with quite a high concentration of myoglobin and cytochromes. It is believed to be stimulated via adrenoceptors.

Heat loss

If body temperature is to be maintained constant, heat gain must be balanced by heat loss. Heat loss can be reduced by insulation. Special insulative qualities have been claimed for fat, but are questionable. A layer of fat, however, does provide insulation, and is also a source of metabolic energy. Insulation is achieved in animals such as pigs, for example, by a layer of cold superficial tissue. Birds have a layer of feathers next to the skin and most mammals have a layer of fur or hair. Heat loss may be further decreased by trapping a thick layer of air by fluffing up the feathers or by erection of the hair. Although piloerection occurs in man as can be seen with the formation of 'goose-pimples', it is ineffective because of the meagre hair cover. However, man traps layers of air in his clothes and nowadays this is achieved with great efficiency by using very lightweight protective clothing. A similar effect is produced in nature by means of hollow hair as in the caribou.

Since heat is lost from the skin, losses can be decreased by curling up or increased by stretching. Heat loss can also be affected by the amount of blood reaching the skin. Skin blood flow and hence heat loss can be decreased by increasing sympathetic vasoconstrictor tone and increased by a reduction in the activity of the sympathetic nerves. If the skin temperature in man drops below 10 °C as a result of intense vasoconstriction, then pain is experienced. In such circumstances cold vasodilatation takes place, which may prevent damage to the skin. The phenomenon is largely due to axon reflexes operating, particularly on the arteriovenous anastomoses. A counter-current heat-transfer system is also important in the regulation of the temperature of the tissues. This arrangement allows the extremities to be maintained at a lower temperature without excessively cold blood returning to the heart. Venous blood returning from the foot is warmed by the arterial blood, which is close proximity to the vein, so its temperature has risen to 37 °C when it re-enters the trunk. Simultaneously the arterial blood is cooled. This system also acts on blood going to the head. Cool blood from the face and skin of the head runs in veins close to arterial blood going to the brain, which then brings about the appropriate responses in the rest of the body. Changes of 0.01 °C in the hypothalamic regions of the brain can cause thermoregulatory effects and the brain temperature is kept remarkably constant. In various animals there is a heat exchange system, the carotid rete, between the arterial blood and the venous blood returning from the nasal cavity, as shown in Fig. 17.3. A similar arrangement comprising bundles of hundreds of intermingled arteries and veins is found in the legs and tails of animals. When heat must be conserved the circulation is restricted and when heat should be lost more blood passes through so that cool rather than warm blood returns to the circulation.

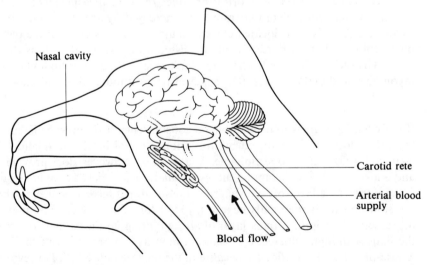

Figure 17.3 Carotid rete.

Evaporative heat loss

In the human about 30 g water per hour may be lost by evaporation from the skin. About 2.4 kJ (0.6 cal) are required to vaporize 1 g water, so that the loss represents about 20 W. This means of cooling has been exploited by birds and mammals in many different ways. Losses from the buccal and respiratory surfaces may be brought about by panting or by gular flutter, which is metabolically less expensive and involves quick fluttering of the floor of the mouth and the upper regions of the throat. Considerable evaporation occurs from the skin, even if there are no sweat glands; pigs, for example, are wallowing animals, and lose heat by conduction and by evaporation of pond water or mud. However, the skin of many mammals especially primates and Equidae is provided with numerous sweat glands. In man, evaporation of sweat is of great importance if the environmental temperature is higher than that of the body, since evaporation then becomes the only possible route of heat loss. Sweat, of course, needs to be evaporated, and not merely allowed to roll off the skin. Man is the only animal to use this thermoregulatory mechanism in environmentally warm conditions, although horses sweat as heat is generated metabolically.

In man there are probably about two million sweat glands distributed over the body surface. As shown in Fig. 17.4, they consist of a secretory coiled terminal portion and an excretory duct which passes through the corium and epidermis to the surface. Two types of sweat gland are found—apocrine and eccrine. The former are found in the axillae and round the nipples and vulva. The eccrine glands are associated with heat loss, producing sweat which is hypotonic to plasma, containing 0.1–0.4 per cent NaCl. The production of sweat is an active process and is elicited by stimulation of the

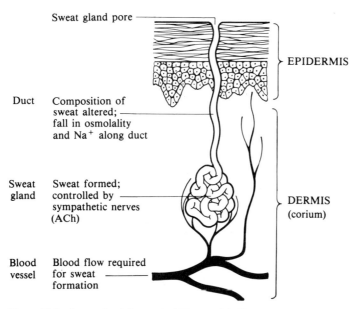

Figure 17.4 Sweat gland (human). ACh, acetylcholine.

cholinergic sympathetic nerves. Thermoregulatory sweating occurs at the expense of salt and water balance. On exposure to a hot or humid climate large amounts of salt and water may be lost in this way so that the blood volume is reduced and circulatory failure may result. A lowered plasma sodium results in muscle cramps. Additional salt as well as fluid should therefore be taken if one exercises in a hot environment. In a humid climate the effectiveness of heat loss through sweating is reduced. At extreme temperatures heat stroke may result in disruption of brain function and death. Exposure to heat leads to increased cardiac output and alterations in the circulation, frequently with increased venous pressure. It seems that the cause of fatal hyperpyrexia may be the cessation of sweating and circulatory failure. Physiological acclimatization to heat provides man with thermoregulatory capacities which can be life-saving. There is an altered pattern of sweating and vasodilatation as well as changes in the regulation of water and electrolyte balance and modified work performance.

Some animals such as the camel are particularly well adapted to live in hot arid conditions. Here the problem is not only the heat, but also the lack of water. Water losses via the respiratory tract and kidney are kept to a minimum and, since sweating is limited, the various other ways of preventing body temperature from becoming too high become important. For example the temperature of a camel may fluctuate considerably. It is allowed to fall quite low at night, thereby enabling a greater accumulation of heat during the day. The animal also shows behavioural responses. Unlike human sunbathers at the coast, camels position themselves so that the minimum surface area is exposed to the rays of the sun and, if they are sitting on the ground, they stay in the same place, thereby avoiding absorption of heat from the ground.

Effects of alteration in oxygen availability

Introduction

The requirement for food and hence for oxygen in different species depends on their resting metabolic rate and their degree of activity. In general, homeothermic species have higher metabolic requirements than poikilotherms. For terrestrial species, at least below 3000 m, the oxygen supply is never a limiting factor, though food may be. For aquatic species, because of the low solubility of oxygen in water, the oxygen supply could limit the animal's energy production, and anatomical or biochemical adaptations for intake and transport of oxygen can be seen. An example of a ventilatory adaptation may be seen in the number of gill lamellae possessed by fish, a larger number being seen in more active fish. Synthesis of haemoglobin, the means of transporting oxygen, can be stimulated in some animals including invertebrates on exposure to hypoxia. Acclimatization through altered metabolism is also well documented.

High altitude

For terrestrial animals low oxygen tensions are generally experienced only at high altitude. Over 10 million people live above 3000 m. The highest level at which people work is at 5700 m (Fig. 17.5) and life is sparse above 5500 m. In the case of cold-blooded animals, of course, this could well be due to the temperature. On rapid ascent to high altitude, man experiences breathlessness together with fatigue, insomnia and cyanosis, in which a bluish tinge is seen in the lips and nail beds, reflecting the colour of incompletely oxygenated haemoglobin. Some people may experience acute mountain sickness, characterized by dizziness, headache, vomiting and nausea, difficulty in breathing and incoordination. If one ascends more slowly, there is time for acclimatization. The first response to the reduced oxygen tension is stimulation of respiration via an effect on the peripheral chemoreceptors. This also has the effect of blowing off carbon dioxide so that respiration is depressed. Periodic breathing may even be seen, respiration being suppressed as carbon dioxide is blown off and then returning to normal as carbon dioxide builds up. The decreased partial pressure of carbon dioxide (P_{CO_2}) is associated with an alkalosis which results in decreased oxygen transport by haemoglobin. The raised pH leads to increased transport of bicarbonate out of the cerebrospinal fluid so that the ratio of carbon dioxide to

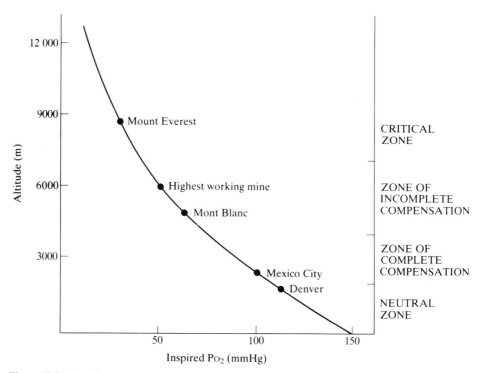

Figure 17.5 Partial pressure of oxygen (P_{O_2}) at various altitudes.

$(HCO_3)'$ ions is brought back to normal. A further adaptation may be an increase in the size of the peripheral chemoreceptors. In this way the increased ventilation may be maintained, but it is, of course, expensive in terms of the energy consumed by the respiratory muscles and heart, and leads to extra water losses.

Transport of oxygen is also improved at high altitude. Hypoxia produces an immediate increase in number of erythrocytes by causing contraction of the spleen via increased activity in the sympathetic nerves. Erythrocyte number remains elevated as multiplication of red cells and haemoglobin synthesis is enhanced through the action of erythropoietin, a hormone produced by the kidney. The haemoglobin oxygen-dissociation curve is shifted to the right as a result of an increase in 2,3-diphosphoglycerate in the erythrocytes. This means that oxygen is more readily released in the tissues. The supply of oxygen to the tissues is also enhanced by an initial increase in cardiac output of some 20–50 per cent. This is not maintained in the long term, but there is an increased number of capillaries in tissues such as muscle, heart and brain. Lastly, in addition to systemic changes there are changes at the cellular level. Thus in muscle, especially heart muscle, there is an increase in myoglobin levels and numbers of mitochondria.

Adaptations for diving

The major groups of terrestrial animals have members adapted to living under water. As with high altitude, the major problem is lack of oxygen, but this is even more extreme under water. For minute animals like the water mite, sufficient oxygen can be obtained by diffusion alone. Although this is not true for large animals, varied arrangements allow members of classes of land vertebrates to stay under water for longer or shorter periods of time. A spectacular example is that of the sperm whale which is reported to go as deep as 1000 m and to remain under water for an hour or more without encountering any obvious problems. The ability of birds and mammals to remain under water depends on oxygen-saving mechanisms, at both physiological and biochemical levels. A very important response is the slowing of the heart (diving bradycardia, Chapter 5), which is accompanied by a fall in the blood flow to the muscles, skin and viscera, so that flow to the brain, heart and adrenal glands is maintained. In a variety of mammals, stimulation by water of receptors in the nasal region triggers the cardiac slowing.

Carbohydrate is the major source of energy during diving. Since the oxygen stores of myoglobin in the muscle are rapidly used up, much lactic acid is soon produced by the tissue and lactate is in turn used by the lung and the heart as a substrate, allowing glucose to be spared for the brain. Diving vertebrates also have a relatively large blood volume and this may be accompanied by the development of large venous reservoirs. As will be discussed shortly, a problem man faces on returning to the surface after a dive is the supersaturation of body fluids with nitrogen. This is not a problem with diving mammals in which there are several anatomical specializations, including the presence of numerous ribs which are not attached to the sternum— 'floating ribs'. Thus during a deep dive the higher surrounding pressure is transmitted to the air space of the lungs, which collapse and restrict the capillary circulation so that excessive amounts of gas are not dissolved.

Since man is not naturally a diving animal and has no special adaptations to facilitate this behaviour, divers working at depth are faced with many problems. A major one is the high ambient pressure, which increases by 1 atmosphere for every 10 m (30 ft). Air must be supplied at the pressure of the surroundings, otherwise the lungs would collapse. This in itself leads to two problems. The first is that oxygen and nitrogen under high pressures are hazardous. Hyperbaric oxygen may cause damage to the lungs and may be detrimental to the nervous system. Nitrogen at high pressures dissolves in the membranes and other lipid structures, resulting in nitrogen narcosis. The excitability of the cells is reduced so that the state resembles that following administration of anaesthetic. Accordingly, in diving bells or helmets, the nitrogen of the air is replaced by helium, which has little effect on the body under high pressure. The second danger, occurring when the diver ascends too rapidly, is the expansion of the gas and its release from solution, which results in decompression sickness. The bubbles may form emboli in the pulmonary, myocardial and cerebral circulation or may become lodged in the joints. To overcome this problem, decompression chambers are employed so that the pressure can be reduced slowly. Immersion in water also makes it harder to maintain thermal equilibrium. Finally, perception is also affected: there is little light at depth and indices of refraction of light travelling from water through glass to the air space in front of the eye make the image appear at only 70 per cent of its actual distance. Water-borne sound impinges on the head and hearing is assumed to be via bone conduction.

Circadian rhythms

The nature of rhythms

Any regularly oscillating process is called rhythmic or periodic; it may follow a sine wave pattern or it may be asymmetric. The physical characteristics of a rhythm are described using the following terms (Fig. 17.6):

cycle	the shortest part of a rhythm which repeats itself indefinitely: it may be taken from trough to trough or peak to peak;
period	the time occupied by a cycle;
amplitude	the distance between the extremes, i.e. the trough and crest.

In addition, the following terms are applied to rhythmic physiological processes:

diurnal	a rhythm whose period is a day;
circadian	a more recently introduced term describing a rhythm whose period is around 24 h;
nycthemeral	the alternation of day and night.

If the rhythmic pattern of a physiological process continues in the absence of external changes, it is called endogenous and is thought to originate within the animal.

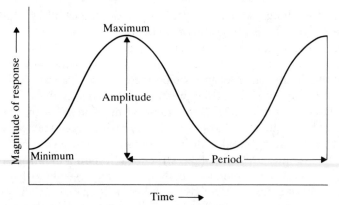

Figure 17.6 A repeating cycle.

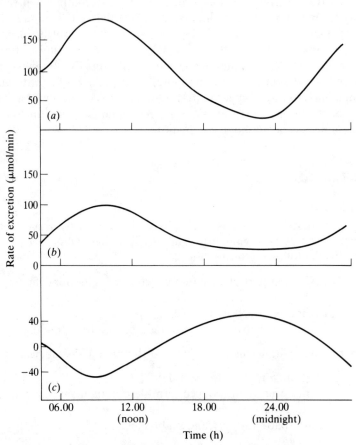

Figure 17.7 Urinary parameters over 24-h day. (*a*) Na$^+$. (*b*) K$^+$. (*c*) H$^+$; excretion of acid is given as titratable acid plus ammonia minus bicarbonate.

However, in the absence of external cues the period of such a rhythm will show deviation from 24 h and the rhythm will gradually shift out of phase with the solar day. Normally, environmental cues such as dark–light transition and temperature adjust the rhythm; such cues are called the *Zeitgeber* or timekeeper. Man's life is dominated by a single periodicity, alternations of dark and light. However, there are many endogenous rhythms with periods varying from milliseconds, as seen in the brain, through minutes, as seen in the pulse and respiration, to hours and days, as seen in the endocrine system.

Since man's habits are largely governed by social and environmental rhythms, it is not surprising to find that many physiological measurements show a more or less regular periodicity. Rhythmic variations in blood pressure, pulse rate and temperature could result simply from a regular alternation of rest and exercise; the pattern of renal excretion (Fig. 17.7) could result from the regularity of ingestion of food and water; and changes in endocrine secretion from variations in alertness and drowsiness. The first step in characterizing a rhythm is to establish the pattern under normal circumstances. Next one must find whether the pattern is exogenous or endogenous. Ideally for an endogenous pattern one should be able to demonstrate a rhythm in the absence of all circadian cues, as, for example, in caves or underground bunkers; and to try to eliminate the effects of posture, human subjects could be maintained recumbent. Finally one can produce a phase shift artificially or by flying across time zones and observe the effect of such a shift on the rhythm. Body temperature is a parameter which shows a circadian rhythm, a fact reported by Davy in 1845. One could argue that it is due to the heat production associated with activity, but it is still seen in people confined to bed and therefore other factors such as heat loss through cutaneous blood flow must be considered. In fact the temperature rhythm is indeed endogenous and is maintained even after a phase shift, though it will finally adapt to the new time.

Rhythms of various parameters

Another series of parameters which have long been known to exhibit circadian rhythms are those of the kidney (see Fig. 17.7). It is well known that urine flow is reduced during sleep. The earliest observation was by Schweig in 1843. This pattern in urine flow results from changes in glomerular filtration rate, tubular function and secretion of hormones. Glomerular filtration rate, for example, is higher during the day. The patterns, of course, are reversed for nocturnal animals. Circadian periodicity has been noted in many circulatory functions, including blood pressure, pulse rate, plasma volume and cardiac output. There is a fall on going to sleep, followed by a gradual increase during the night. There is also variation in skin temperature, presumably reflecting skin blood flow: it is at a minimum at 08.00–16.00 h and at a maximum at 20.00–04.00 h. The heart rate and temperature curves are closely superimposable. There are marked changes in ventilation during sleep with a fall in ventilation rate and an increase in P_{CO_2}. The respiratory minute volume falls to 2 litres/min and the ventilatory rate becomes less responsive to a rise in P_{CO_2}. The vital capacity falls during the day to a minimum value around midnight and then climbs until the normal time of waking.

Endocrine rhythms

Hormone secretory patterns show very marked rhythms, especially those of the anterior pituitary. Particularly marked are the rhythm of corticotrophin releasing factor and adrenocorticotrophic hormone (ACTH) and of the associated glucocortic-

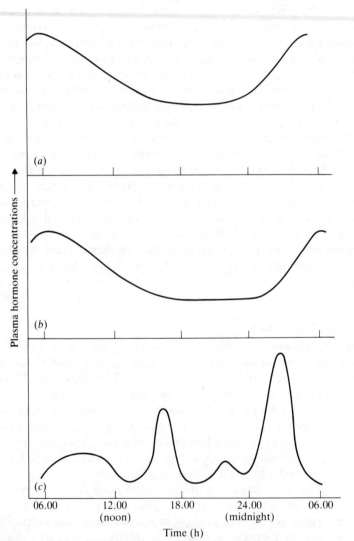

Figure 17.8 Fluctuations in plasma levels of three hormones. (*a*) ACTH. (*b*) Cortisol. (*c*) Growth hormone.

oid, cortisol, shown in Fig. 17.8. As described in Chapter 14, glucocorticoid concentration increases in the early morning to a peak on waking. When one travels through a time zone the rhythm takes about a week to adapt. It can also be observed in blind subjects and people isolated from geophysical inputs. The other adrenal hormone, aldosterone, also shows a maximum plasma concentration in the morning and a minimum on retiring. In contrast to the glucocorticoid rhythm, it is abolished by enforced recumbency and reversed within one day of reversing the light–dark pattern. The rhythm of potassium coincides with that of aldosterone but persists when the aldosterone pattern is shifted. Many other hormones show enhanced secretion during the evening as, for example, prolactin and growth hormone, which are elevated during the early onset of sleep, particularly in children. The hormone pulses are not seen if sleep is delayed. Circadian changes in gonadotrophins are complex and show species differences, depending on a number of factors. For example in seasonal breeders, patterns are related to day length. In animals such as the rat the luteinizing hormone (LH) surge is tightly linked to the light–dark cycle. There is no evidence of circadian organization of reproductive cycles in primates. However, the onset of puberty in the human is marked by increased LH pulses, especially during the night. Even the delivery of the human infant is most likely to occur in the early morning.

Basis of the circadian rhythms

In the human at birth there is a 50- to 60-min rest–activity cycle; a 4-hour sleep–wake pattern gradually develops. Soon, long sleep periods develop with naps during the day. A more or less adult pattern is established by the age of 4 years. The pattern of body temperature is clear by 6 months and fully established by 2 years.

There has been considerable discussion as to the basis of the diurnal responses. It has been suggested that in some species the pineal gland plays a role. The pineal contains an indole called melatonin because it lightens the skin of tadpoles by an action on the melanophores. Melatonin is released from the pineal with a marked circadian rhythm entrained to a light–dark cycle. The pineal in lower vertebrates is photosensitive. In mammals there is a pathway from the retina to the pineal. The function of the pineal in mammals is not clear although melatonin can inhibit gonadal activity and may play some role in regulating photoperiodic control of seasonal breeding in species such as the hamster. The suprachiasmatic nucleus also receives an input from the retina, and in rodents destruction of the nuclei disrupts circadian rhythms, as, for example, the pattern of secretion of ACTH. In higher mammals such as primates a more complex regulation of circadian rhythm is apparent, where there is a greater capacity for the dissociation of endogenous rhythms.

Significance of circadian and other rhythms

Circadian rhythms linked to sleep–activity patterns may allow enhancement of performance during the active phase and saving of energy during resting periods in most species. In man these rhythms are important in many situations, for example at work and in medical contexts. Human performance is affected by circadian swings and this is very important in the arrangements for working, especially for shift workers. The clinical implications of circadian rhythms are manifest both in biochemical estimations and in the efficiency of drugs. For example it is important to know that cortisol secretion exhibits a circadian rhythm, otherwise a misdiagnosis could be made when plasma hormone concentrations were being assessed. Again drugs have different degrees of effectiveness, rates of metabolism and rates of excretion at different times of the day. For example, dexamethasone produces a more marked decrease of cortisol level when given at midnight than when given at 08.00–1600 h. Examples of differences in the rate of metabolism and excretion of drugs are seen with such drugs as amphetamines and salicylate (Fig. 17.9).

Lunar and annual cycles are also of significance in the evolution of cyclical biological phenomena. Many cycles have been described which coincide with the lunar cycle or some particular phase. An amazing example is the mass spawning of the Pacific grunion, which occurs two to four nights after the full moon during March, April, May and June. The fish (both sexes) swim up the beaches, spawn, and return to the water after the turn of the tide. This synchronism is said to increase the chances of successful reproduction, perhaps by carrying the fertilized ova well offshore on the low ebb of spring-tides. Annual rhythms may be seen in birds, molluscs, arthropods, reptiles and mammals. For instance golden-mantled ground squirrels can maintain their rhythm of hibernation for up to 4 years even if constant temperature and day length are artificially maintained.

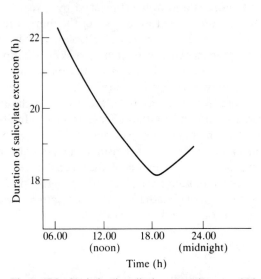

Figure 17.9 Variation in salicylate excretion over 24 h.

Summary and conclusions

It may be seen that animals are capable of many adaptations to allow them to live in extremes of environment or to cope with changes in the environment. Many systems of the body contribute to this adaptation and the integrated responses allow survival of the animal. Thus in thermoregulation many organs and tissues contribute to the balance of heat gain and heat loss. At high altitude a variety of changes allows oxygen to be more readily taken up, transported to the tissue and used more effectively. At great depths under water, there are adaptations not only to allow the efficient uptake and use of oxygen, but also to allow the animal to withstand the elevated ambient pressures. These are just a few examples of the way in which animals become adapted to ambient conditions. One has only to look at the diverse species to appreciate the multitude of anatomical adaptations; physiological adaptations are not always so readily apparent. Rapidly reproducing life-forms such as bacteria show the greatest rate of adaptation and are able to live under the most inhospitable conditions. Modern man has a great capacity to alter the environment; but he only rarely reveals the ability to respond, by physical adaptations, to such changes of his own making.

18 Conclusion: some properties of physiological processes

On surveying the particular physiological systems considered in this book, certain general aspects of physiological processes become apparent. Consideration of these general aspects may help readers going on to study other systems, or to study these same systems in greater depth. Many physiological processes can conveniently be analysed into three components in sequence: perturbation → effect → consequence; or, to put it in biological terms: stimulus → response → change in whole body (or whole cell, tissue or organ). This could take place at the level of a single cell, where the sequence might be: excess sodium within the cell → increased activity of the sodium pump → restoration of normal composition and volume of the cell. It could occur at the level of the blood, as for example: high concentration of plasma solute → retention of water by kidney → dilution of whole extracellular fluid. Again, a whole group of organs of the body might be involved: stretching of the wall of the carotid arteries → slowing of the heart beat and also to dilatation of arterioles → lowering of arterial blood pressure all over the body. A knowledge of the sequence of these three components, and particularly of the intermediate steps between the first two, is fundamental in understanding the working of the body.

It is nearly always helpful in any consideration of a physiological process to define the initial event, or initial state, or starting point. What is the stimulus? What parameter has been altered? Has the alteration come from outside the body or within it? Among the initial events considered in this book are:

1. changes of concentration of solutes in intracellular and extracellular fluid;
2. changes in membrane potential;
3. changes of sensory input via sense organs such as muscle spindles or cardiovascular stretch receptors.

Examples of initial states arising from within the central nervous system (CNS) (largely independent of afferent input or internal chemical signals) are:

1. the inherent rhythm of the respiratory centre at the base of the brain, which, though

influenced by input from sense organs, does not seem to be dependent on any input to keep it going;

2. states of emotion such as fear or excitement, leading to widespread stimulation of the sympathetic nervous system;
3. conscious voluntary effort initiating muscular movement.

Sometimes the physiologist may have to make his own somewhat arbitrary decision about where a process starts. In considering intestinal absorption, for instance, we started at the point where foodstuffs are already broken down into absorbable molecules. In reality, digestion of some foods is continuing alongside absorption of others, and indeed digestive juices are among the materials being absorbed. Physiological processes are continuous and interlocking, and this simultaneity should not be overlooked in our efforts to divide and classify them.

Having determined the starting point or initial event, the student must consider the activity set in motion by this event. The response may occur in a series of steps, each one acting as the stimulus for the next in the series. Indeed the more detailed one's knowledge, the more numerous are the intermediate steps which can be described. One of the most interesting parts of physiological study is the disentangling of these intermediate steps. The bald statement 'Excitement causes a rise in blood glucose level' is relatively uninformative. The sequence of events is: emotional excitement → increased activity of nerves to adrenal glands → increased secretion of adrenaline into blood → uptake by liver cells of blood-borne adrenaline → stimulation of glycolytic enzymes of liver cells → increased breakdown of liver glycogen → increased supply of glucose to blood → rise of blood glucose concentration. Even these six intermediate steps between the initial and the final event cannot be the whole story. One might ask: How do the nerve impulses cause release of adrenaline into the blood? Why should adrenaline affect specifically liver cells (and a few other types of tissue) and not every cell of the body reached by the blood? How can adrenaline alter the amount or activity of an intracellular enzyme? How (to begin with) does emotion cause stimulation of certain peripheral nerves? So a full description of this phenomenon of rise of blood sugar could require biochemical, pharmacological and even psychological insight, as well as purely physiological knowledge.

Again, stimulation of a single group of receptors may lead to numerous responses in several different parts of the body: simultaneous rather than sequential events. For example we may consider the chilling of the body of a mammal or bird in a cold environment. The effect of the cooled blood perfusing certain nerve cells at the base of the brain leads to:

1. constriction of blood vessels of the skin;
2. shivering or increased muscle tone of striated muscles;
3. erection of hair, fur or feathers.

None of these three events causes either of the other two, and the three types of tissue involved are different. All three responses working together have the effect of raising body temperature by retaining existing heat and generating more heat. It is sometimes difficult in the study of physiological processes to work out whether a group of events are simultaneous or sequential and, if sequential, the precise order in which they occur. In the cardiovascular system, for instance, the sequence of events may be very rapid—the time occupied by two or three heart beats. For instance when an animal is startled, its heart suddenly beats more quickly. An increase of the volume of blood put out by the heart leads to a rise in pressure in the main arteries, which stretches their walls, which stimulates stretch receptors, which initiate an increase in the number of impulses up sensory nerves to the brain; this stimulates the vagus nerves to the pacemaker of the heart; these nerve impulses have the effect of slowing the heart, thereby decreasing its output. But the whole cycle of events starting and finishing with the heart can take place within a couple of seconds. In actual situations it is sometimes only by careful scrutiny that the observer can see which event comes first in the time sequence and might thus be the stimulus starting the whole train of responses.

One kind of immediate response to the initial event or stimulus consists of an alteration of the level of activity of one organ or of the entire body. For example a standing man takes a step; a resting animal starts to run; the stomach and duodenum, almost empty and moving little in the fasting state, suddenly increase in motility and secretion when loaded with a meal. In many instances the response to a stimulus is a matter simply of increasing (or decreasing) the rate of a process that is already in action, rather than initiating an entirely new process. Vasomotor nerves, for instance, are constantly conveying impulses which keep the muscular wall of the arterioles partially constricted; one kind of stimulus elicits an increase in impulse rate, another kind leads to a reduction in rate, causing respectively more constriction or more dilatation of the arterioles. The sodium pump in the cell membrane is constantly at work: entry of Na^+ ions during conduction in excitable tissues increases the pump rate. Many hormones work at the cellular level by altering the rate of one of the cell's enzyme reactions at the expense of others, forcing metabolism in a certain direction but not starting an entirely new metabolic pathway. There do exist physiological activities which start some entirely new process; perhaps enzyme induction might be considered an example of this. But such actions are rare compared with the numerous examples in which the response is a change of rate in an ongoing process.

At the end of this consideration of 'cause' and 'effect' or 'stimulus' and 'response' in biological systems, the reader is reminded that by no means all processes occurring in the animal body are, strictly speaking, unique to biological systems. A great many processes can be interpreted in purely physicochemical or mechanical terms, without the need to invoke biological energy changes. The living body is, of course, part of the material world and subject to its laws. Within the body, as outside it, the direction and rate of a chemical reaction are determined by the Law of Mass Action; particles of opposite sign attract and those of the same sign repel, within living cells as everywhere else; the relationship of surface tension, internal pressure and radius of a gas-filled sphere is the same for a balloon, soap bubble and the alveolus of the lung; gravity takes blood to the feet when a person stands; oncotic pressure of plasma protein brings water from intestine to portal blood. Such physical and chemical processes are a frequent component of the response pattern and one should always be on the lookout for them. There are indeed still a great many mysteries about the working of cells and organisms. But there is no need to add to the mysteries if a straightforward explanation in terms of well-established laws of physics and chemistry is available. Such an explanation should always be the object of one's first search.

We have seen instances of connections between the first two elements (stimulus and response) of the three components into which physiological processes can be usefully analysed. Something can now be said about the relationship between the response (or pattern or sequence of responses) and the effect on the whole organism or whole cell. This effect is sometimes given the title 'biological advantage' or 'physiological significance'.

The examples given in the preceding paragraphs illustrate a function of a great many physiological processes: their final outcome is the stabilizing of some variable property (parameter) of the body. In the case of the mammal or bird undergoing chilling the various responses lead to the restoration of the body temperature. In the case of the cardiovascular system the cycle of events described earlier keeps the cardiac output at a steady level. This type of physiological process—the alteration of a parameter starting a sequence of responses which leads to the restoration of the parameter to its original value—is negative feedback. Implicit in negative-feedback systems is the continuous slight change of the parameter (e.g. body temperature, cardiac output) above and below a certain value. This slight up-and-down variation in biological systems is known as 'hunting', a technical term used also for mechanical stabilizers. The outcome of feedback systems for the whole body (or cell, or organ) is the maintenance within it of a certain degree of stability, or reduction of the effect of a disturbance. Indeed so common are negative-feedback systems that it is sometimes difficult to remember that not all physiological processes are of this type.

The final outcome or biological advantage of most physiological processes is obvious and hardly needs spelling out. Three points should be brought to the reader's attention here.

1. It is important not to become so concerned with the fine details and intricacies of the mechanisms in the connection of 'stimulus' and 'response' that one misses the physiological significance of the whole pattern. It is all too easy to fail to see the wood when examining the trees. In the study of neurophysiology, for example, one may find the details of a series of interlocking postural reflex arcs so absorbing that one can overlook the general outcome: the animal stands upright and moves smoothly.

2. Perhaps an even greater danger is to argue backwards from 'biological advantage' to 'mechanism'. It is not the 'need' or 'requirement' for the biological advantage that elicits the mechanism. It is not, for instance, the requirement for additional oxygen that causes an animal to breathe more quickly during exercise. The final outcome of a whole series of physiological processes leading to quick breathing (and rapid blood flow) during exercise is indeed that more oxygen is taken into the body and brought to the actively working muscles. However, this is not in any

physiological sense the *cause* of the rapid breathing and blood flow, but rather the eventual biological outcome. Ultimately, mechanisms which survive, in the evolutionary sense, must have some biological advantage. But to argue, for any biological mechanism: 'It must happen like this, because in these conditions an animal would need ...' is a muddle-headed confusion of cause and effect.

3. There may well be physiological processes for which there is no perceptible biological advantage. Evolutionary 'relics' provide examples of such processes. In many mammals and birds, smooth muscles in skin follicles are stimulated to contract in cold conditions, with consequent raising of fur or feathers and thickening of the layer of trapped air close to the skin; so a thicker layer of insulation is created, a clear biological advantage in the cold. Humans have the same cold-reflex: in sudden cold the hair on the head and arms is raised. But it is doubtful whether even primitive man had enough hair for this reflex to make any difference to his insulation or heat loss (and of course for modern man there is no biological advantage whatever). Another curious process, also a response to cold, is that many humans find that stimulation of cold-receptors of the skin elicits urination, or the sensation of the need to urinate; and it is hard to find any biological advantage for this, for man or any other species. To argue, as some have done: 'The process must have some biological advantage, otherwise it would not exist' is a wrong-headed approach. There is certainly much redundancy in biological systems. To search frantically for 'biological advantage' in every observed process or biochemical reaction is a waste of effort.

Biological significance, though not to be forgotten during the study of the process, must never be used as a 'short-cut' or 'explanation', a substitute for the sometimes tedious business of working out all the steps of the response. Some areas in the study of animal physiology are better known than others. Many readers will be well aware that the description of those processes discussed in this book could have been more complete by including reactions of cell biology at one end of the scale and of animal behaviour at the other. No biological description is ever complete, and scientists still have far to go, in matters of knowledge, understanding and explanation. The phrase 'This process is not completely understood' could be used of virtually all, if not all aspects, of physiological study. It is never an excuse for failure to try to understand and make sense of the known facts. To help readers to set about this understanding is the purpose of this book.

Appendix 1 Osmotic and ionic equilibrium across a membrane: Nernst equation

The question is sometimes asked: why is a *logarithmic* relationship involved in the concentration difference across a membrane in the Nernst equation? The brief answer is: because it is derived from an integral; and even students with little knowledge of calculus should be able to follow the general argument.

The osmotic pressure of a solution, P, is given by RTc, (where R = gas constant, T = absolute temperature and c = concentration). The free energy inherently present in a simple solution is capable of doing osmotic work. The amount of work could be measured by a simple machine (Fig. A1.1) consisting of a cylinder containing a piston made of a membrane permeable to water but not to solute. Water is above the membrane, the solution below it. Water moves across the membrane into the solution, increasing its volume, and the piston moves upwards. If there is a weight at the top of the piston rod, this upward movement gives the weight greater potential energy, an increase measurable when the system has reached equilibrium. The solution has become more dilute, going from c_0 to c_1, as the piston moves from x_0 to x_1. The area of the piston is A.

The maximum work which the solution can do in moving the piston by a small amount, dx, is:

$$PA\, dx - RTcA\, dx$$

So the maximum work that the solution can perform in moving the piston all the way

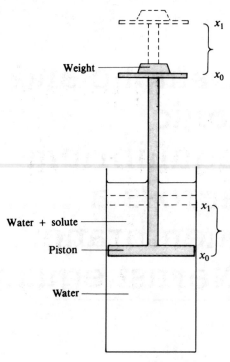

Figure A1.1 Osmotic work during dilution, with a piston of semipermeable membrane. See text for explanation.

from x_0 to x_1, the equilibrium position, is:

$$RT \int_{x_0}^{x_1} Ac \, dx$$

The concentration of the solution is inversely proportional to the height, i.e.

$$c_0 x_0 = c_1 x_1 = cx$$

If 1 mole is originally present,

$$c_0 x_0 A = 1 \quad \text{or} \quad cxA = 1 \quad \text{or} \quad Ac = \frac{1}{x}$$

So maximum work done

$$= RT \int_{x_0}^{x_1} \frac{1}{x} \, dx$$

$$= RT \ln\left(\frac{x_1}{x_0}\right)$$

$$= RT \ln\left(\frac{c_0}{c_1}\right)$$

This therefore is the free energy change per mole as the concentration goes from c_0 to c_1.

If the solution contains ions, and the ions are also in equilibrium, across the membrane, we must consider the work done in moving ion-moles across a membrane. If the membrane becomes charged at equilibrium, to E (volts), the work done in moving one ion-mole is ZEF, where $Z =$ valency and $F =$ Faraday's constant. (If the ion is taken from the low-voltage to the high-voltage side of the membrane, the work is positive for cations, negative for anions.)

So for each ion at equilibrium, electrical work done in one direction balances osmotic work done in the other:

$$ZEF = RT \ln \left(\frac{c_0}{c_1} \right)$$

$$\text{or} \quad E = \frac{RT}{ZF} \ln \left(\frac{c_0}{c_1} \right)$$

Appendix 2 Electrochemical potential gradients

The useful energy, μS, in joules/mole, of a charged particle S in solution is defined in terms of two components: a chemical part and an electrical part.

$$\mu S = RT \ln \gamma [S] \qquad + ZF\Psi$$

(Chemical part, assuming constant temperature and pressure)   (Electrical part)

R = gas constant, T = absolute temperature, Z = valency, F = Faraday's constant, and Ψ = voltage with respect to a reference point.

In biological systems interstitial (extracellular) fluid is by convention considered to be the reference point, 'zero voltage', as is 'earth' in physical systems.

$\gamma [S]$ = activity: γ = activity coefficient, which is close to 1 in most biological systems, so the chemical part becomes, as a close approximation, $RT \ln [S]$.

If the ion is present at different concentrations, $[S]_1$ and $[S]_2$, inside and outside the cell, the membrane of which carries a charge of $\Delta \psi$ (difference in electrical potential), then the electrochemical gradient driving it towards its thermodynamic equilibrium across the membrane would be the difference in 'useful energy' on the two sides of the membrane:

$$= \Delta \mu S = (RT \ln [S]_1 - RT \ln [S]_2) + ZF\Delta\psi$$

(Chemical gradient)   (Electrical gradient)

$$= RT \ln [S]_1 - \ln [S]_2) + ZF\Delta\Psi$$

$$= RT \ln \left(\frac{[S]_1}{[S]_2} \right) + ZF\Delta\Psi$$

Appendix 3 Electro-cardiogram

The electrical changes in the heart during waves of excitation and relaxation at each heart beat can be recorded from the surface of the body through electrical leads placed on the skin surface and connected to sensitive galvanometers or other recording equipment. The pattern of changes during each cardiac cycle is called the electrocardiogram (ECG). It can be recorded in several ways. One way is to use a strip of paper moving rapidly past the ink-filled galvanometer needle. The ECG is used for diagnostic purposes because it shows certain characteristic changes in specific cardiac disorders.

The wave of excitation spreading over the myocardium can be considered as a moving dipole. (A dipole is a pair of equally charged positive and negative poles such as battery terminals, but infinitely close together.) Figure A3.1a shows the wave of excitation (depolarization) on the membrane of a cardiac muscle fibre moving from left to right, the edge of the wave being represented by a dipole, leading edge positive.

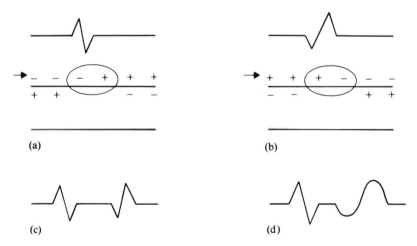

Figure A3.1 Electrocardiogram records. (a) Excitation. The edge of the wave of excitation is represented by a dipole, shown in a circle. (b) Recovery. (c) Theoretical record. (d) Actual record from ventricular surface.

The galvanometer is wired in such a way as to give an upward deflection as the positive pole of the dipole moves towards it, and a downward deflection as the dipole moves away from it. So as the edge of the excitation approaches, passes directly under it, and then moves on, a quick up-and-down fluctuation is recorded, as shown in Fig. A3.1a. The recovery phase of the myocardial muscle, the recharging of the membrane, is represented in Fig. A3.1b. Here the leading edge of the dipole is negative, so the galvanometer gives a quick down-and-up sweep, as the wave of electrical recovery passes below it. So each portion of the myocardium in turn should produce a series of galvanometer recordings as seen in Fig. A3.1c. In fact records taken directly from the ventricular surface are more like those shown in Fig. A3.1d, because the recovery phase always takes longer than the excitatory phase, so the deflections are more splayed out; and the first part of the recovery record is usually obliterated by other electrical activity.

An ECG record taken from leads on the body surface includes atrial as well as ventricular activity, and often appears as in Fig. A3.2. The various peaks and troughs have been named by letters. The P peak represents atrial depolarization. (The atrial repolarization is lost among the fluctuations of greater amplitude caused by ventricular events occurring at the same time.)

Surface leads are commonly attached to the right arm (RA), left arm (LA) and left foot (LF), and these are joined in pairs with a galvanometer between each two. The pairs are conventionally numbered: Lead I (RA and LA), Lead II (RA and LF) and Lead III (LA and LF) (Fig. A3.3). The triangle joining the three points of contact on the body surface is called the Einthoven Triangle, named after the cardiologist who established the conventional leads.

In most normal people the electrical axis of the heart, like the anatomical axis, runs obliquely downwards and to the left. The ECG deflections during a cardiac cycle will be largest in the lead lying parallel with the direction of the wave of excitation and relaxation: that is, Lead II. In certain abnormal conditions the main axis of the heart

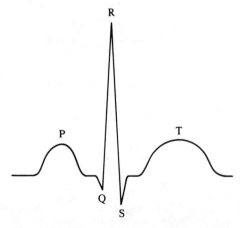

Figure A3.2   Shape of electrical record with conventional lettering.

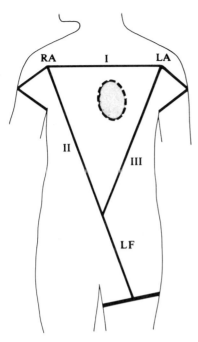

Figure A3.3 Einthoven Triangle. Leads I, II and III join, in pairs, surface leads attached to the right arm (RA), left arm (LA) and left foot (LF).

may shift to lie more nearly horizontal. (This may be associated with a change in the position of the diaphragm, a hypertrophy of the left ventricle, or other thoracic defect.) In this case the greatest deflection in the ECG waves appears in Lead I. In other conditions the heart tilts towards a more nearly vertical position, and in this case it would be Lead III that records the largest ECG deflections. In left ventricular hypertrophy the greatly thickened muscular tissue causes a delay in the whole process of depolarizing and repolarizing, so the Q–R–S complex is splayed out along the time axis, compared with a normal ECG. Another abnormality detectable by ECG is poor conduction between atria and ventricles. This is revealed by an unusually long P–R interval.

Appendix 4 Lung compliance and pressure-volume relationship

Compliance of the lung—an indication of the elasticity of the organ—is defined as the change of volume produced by unit change of pressure, $\Delta V/\Delta P$, and is measured in units of ml/mmHg or ml/cm water. If the lungs of an animal are inflated with air, the volume does not change uniformly as the pressure increases (see Fig. A4.1). From 0 to

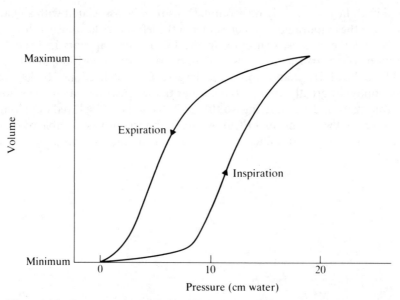

Figure A4.1 Pressure–volume relationship during inspiration and expiration (hysteresis loop).

9 cm water pressure there is very little change in volume (low compliance). Then compliance increases rather suddenly and volume increases rapidly for the next pressure increase, up to a maximum. As pressure decreases, volume does not return by a reversal of the same path, but remains rather higher, then falls steeply to the starting point. The route drawn by the volume–pressure graph is called a hysteresis loop. (Hysteresis means 'lagging behind'. Hysteresis loops are familiar to students of physics.) The hysteresis loop described for artificial inflation and deflation of an animal's lung occurs also in natural breathing. Comparison with the graph for surface tension of water in the presence of lung surfactant (Fig. 6.4) shows the chemical basis for the volume–pressure change in the lung. If in an animal's lungs the inflation–deflation is carried out with a saline solution instead of air, thereby eliminating the air–water interface, at least 80 per cent of the hysteresis is abolished. (Presumably the remainder of the effect is due to some elastic property of the thoracic cavity.)

The molecular basis for the hysteresis loop of lung surfactant and of the lung volume during breathing is unknown; nor do we know whether it has any physiological importance.

Lung compliance alters in characteristic ways in certain lung diseases; it falls in pulmonary fibrosis, and increases in emphysema.

Appendix 5 Exercise and training

Dynamic exercise such as running or swimming not only makes demands on skeletal and cardiac muscles, but also entails adjustments of several physiological systems including the respiratory, the endocrine and the whole cardiovascular systems. Some of these physiological adjustments are summarized in Fig. A5.1. Autonomic and endocrine processes occur even before the beginning of exercise ('Anticipation'). A number of cardiovascular and respiratory changes take place during the exercise as described in Chapters 5 and 6, and biochemical and thermal responses also occur. However, the exercise, in spite of these adjustments, cannot continue indefinitely ('Starting to tire' in Fig. A5.1).

The break-point at which the exercising person stops (or collapses) may be governed by temperature: heat dissipation fails to keep pace with the rate at which heat is being generated and the consequent rise of core temperature may force the runner to stop; or it may be a matter of depletion of the body's energy stores, including the glycogen of the exercising muscles. Although the discomfort of the sensation of 'breathlessness' may force a runner to stop, there is evidence that the respiratory system does not limit physical performance: respiratory movements at the break-point are more than sufficient to keep the blood leaving the lungs fully saturated with oxygen and to remove additional carbon dioxide at the rate of its production.

Physical training is aimed at allowing the exercise to continue for a longer time before the break-point is reached, or allowing more intense exercise (such as faster running), or both. The effects of training are often assessed by measurement of a person's maximum oxygen intake (in ml/kg body weight/min) during his most vigorous exercise. The physiological results of training are as follows:

1. Stroke volume of the heart increases as the ventricles enlarge.
2. Oxygen uptake per breath increases; this may be because all the lung alveoli are open all the time.
3. Total blood volume increases, and so also does the total amount of haemoglobin in the body.
4. There is an increase in the number of muscle capillaries.
5. There is an increase in the myoglobin of red muscles, and of mitochondria, and of several of the enzymes concerned in oxidative metabolism.
6. During exercise, circulating levels of intermediary fat metabolites are lower, implying an increased uptake by trained as compared with untrained muscles.

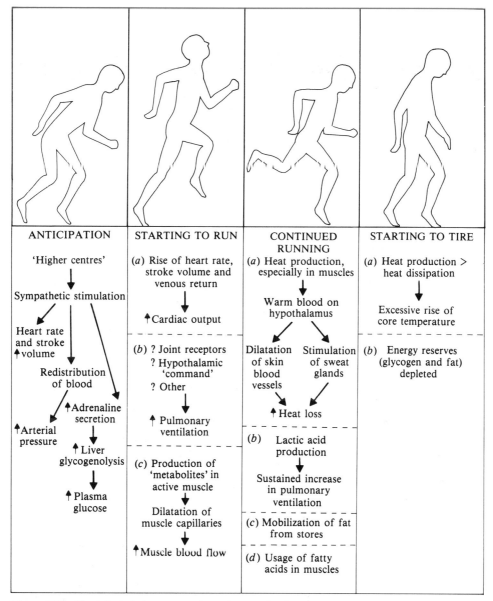

Figure A5.1   Physiological changes accompanying running (man).

These adaptations, particularly the development of additional muscle capillaries, are of great interest to physiologists as well as to athletes and trainers. All the changes consequent on athletic training are reversible: the skeletal muscle and heart can be deconditioned by bed-rest as quickly as they are trained by exercise.

Appendix 6 Blood groups and polymorphism

Human erythrocytes were the first cells on which blood group substances were found. The blood group substances are glycoproteins—proteins with a polysaccharide attached—which occur on the surface membrane of erythrocytes of mammals and birds in all species so far examined. The substances have slightly different chemical forms in different individuals of the same species; all individuals having the same chemical form of a particular substance are said to belong to the same blood group. The production of blood group substances is genetically controlled. In man there are about 14 different systems of erythrocyte blood group substances, and thus 14 different clusters of genes controlling their formation.

The ABO group substances in man have been studied for many years. Individuals can carry on their red cells either the A substance or the B substance or both. The *A* and *B* genes are dominant to their absence, so a genotype of *AO*, for instance, would produce a phenotype of Group A. A genotype of *OO* would produce a phenotype with neither A nor B glycoprotein—a Group O individual. Many blood group substances have been given letter-names: for instance another set of human blood group substances is called Rh, controlled mainly by a gene called *D*, and another is called the MNSs group.

Blood group substances are antigenic: that is, antibodies are formed in the plasma of an animal of a given blood group when erythrocytes of a different blood group are injected into it. The antibody plasma on subsequent mixing with the antigenic erythrocytes causes them to clump together (agglutination); or, in the presence of 'complement' (a series of membrane-associated enzymes) the antigenic erythrocytes break down (haemolysis). These processes have been the basis for a convenient identification of blood group substances and hence of the genetic make-up of individuals. This identification has been of great assistance in the study of population genetics and in immunochemistry, and also in physical anthropology since the incidence of different blood groups varies among different human populations.

In sheep a blood group substance of some biochemical interest has a relationship to the sodium–potassium exchange pump on the red cell membrane. The presence of the so-called 'L-substance' causes alteration in the rate of this ionic exchange, with the result that the erythrocytes contain a rather low K^+ concentration. So sheep of all breeds can be grouped as 'high-potassium' or 'low-potassium' individuals. 'Low-potassium' sheep are in no way harmed by having this low potassium level in their erythrocytes.

As far as is now known, the existence of blood group substances has no relevance to survival in man or any other species, and confers no direct biological advantage or disadvantage on individuals or populations.

Practical applications in man

In man there happen to be naturally occurring antibodies to the A and B blood group substances. Individuals with A erythrocytes carry anti-B antibodies in their plasma, and people with B erythrocytes carry anti-A plasma; people of Group O carry both sets of antibodies in their plasma. It is therefore important to cross-match blood before transfusion to make sure that the recipient's plasma will not agglutinate the transfused red cells. Cross-matching for other blood groups may become important if a sufferer from, say, haemophilia or chronic anaemia has to receive multiple blood transfusions. An initial transfusion with blood of M erythrocytes into an N patient, for instance, may cause formation of anti-M antibodies in the recipient's plasma, so a subsequent M-containing transfusion might lead to intravascular haemolysis. The Rh-substance may also be of clinicial importance. Most people of most human races carry Rh (Rh-positive). A few people do not (Rh-negative). Rh-negative pregnant women with an Rh-positive fetus may form anti-Rh antibodies, which during the same or a subsequent pregnancy may cross the placenta and haemolyse the erythrocytes of the fetus. The newborn infant, or even the fetus, can be saved from this disaster by exchange transfusion, replacing its own red cells with those of Rh-negative donor blood.

Polymorphism in other glycoproteins

The existence of slightly different forms of a glycoprotein (and thus of the gene complex controlling its formation) occurring in different individuals of a population is a phenomenon called polymorphism. The polymorphic glycoproteins of erythrocytes and of lymphocyte surfaces have been studied in some detail, but they occur also on other types of cells.

A set of genes called MHC genes (major histocompatibility complex) controls the glycoprotein structure of surfaces of many cells of the body of mammals and birds, but especially of lymphocytes. These glycoproteins are important in connection with an animal's immune response, which in turn depends on whether it is able to recognize as 'foreign' the proteins of viruses or bacteria or other invading pathogenic parasites. (If the animal does recognize the protein as 'foreign', the animal's lymphocytes come into action: T-lymphocytes are cytolytic; they break down the cells carrying the foreign protein; B-lymphocytes become plasma cells, which generate the specific antibody.) If the glycoprotein product of a certain MHC gene group fails to form an association with the pathogenic protein, the foreign protein cannot be recognized as such, and no immune response can be started. But perhaps another individual with a different set of MHC genes *can* recognize and deal with this pathogen. Every species has a large pool of genetic MHC material, giving rise to highly polymorphic glycoproteins. So even if some individuals die during an epidemic of a disease, there is a good probability that some individuals have the natural immunity which will enable the species as a whole to survive.

At a practical level the existence of the MHC gene complex is assisting selective breeding of livestock for natural immunity to various diseases. In the matter of organ transplants in man it is of course necessary to try to prevent recognition of the donor organ as 'foreign' to the recipient, by matching tissue types as closely as possible.

Appendix 7 Voltage clamp

The voltage clamp is a device which allows an observer to maintain a constant predetermined potential on the membrane of a nerve axon, thus eliminating the action potential, while observing and measuring the ionic currents that normally accompany the transmission of the nerve impulses.

The two electrodes which maintain the required potential on the membrane of the axon (say a squid giant axon) run the whole length of the axon; one, a silver wire, lies in the axoplasm, and the other is a metal cylinder outside the membrane in a bath of sea water (Fig. A7.1). If only a short length of membrane were to be voltage-clamped, this part would act as a source of stimulus initiating an action potential in the remaining portion. A second pair of electrodes, one in the axoplasm and one exterior to it, can be used for passing a current across the membrane from a feedback circuit. When the observer clamps the voltage to a potential at or above threshold for the nerve, the ionic currents which would (in the unclamped axon) be associated with the start of an action potential are 'opposed' by passing an equal and opposite current across the membrane from the feedback circuit, to maintain the constant voltage. Measurements of the size (in mA) and time-course of the currents required for this voltage maintenance indicate the size and time-course of the ionic currents normally occurring at this potential. Examples are given in Fig. 9.3.

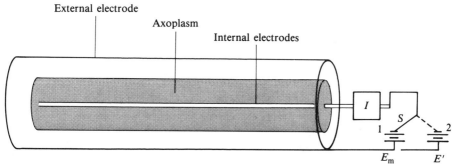

Figure A7.1 Voltage clamp. The axon (shaded) contains a pair of internal electrodes (fine wires), one to apply voltage and one to record current. An external electrode (cylinder) lies outside the membrane, but not touching it. When the switch (S) is in position 1, connected with battery of voltage equal to membrane potential (E_m), no net ionic current flows through the membrane. When the switch is moved to position 2, connected with a known voltage (E') chosen by the observer, ionic currents start flowing through the membrane. Their direction, size and time-course can be recorded by the ammeter (I).

Appendix 8 Conduction velocity in unmyelinated nerves

Conduction velocity in an unmyelinated axon depends on a property called the length constant (λ), which indicates how far ahead of the action-potential spike the local-response potential is large enough to reach the threshold of that particular axon. If axoplasmic resistance is high, the local-response potential cannot spread far; it falls off along the line r_1 (Fig. A8.1) and each local circuit will be short (S to h_1 in the figure) and velocity will be low. If axoplasm resistance is low, the local-response potential spreads well ahead of the spike, and local circuits are long (S to h_2) and conduction velocity is rapid. The membrane resistance is also important: if it is too low, the potential in the axoplasm simply leaks away into the extracellular fluid and a portion of membrane well ahead of the spike is never brought to threshold. Thus, long local circuits and fast conduction will be achieved by axons which have a rather high membrane resistance r_m and a rather low axoplasm resistance r_a: velocity therefore is likely to be proportional to r_m and inversely proportional to r_a. In fact the longitudinal spread of potential in the axon, and thus the ability to generate a local circuit ahead of the spike, depends on r_m/r_a. This is the length constant, λ.

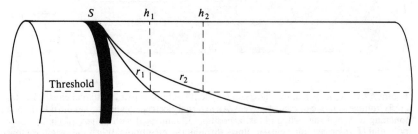

Figure A8.1 Fall-off of local response potential in axon of high axoplasmic resistance (line r_1) and low axoplasmic resistance (line r_2). See text for explanation.

The resistances r_m and r_a depend on the materials of which the membrane and axoplasm are made, and also on the dimensions of the axon, i.e. the total *area* of membrane along the length h, in which the local circuit is generated, and the total *volume* of axoplasm in the cylinder of that length. To compare resistances (and thus velocities) of one axon with another, we need to compare resistance *per unit length* of axon (Fig. A8.2). These values are known as the *specific resistances* of the membrane and axoplasm, R_m and R_a.

To express r_m and r_a in terms of R_m and R_a, we may make a small calculation assuming that the axon is cylindrical and using the formulae for surface area and volume of a cylinder. It will be recalled that resistance is *inversely* related to volume or area (the smaller the volume or area, the greater is the resistance). The resistances for the cylinder in Fig. A8.2, for length h and radius x, are r_m and r_a. So for unit area and volume:

$$R_m = r_m(2\pi x h),$$

Therefore

$$r_m = \frac{R_m}{2\pi x h}$$

$$\text{and } R_a = r_a(\pi x^2 h)$$

Therefore

$$r_a = \frac{R_a}{\pi x^2 h}$$

Thus

$$r_m/r_a = \frac{R_m \pi x^2 h}{R_a 2\pi x h}$$

$$= \frac{R_x x}{2R_a}$$

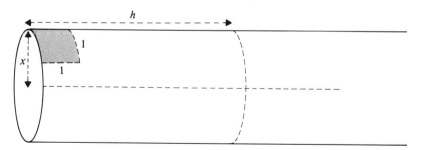

Figure A8.2   Dimensions of axon cylinder, radius x. Total resistance of membrane surface along length $h = r_m$. Specific resistance of 1 mm^2 (shaded area) $= R_m = r_m 2\pi x h$. (Resistance is inversely proportional to area.)

and

$$\lambda = \sqrt{(r_m/r_a)}$$

$$= \sqrt{\left(\frac{R_m x}{2R_a}\right)}$$

Now R_m and R_a, the specific resistances for all non-myelinated nerves in any one type of animal, will be similar; the materials of which nerves are composed do not vary much. So R_m and R_a can be regarded as constants, and the important variable in determining λ, the spread of local excitory potential ahead of the spike, is therefore $\sqrt{x}$, the square-root of the radius (or diameter). Indeed it has been found experimentally that velocity in non-myelinated nerves is fairly closely related to the square-root of the diameter.

Glossary

Acclimatization   adaptive change of physiological systems to an altered environment.

Acquired immunity   the presence of an antibody against a specific antigen as a result of exposure to the antigen (active) or transfer of exogenous antibody (passive).

Acrosome   the anterior end of the head of a spermatozoon.

ACTH   adrenocorticotrophic hormone, a polypeptide hormone produced by the anterior pituitary, which has a trophic effect on the adrenal cortex.

Adaptation (*neural*)   decrease in the rate of transmission of impulses in a sensory neurone in the face of constant stimulation.

Adenohypophysis   anterior part of the pituitary gland, consisting of the pars distalis, tuberalis and intermedia.

Adrenergic   describing nerve fibres which release noradrenaline at their nerve endings.

Afferent   describing nerves which conduct impulses *towards* the central nervous system; or arterioles taking blood *towards* the renal glomeruli.

Agglutination   the process of coming together to form a mass, as for example red cells or bacteria.

Anabolism   the synthesis of molecules from small molecular fragments.

Angiotensin I   decapeptide with slight vasoconstrictor effect, formed from the splitting of a plasma protein (angiotensinogen) by renin.

Angiotenin II   an octapeptide with a powerful vasoconstrictor effect and the ability to stimulate release of aldosterone from the adrenal cortex.

Antagonist   a muscle whose activity opposes a given action; thus flexor muscles are antagonists of extensor muscles.

Antidiuretic hormone   see Vasopressin.

Antigen   a foreign substance, usually protein, causing production of antibodies.

Ascites   pathological accumulation of fluid in the abdomen.

Baroreceptor a receptor sensitive to pressure or stretch.

B-cells lymphocytes which on activation proliferate and differentiate into plasma cells producing circulating antibodies.

Blood–brain barrier a specialized anatomical barrier which controls the rate of passage of substances from the blood to the extracellular space of the brain.

Calcite crystalline form of calcium carbonate.

Calcitonin peptide hormone produced by the parafollicular cells of the thyroid and which influences the blood levels of calcium.

Calmodulin intracellular protein which binds calcium and mediates a number of second messenger functions.

Carotinoid collective term for the carotenes, a group of yellow-orange pigments of plants.

Cerebrospinal fluid fluid which fills the cerebral ventricles and subarachnoid space and which cushions the central nervous system.

Choroid plexus capillary network involved in the production of cerebrospinal fluid.

Circadian describing events that recur at approximately 24-h intervals.

Colligative property property of solution which depends on the number of solute particles present but not on their nature (e.g. freezing point or boiling point of solution).

Colostrum milky fluid produced by the mammary gland immediately after birth.

Complement system of plasma proteins which when activated kills microbes and facilitates the steps of the inflammatory process.

Contralateral on the opposite side (to).

Convergence property of neuronal circuits in which a number of presynaptic neurones form synapses on one nerve cell body.

Coronary describing blood vessels supplying the heart muscle.

Corpus luteum ovarian structure formed from the remaining cells of the follicle after its rupture; it produces oestrogen and progesterone.

Cortisol steroid hormone produced by the adrenal cortex which controls aspects of carbohydrate metabolism and is anti-inflammatory.

Cyclic AMP cyclic 3′:5′-adenosine monophosphate, a cyclic nucleotide which serves as a second messenger for many peptide hormones and neurotransmitters.

Dendrite short branched process of a neurone that conducts impulses towards the cell body.

Dextrin small water-soluble polysaccharide composed of glucose units.

Diuresis production of abnormally large amounts of urine.

Divergence property of a neuronal circuit in which a single presynaptic neurone influences a number of postsynaptic neurones.

Dopamine an amine neurotransmitter and the precursor of adrenaline and noradrenaline.

Dorsal root point at which a group of afferent nerve fibres connect with the dorsal side of the spinal cord.

Efferent describing nerves conducting impulses, or impulses travelling, *away from* the central nervous system; or arteriole taking blood *away from* renal glomeruli.

Endocrine gland ductless gland which secretes chemicals (hormones) into the bloodstream.

Endogenous arising from within the body or organ.

Endorphins internally produced morphine-like substances which act as neurotransmitters, paracrines and hormones.

Endothelium epithelium lining internal surfaces such as blood vessels and lymphatics.

Endothermic describing chemical reactions which absorb heat.

Enkephalin peptide which functions as a neurotransmitter at synapses activated by opiate drugs; it has a pain-killing effect in the central nervous system.

EPSP excitatory postsynaptic potential, a graded depolarizing potential present in a postsynaptic neurone when excitatory inputs are activated.

Exogenous arising from outside the body or organ.

Exothermic describing heat-producing chemical reactions.

Extensor muscle muscle whose contraction produces the straightening of a limb joint.

Eukaryotic describing cell or organism in which the DNA is organized into chromosomes and surrounded by a membrane.

Eutherian describing group of mammals in which there is a well developed placenta (i.e. marsupials excluded) and which bear living young (i.e. monotremes excluded).

Feedback a characteristic of control systems in which the output controls the process producing the input.

Fibrinogen plasma protein that is the precursor of fibrin in blood coagulation.

Flexor muscle muscle whose contraction produces bending of a limb joint.

FSH follicle-stimulating hormone, a glycoprotein hormone produced in the anterior lobe of the pituitary; one of the gonadotrophins which stimulates sex-cell development in both male and female.

Gamma motor neurone nerve which controls the length of the muscle spindle fibres.

Glucagon hormone synthesized in the cells of the pancreas which increases plasma glucose concentration.

Gluconeogenesis synthesis of glucose from non-carbohydrate sources.

Glycogenolysis breakdown of glycogen to yield glucose.

Helper T-cells a class of T-cells which enhance production of antibodies and cytotoxic T-cell function.

Heparin an anti-clotting agent produced by various tissues especially liver and lung.

Histamine amine derived from mast cells of skin and other connective tissue which contributes to the inflammatory process by dilating capillaries and increasing their permeability.

Homeostasis maintenance of constancy of internal environment of the body; maintenance of equilibrium between organism and environment.

Hyper- (prefix) large; greater; excessive; above.

Hypo- (prefix) small; lesser; too low; below.

Hypothalamus region below the thalamus in the third ventricle of the brain, site of integration of basic behavioural patterns.

Hypoxia too low level of oxygen (in gas mixture, blood or tissue).

Immunoglobulin gamma-globulin or antibody.

Insulin polypeptide hormone produced by the beta cells of the pancreas which lowers plasma glucose.

Ipsilateral on the same side (as).

IPSP inhibitory postsynaptic potential, a graded hyperpolarizing potential which develops in the postsynaptic neurone when inhibitory inputs are activated.

Isosmotic; Isosmolar having the same osmolar concentration; appropriate to the maintenance of the same osmolar concentration.

Juxta-glomerular apparatus specialized region of the nephron adjacent to the glomerulus that detects changes in the fluid flow rate in the nephron and adjusts glomerular filtration rate.

LH luteinizing hormone, a glycoprotein hormone produced in the anterior pituitary and necessary for ovulation and corpus-luteum formation.

Ligament(s) band of fibrous tissue connecting two or more bones.

Limbic system group of interconnected brain structures involved with emotion and learning.

Leydig cells interstitial cells of the testis.

Macrophage cell type found in blood vessel walls and body tissues which functions as a phagocyte and becomes mobile when inflammation occurs.

Mast cells round or ovoid cells found mainly in loose connective tissue and containing histamine and heparin; they appear to have a role in inflammation.

Matrix medium in which structure is embedded.

Median eminence region at the base of the hypothalamus containing capillary tufts into which hormones are secreted.

Memory cells B- and T-lymphocytes produced on first exposure to an infection which respond rapidly on subsequent exposure to the same antigen.

Mendelian recessive character or property of which the inheritance follows Mendel's Laws and which is dependent on a recessive gene; i.e. gene, derived from one parent, of which the expression is suppressed in the presence of an alternative (dominant) gene derived from the other parent.

Mesentery fold of connective tissue in abdominal cavity serving to hold organs in place.

Metabolism the sum of the chemical changes, constructive (anabolic) and destructive (catabolic), occurring in living organisms.

Metabolite any product of metabolism, usually a catabolic product.

Modality manner or quality, especially type of sensation.

Motor unit motor neurone together with the muscle fibres which it innervates.

Myeloma cells cells comprising bone-marrow tumours; they reproduce rapidly and can be grown in culture medium outside the body.

Myocardium heart muscle as a whole.

Myogenic arising in muscle independently of nerves or other external stimuli.

Natriuretic hormone   hormone inhibiting sodium reabsorption in the renal tubule.

Natural killer cells   a class of cells which bind non-specifically to cells bearing foreign antigens and kill them directly.

Neurohypophysis   the posterior part of the pituitary gland comprising the pars nervosa, infundibulum and median eminence.

Nucleoside   compound made up of one of four possible nitrogenous bases linked to ribose or desoxyribose.

Nucleotide   compound formed from nucleoside linked to phosphoric acid, which when polymerized forms nucleic acid.

Occipital region   part of brain or skull at back of head adjacent to dorsal side of neck.

Odiferous   having an odour or smell.

Oestrogen   a follicular steroid hormone responsible for female secondary sex characters and cyclical changes of the uterine endometrium.

Organelle   structure within cell which has a specific function.

Osmoreceptor   nerve cell in central nervous system responding to changes in the osmolarity of the extracellular fluid.

Oxytocin   a nonapeptide hormone synthesized in the hypothalamus and released from the posterior pituitary; it causes contraction of the uterus and milk ejection.

Partition coefficient   ratio of the concentrations of a solute found in two adjacent non-miscible solvents at equilibrium.

Periosteum   outermost layer of bone containing many blood vessels.

Periphery; Peripheral   (near or towards) edges, surroundings; away from the centre.

Peritoneum   membrane lining the walls of the abdominal cavity and also forming the mesentery in which abdominal organs are held.

Photo- (prefix)   related to light (e.g. photosensitive).

Photochemical   chemical effect initiated by light.

Pineal gland   small gland that projects upwards from the diencephalon (region below the cerebral hemispheres of the brain) which produces melatonin.

Platelet   a formed element of the blood derived from a megakaryocyte; it has a role in blood clotting.

Plexus   network of slender nerves or capillaries.

Primate   group of mammals including monkeys, apes and man, with limbs adapted for climbing and leaping; some species have upright posture.

Progesterone steroid hormone produced by the corpus luteum; stimulates secretion by the uterine glands and development of the mammary glands.

Pro-opiomelanocortin large protein precursor molecule from which a number of peptides are derived, including ACTH and the endorphins.

Protein kinase type of enzyme which catalyses the addition of a phosphate to a specific protein.

Recruitment activation of an increased number of cells on exposure to a stimulus of increasing magnitude.

Renin enzyme produced in the kidneys which catalyses the cleaving of angiotensin I from angiotensinogen in the blood.

Ringer solution solution containing salts in the same concentrations and proportions as they are present in plasma.

Ruminant group of mammals (including cow, sheep and deer) which have a rumen in the alimentary canal; type of digestion in such animals.

Sagittal axis (plane) median longitudinal axis (plane) dividing body into left and right.

Salt-bridge link (analogous with electrostatic attraction of cation and anion of a salt) formed between adjacent oppositely charged side-chains of a folded peptide chain in a protein.

Schwann cell a glial (supporting) cell which forms the myelin sheath around myelinated nerves.

Second messenger a substance such as cyclic AMP or calcium whose concentration within a cell increases in response to combination of a hormone with receptors in the cell's plasma membrane; it brings about changes mediating the tissue's response to the hormone.

Secretion substance or fluid manufactured by cells or tissue and passed out from its source; process of passing out such fluid.

Seminiferous tubule tubule within the testis in which spermatogenesis occurs.

Sensitize render sensitive to an antigen by repeated exposure to that antigen.

Septum partition separating two cavities or masses of tissue.

Sertoli cells cells of the testes associated with nourishment and maturation of the sperm.

Somatomedins a group of growth-promoting steroids produced largely in the liver, mediating the action of growth hormone.

Somatostatin growth hormone release inhibiting hormone produced by the hypothalamus; also produced in the stomach and pancreas—a possible neurotransmitter.

Spatial summation   the addition of simultaneous stimuli to different parts of a cell producing a greater change in potential than that generated by a single synaptic input.

Stearic hindrance   prevention of proximity or reaction between two molecules because of their three-dimensional structure.

Suppressor T-cells   the class of T-lymphocytes inhibiting antibody production and cytotoxic-cell function.

T-cells   lymphocytes processed by the thymus and able to combat foreign tissues, viruses and parasites that have entered the body.

Temporal   (a) related to time; (b) the side (of the eye) near the temporal bone of the skull.

Temporal summation   the additon of two or more stimuli arriving at different times and producing a greater change than that produced by a single synaptic input.

Testosterone   a steroid hormone produced by the interstitial cells of the testes; it maintains growth and development of the reproductive organs.

Threshold   minimum stimulus necessary to elicit a response from an excitable cell, tissue or organ.

Thyroxine   an amine hormone secreted by the thyroid gland and containing four iodine atoms in each molecule.

Tone   continuous slight asynchronous activity of nervous or muscular tissue.

Tritiated water   water in which one or both hydrogen atoms of the molecule have been replaced by the radioactive isotope tritium (^3H).

Trophic   growth-promoting and nourishing.

Vascular   related to, or abundantly supplied with, blood vessels.

Vaso- (prefix)   related to blood vessels.

Vasopressin   a nonapeptide hormone synthesized in the hypothalamus, released from the posterior pituitary and serving to promote water retention and vasoconstriction; also called antidiuretic hormone (ADH).

Ventral root   a group of efferent fibres leaving the spinal cord at the ventral side of the body.

Vesicle   small sac containing fluid.

Visceral   related to the internal organs of the abdominal and thoracic cavities, especially the intestines.

Zona fasciculata, glomerulosa and reticularis   three zones of the adrenal cortex producing steroid hormones.

List of abbreviations

ACh	acetylcholine
ACTH	adrenocorticotrophic hormone
ADH	antidiuretic hormone
ADP	adenosine 5'-diphosphate
AMP	adenosine 5'-phosphate
cAMP	cyclic adenosine 3': 5'-phosphate
ANF	atrial natriuretic factor
ATP	adenosine 5'-triphosphate
AV	atrioventricular
CCK	cholecystokinin
CNS	central nervous system
CRF	corticotrophin releasing factor
CSF	cerebrospinal fluid
DCT	distal convoluted tubule
DIT	di-iodotyrosine
DNA	deoxyribonucleic acid
DPG	2,3-diphosphoglycerol
DPPC	dipalmitoyl phosphatidyl choline
ECG	electrocardiogram
EM	electron microscopy
EPSP	excitatory postsynaptic potential
ER	endoplasmic reticulum
FSH	follicle stimulating hormone
GFR	glomerular filtration rate
GH	growth hormone
GnRH	gonadotrophin releasing hormone
GTP	guanosine 5'-triphosphate
HCG	human chorionic gonadotrophin
IPSP	inhibitory postsynaptic potential
LGB	lateral geniculate body
LH	luteinizing hormone
LHRH	LH releasing hormone
LM	light microscopy
mepp	miniature endplate potential

MHC	major histocompatibility complex
MIT	mono-iodotyrosine
MSH	melanocyte-stimulating hormone
NK	natural killer
PCT	proximal convoluted tubule
PD	potential difference
PG	phosphatidyl glycerol
Rh	rhesus
RNA	ribonucleic acid
mRNA	messenger RNA
RQ	respiratory quotient
SA	sinoatrial
SI	Système International d'Unités
SR	sarcoplasmic reticulum
T_3	tri-iodothyronine
T_4	thyroxine
TRH	thyrotrophin releasing hormone
TSH	thyroid-stimulating hormone
TOC	total osmolar concentration

Suggestions for further reading

3 Cell structure and function
Allen, R. D., 'The microtubule as an intracellular engine', *Scientific American*, **256**, 2, 26–33, 1987.

Willingham, M. C. and I. Pastan, 'Endocytosis and exocytosis: current concepts of vesicle traffic in animal cells', *International Review of Cytology*, **92**, 51–92, 1984.

4 Feeding, digestion and absorption
Dockray, G. J., 'Comparative biochemistry and physiology of the gut hormones', *Annual Review of Physiology*, **41**, 83–95, 1979.

Forte, J. G., T. E. Machen and K. J. O'Brink, 'Mechanisms of gastric H^+ and Cl^- transport', *Annual Review of Physiology*, **42**, 111–126, 1980.

Schultz, S. G., 'A cellular model for active sodium reabsorption by mammalian colon', *Annual Review of Physiology*, **46**, 435–451, 1984.

5 Cardiovascular system
Crone, C., 'The function of capillaries', in *Recent Advances in Physiology*, vol. 10, P. F. Baker (ed.), Churchill-Livingstone, Edinburgh, 1984.

6 Respiration
Bangham, A. D., 'Breathing made easy', *New Scientist*, **85**, 408–410, 1980.

Bye, P. T. P., G. A. Forbes and C. Roussos, 'Respiratory factors limiting exercise', *Annual Review of Physiology*, **45**, 439–451, 1983.

Perutz, M., 'Regulation of oxygen affinity for haemoglobin', *Annual Review of Biochemistry*, **48**, 327–386, 1979.

7 Body fluids and the kidney
Creger, R., 'Ion transport mechanisms in thick ascending limb of Henle's loop of mammalian nephron', *Physiological Reviews*, **65**, 760–795, 1985.

De Wardener, H. E. and E. M. Clarkson, 'Concept of natriuretic hormone', *Physiological Reviews*, **65**, 658–759, 1985.

Sherwood, J. E., 'The chemistry and physiology of erythropoietin', *Vitamins and Hormones*, **41**, 161–211, 1984.

8 Control of the pH of plasma

Halperin, M. L., and R. L. Jungas, 'Metabolic production and renal disposal of hydrogen ions', *Kidney International*, **24**, 709–713, 1983.

Haüssinger, D., W. Gerok and H. Sies, 'Hepatic role in pH regulation: intercellular glutamine cycle', *Trends in Biochemical Sciences*, **9**, 300–307, 1984.

9 Conduction in nerve fibres

Benzanilla, F. and C. M. Armstrong, 'Gating currents of the sodium channels: 3 ways to block them', *Science*, **183**, 753–754, 1974.

Keynes, R. D. and D. J. Aidley, *Nerve and Muscle*, Cambridge University Press, Cambridge, 1981.

10 Autonomic nervous system

Guyton, A. C., 'The autonomic nervous system: the adrenal medulla', in *Basic Neuroscience: Anatomy and Physiology*, pp. 262–273, Saunders, Philadelphia, 1987.

Mrosovsky, N., 'The adjustable brain of hibernators', *Scientific American*, **218**, 3, 110–118, 1968.

Stanier, M. W., L. E. Mount and J. Bligh, *Energy Balance and Temperature Regulation*, Cambridge University Press, Cambridge, 1984.

11 Muscle

Gabella, G., 'Structure of smooth muscles', in *Smooth Muscle: An Assessment of Current Knowledge*, E. Bulbring, A. F. Brading, A. W. Jones and T. Tomita (eds), Arnold, London, 1981.

Goldman, Y. E. and B. Brenner, 'Molecular mechanisms of muscle contraction: general introduction', *Annual Review of Physiology*, **49**, 629–636, 1987.

12 Sense organs and sensation

Cross, A. and L. H. Rees, 'The neuroendocrinology of opioid peptides', *British Medical Bulletin*, **39**, 83–88, 1983.

Gregory, R. L., *Eye and Brain: The Psychology of Seeing*, Weidenfeld & Nicholson, London, 1966.

Hasland, R. H., 'The functional architecture of the retina', *Scientific American*, **255**, 6, 90–99, 1986.

Jessell, T. M., 'Pain', *Lancet ii*, 1084–1088, 1982.

Pettigrew, J. D., 'The neurophysiology of binocular vision', *Scientific American*, **227**, 2, 84–95, 1972.

Stryer, L., 'The molecules of visual excitation', *Scientific American*, **257**, 1, 32–40, 1987.

13 Introduction to the central nervous system

Blakemore, C., 'The nature of explanation in the study of the brain', in *Functions of the Brain*, C. Coen (ed.), Clarendon Press, Oxford, 1986.

Merton, P. A., 'How we control the contraction of our muscles', *Scientific American*, **226**, 5, 30–37, 1972.

Stein, J. F., 'The control of movement', in *Functions of the Brain*, C. Coen (ed.), Clarendon Press, Oxford, 1986.

14 Endocrine system

Berridge, M. J., 'The molecular basis of communication in the cell', *Scientific American*, **253**, 4, 124–134, 1985.

Cantin, M. and D. Genest, 'The heart as an endocrine organ', *Scientific American*, **254**, 4, 62–67, 1986.

Nathanson, J. A. and P. Greengard, '"Second messengers" in the brain', *Scientific American*, **237**, 2, 108–119, 1977.

O'Riordan, J. L. H., P. G. Malan and R. P. Gould, *Essentials of Endocrinology*, Blackwell, Oxford, 1988.

Shiu, R. P. C. and H. G. Friesen, 'Mechanism of action of prolactin in the control of mammary gland function', *Annual Review of Physiology*, **42**, 83–90, 1980.

Synder, S. H., 'The molecular basis of communication between cells', *Scientific American*, **253**, 4, 114–123, 1985.

15 Reproduction

Hogarth, P. J., 'Viviparity', in *Studies in Biology*, no. 75, Arnold, London, 1976.

Lagercantz, R. and T. A. Slotkin, 'The stress of being born', *Scientific American*, **254**, 4, 92–98, 1986.

Nathanielsz, P. W., 'Endocrine mechanism of parturition', *Annual Review of Physiology*, **40**, 411–445, 1978.

Widdowson, E. M., 'The role of nutrition in mammalian reproduction', in *Environmental Factors in Mammalian Reproduction*, D. Gilmore and B. Cook (eds), Macmillan, London, 1981.

16 Defence mechanisms of the body

Ada, I. I. and G. Nossal, 'The clonal selection theory', *Scientific American*, **257**, 2, 50–57, 1987.

Cohen, I. R., 'The self, the world and autoimmunity', *Scientific American*, **258**, 4, 34–41, 1988.

Lawn, R. M. and G. A. Vehar, 'The molecular genetics of haemophilia', *Scientific American*, **254**, 3, 40–46, 1987.

Marrack, P. and J. Kappler, 'The T-cell and its receptor', *Scientific American*, **254**, 2, 28–37, 1987.

Raff, M. C., 'Cell surface immunology', *Scientific American*, **234**, 5, 30–39, 1976.

Tonegawa, S., 'The molecules of the immune system', *Scientific American*, **253**, 4, 104–112, 1986.

Young, J. D. and A. Cohen, 'How killer cells kill', *Scientific American*, **258**, 4, 28–34, 1988.

17 Adaptation to the environment

Gwinner, E., 'Internal rhythms and bird migration', *Scientific American*, **254**, 4, 76–84, 1986.

Harrison, R. J. and G. L. Kooyman, 'Diving in marine mammals', *Carolina Biology Readers*, no. 6, 1981.

Montagna, W., 'Human skin', *Carolina Biology Readers*, no. 159, 1986.

Rambaut, P. C., 'Space medicine', *Carolina Biology Readers*, no. 166, 1985.

Zapul, W. M., 'Diving adaptations of the Weddell seal', *Scientific American*, **256**, 6, 80–85, 1987.

References

Bayliss, W. M. and E. H. Starling, 'The mechanism of pancreatic secretion', *Journal of Physiology*, **28**, 325–353, 1903.

Blakemore, C., 'Developmental factors in the formation of feature extracting neurones', *The Neurosciences Third Study Program*, ed. F. O. Schmitt and F. G. Worden, Cambridge MA, M.I.T. Press, 1974.

Davy, J., 'Miscellaneous observations on animal heat', *Philosophical Transactions of the Royal Society*, **1**, 57–64, 1844.

Edkins, J. S., 'On the chemical mechanism of gastric secretion', *Proceedings of the Royal Society*, **76B**, 376, 1905.

Eldridge, F. L., J. P. Kiley and D. E. Millhorn, 'Respiratory responses to medullary hydrogen ion concentration in cats: different effects of respiratory and metabolic acidoses', *Journal of Physiology*, **358**, 285–297, 1985a.

Eldridge, F. L., D. E. Millburn, J. P. Kiley and T. G. Waldrop, 'Stimulation by central command of locomotion, respiration and circulation during exercise', *Respiration Physiology*, **59**, 313–337, 1985b.

Hodgkin, A. L., 'The relation between conduction velocity and the electrical resistance outside a nerve fibre', *Journal of Physiology*, **94**, 560–570, 1939.

Huxley, A. F. and R. Stämpfli, 'Evidence for saltatory conduction in peripheral myelinated nerve-fibres', *Journal of Physiology*, **108**, 315–339, 1949.

Langley, J. N., *The Autonomic Nervous System*, Heffers, Cambridge, 1929.

Leaf, A., 'Maintenance of concentration gradients and regulation of cell volume', *Annals of the New York Academy of Sciences*, **72**, 396–404, 1958.

Pavlov, I. P., *Conditioned Reflexes: An Investigation of Physiological Activity of the Cerebral Cortex*, G. V. Anrep (ed. and trans.), Oxford University Press, Oxford, 1927.

Penfield, W. G. and H. H. Jasper, *Epilepsy and the Functional Anatomy of the Human Brain*, Little, Brown, Boston, 1954.

Rushton, W. A. H., 'A theory of the effects of fibre size in medullated nerve', *Journal of Physiology*, **115**, 101–122, 1951.

Schweig, *Untersuche über periodische Vorange*, 1843. Quoted in Speck, H., *Archives of Experimental Pathology and Pharmacology*, **15**, 81–145, 1882.

Sherrington, C. S., 'The mammalian spinal cord as an organ of reflex action', *Proceedings of the Royal Society*, **61**, 220–221, 1897.

Index